This operation split the history of suffering mankind into two parts: torture before the invention of anesthesia and calm sleep after the first painless operation on October 16, 1846.

TRIUMPH OVER PAIN

by

RENÉ FÜLÖP-MILLER

TRANSLATED

BY

EDEN AND CEDAR PAUL

THE LITERARY GUILD OF AMERICA, INC.

NEW YORK   N. Y.

TO

ERIKA RENON

FRIEND AND COMPANION

IN GRATITUDE

Prefatory Note

My book is the outcome of personal experience of pain, and is an attempt of the reason to unravel its mystery.

I describe an arduous struggle against the mighty forces of pain, recounting the boldest adventure of the human mind and a brilliant victory of science over the cruelty of nature.

The alleged significance of pain and the means used to dispel or assuage it are considered from the earliest days down to the present time. Yet such a topic cannot be definitely handled; for science, whose aims are infinite, can set no bourn. What today is acclaimed as the last word can tomorrow be superseded; and what seems the most decisive triumph may be but the prelude to unanticipated achievement.

The data available for a description of the origin and fate of a discovery are furnished, above all, the trustworthy accounts of eye-witnesses, friends or foes; letters, conversations, speeches made at congresses; by pamphlets, newspaper reports, and the minutes of proceedings in the law courts—documentary evidence in which there lingers the warmth of human activity.

To liberate mankind from pain, heaven and hell were opened; heroic courage, profound sympathy and the spirit of self-sacrifice provided the aureole; while perfervid ambition, sordid avarice and a futile hunger for fame tarnished the quest. Amid a drama of passions unchained, the redemption of sufferers was prepared.

The nature of the content has determined the method of presentation. Something more was needed than a consecutive catalogue of dry and manifest facts, for when marshaled without artistry what are termed facts are but half-truths. Using his imagination the dramaturge conjures up the scene, instills vitality into forgotten gestures and enables hushed voices to make themselves heard anew. In virtue of his creative privilege, he breathes into the dead past until it regains a living soul.

Contents

Contents

Illustrations

TRIUMPH OVER PAIN

CHAPTER ONE

The Thorn in the Flesh

IN THE nineteenth century a sixth continent was discovered. Archeologists set forth, at the head of expeditions equipped with picks and shovels, to discover the buried land of lost civilizations.

When the time was ripe they were resurrected, these civilizations, arising from the womb of earth to return into the glad light of day. The excavators found city after city, country after country, of which, in writings and sagas, rumor had come down from the ancients: Ashur and Babylon, Nineveh and Erech, dead cities of the Pharaohs, Mycene and Troy; the towns of the Hittites and the Etruscans, with their palaces, tombs, temples and libraries. Stone monuments, clay tablets and papyrus rolls inscribed with mystifying characters were disinterred from among the ruins.

Jean François Champollion, Egyptologist and director of the Louvre, obtained the key which enabled him to decipher the hieroglyphs. Grotefend, rector of the Gymnasium at Frankfort-on-the-Main and subsequently chief of the Hanover Lyceum, and Sir Henry Rawlinson, famous soldier and orientalist—the German and the Englishman alike guided by the guesses of genius—succeeded in reading the cuneiform inscriptions. Forgotten tongues began to speak from the dead rubble of monuments and clay slabs; from palimpsests and papyri. The laws of Egyptian Pharaohs and legendary rulers of Ur and Babylon could be studied by moderns eager for knowledge; latter-day doctors could pore over the pre-

scriptions of their long-forgotten colleagues who were wizards
rather than men of science; officials reported, priests prayed, princes
consulted the oracles, court chroniclers recorded the deeds of
monarchs who for ages have been mingled with the dust.

The old world had risen from the tomb, and spoke across the
ages to the century whose bold conjurations had summoned it from
the realm of the dead.

In the cuneiform writing on a clay tablet from Nippur is the
prayer of a king's daughter in Babylon. After thousands of years
the woman's anguished appeal, the first known written record of
the kind, reaches our ears: "Pain has seized my body. May God
tear this pain out."

As the number of deciphered texts increase, so do the number
of the cries of agony that issued from tortured lips. Tablets and
potsherds from the library of Sardanapalus at Kuyunjik, papyri
written in the days of the pyramid-builders, leathern documents
belonging to the era of Zarathustra, Mycenean and Minoan inscriptions, sacrificial hymns from the Rig-Veda, parchment rolls,
prayers, spells, exorcisms and incantations—one and all, in every
civilization, in every century, they bear witness to the unceasing dominion of pain.

A Greek investigator laid bare the shrines of Æsculapius at
Cos and Epidaurus. At each of these a touching miscellany of dis-
eased fragments of the body meets the eye: stone or metal repro-
ductions of pain-smitten heads, trunks, arms, breasts and inwards;
votive tablets and offerings, with Dorian inscriptions to record how
prolonged and terrible had been the suffering of each pious votary
—until, by the compassion of Æsculapius, he or she had been
delivered from woe.

Classical authors relate the lives of the heroes; medieval
chroniclers tell the legends of the saints; and saga and legend alike
have much to say about pain. With the dawn of modernity comes
the era of the famous ones who claimed neither heroism nor sanctity: discoverers and inventors, reformers, artists and philosophers.
These were the persons to whom, thenceforward, veneration was
paid. Though they were not heroes or saints, their "profane life"
was recorded for the benefit of posterity, that everyone might know

how they had lived and suffered, for suffering was the badge of all their tribe. In the story of the great, one chapter is invariably entitled "Pain."

Whether such a man was, like Columbus or Magellan, the discoverer of previously unknown parts of the world; like Jesus or Mahomet, the founder of a new faith; like Spinoza or Schopenhauer, the pioneer of a philosophical system; a famous scientist, painter, sculptor or author—he suffered, he suffered, was plagued by illness, tortured by pain, even as I who write and you who read are plagued and tortured. Magellan was wounded (not for the first time) during the Moroccan campaign of 1513, and limped for the rest of his life; Columbus had a bad attack of gout on the high seas when making his third voyage to the West Indies. Erasmus of Rotterdam, prince of humanists, writing to Paracelsus, complains of being continually racked by calculus. Luther was gouty likewise, and when he was wrestling at the Wartburg and at Smalkald on behalf of freedom of conscience his work was hampered by gravel, headache and earache. "I am again afflicted as with labor pains, pestered by stone, by the German disease," he writes after a fierce attack of renal colic. Calvin had such violent paroxysms of migraine that when they came on he could scarcely speak; and in his accesses of gout, "for which there seems to be no remedy," he could hardly crawl from bed to writing table. Swift's declining years were one long agony, of which after two centuries it is almost unbearable to read, and which drove him crazy. Michelet, the celebrated French historian, describing the reign of *le Roi Soleil* Louis XIV, divides it into two periods, "before and after the fistula." Napoleon's gastric crises had a good deal to do with the heavy losses of the *Grand' Armée* at Borodino and with the Emperor's final defeat at Waterloo. In exile on St. Helena, during the last months, he would often wail, "The pain cuts like a knife. *O mon pylore, O mon pylore!*"

Dürer sent his doctor a sketch which shows the artist as he stands naked, pointing to the left lumbar region, to show the site of the enlarged spleen which he regarded as the cause of his miseries. Underneath, in his handwriting, are the words: "Where you see the yellow spot toward which the finger points—that is where it hurts." Titian died of the plague in Venice, as a centenarian. Gout struck the paintbrush from Rubens' hand. Beethoven suffered horribly from gallstone colic. Rousseau died upon the nightstool, after a bout of agonizing pain in the belly. Montaigne, d'Alembert, La Rochefoucauld and Leibnitz were great sufferers. Molière was attacked with intense pain when playing his own *malade imaginaire*. He did his best to mask the torments with a forced smile, but directly the performance was over he had to be carried home, writhing in agony, and died a few hours later.

We are told by Charles Darwin's son that the great naturalist "scarcely enjoyed a day's good health during forty years, his life being one long struggle with pain." Nietzsche says of himself: "Throughout life I have seldom known respite from pain, having had at least two hundred days of suffering every year."

Voltaire and Sir Walter Scott had recourse to narcotics for relief. Heinrich Heine, bedridden by spinal disease for more than a decade, used to spend six hundred francs a year upon opiates. "The cramps afflict me night and day, and I can only get ease by dulling my senses with morphine." Maupassant inhaled ether during his attacks of headache. In *Sur l'eau* he writes: "Migraine is atrocious torment, one of the worst in the world, weakening the nerves, driving one mad, scattering one's thoughts to the winds and impairing the memory. So terrible are these headaches that I can do nothing but lie on a couch and try to dull the pain by sniffing ether."

Fate lifts one among thousands into prominence; one among thousands finds biographers—and clinicians—to tell the story of his pain.

But pain visits also the inconspicuous, the millions who are neither heroes nor saints and have no title to greatness, for man is born unto trouble as the sparks fly upward. No one asks about it, no one records it. Pain streaks the lives of millions who go down to death unwept, unhonored and unsung.

The sufferings of these become a historical event only when they occur in persons who are under the scourge of pestilence and are, therefore, raised to the rank of a mass phenomenon. Classical historians and medieval chroniclers deign in such cases to give heart-rending reports. In the triumphs of imperators, during the festivals held to honor the gods, amid the pomp of crusading knights, on the merchantmen and the war-galleys, athwart the solemnity of processions, around the wells and in the market places, and at the groaning boards of the hospitable rich, this dread specter may walk. Then pain racks the bowels, the skin and the limbs of all and sundry; by tens and hundreds and thousands people are speeded to death, whole armies of them, the populations of town and countryside, perhaps of an entire continent. Its might will in a trice transform banquet or crusade, galley or triumph or procession, into the spectacle of myriads of pain-fraught visages, heaps of contorted bodies, into cries of pain and terror forced from unnumbered throats, clamoring down the centuries into our own time, to be stilled only when death commands silence.

Since no description suffices, annalists and statisticians have tried to show forth the temporal and spatial dimensions of the evil by a huge aggregate of figures. Here pain—that of bubonic plague, leprosy, anthrax, cholera, syphilis, smallpox, typhus, and typhoid —has ravaged intestines and blood, skin and limbs, laying whole districts low; there the epidemic has spread from Persia to the Rhine. Now and again a third of the inhabitants have perished in such a visitation, inaugurating new epochs and filling a century with lamentation. Thirteen millions perished thus in Greece. Athens was devastated in her prime. Byzantium suffered from the Plague of Justinian in the days of her greatest glory. The proudest cities of the Middle Ages became places of fruitless mourning.

Descriptive medicine was almost unknown before the eighteenth century. Pinel made a beginning at the Salpêtrière. Thenceforward symptoms were carefully noted in the hospitals, and clinical histories were kept. Thus originated the archives—Archives of Pain.

The body, to whatever epoch it may belong, no matter whether it be the body of someone with undying fame or of a nameless unit of the masses, is a perpetual source of pain. The blood inherits or may acquire the poison of all diseases, the bones are liable to soften or to be broken or to be eaten away, the nerves may thrill to every ache. With few exceptions, any organ can give rise to pain, which is an almost inseparable accompaniment of illness, is present during the sacred act of birth and attends our dying. "This is the noble truth of suffering," announced Sâkya Muni in one of his sermons at Benares, "that to be born is to suffer, to die is to suffer, and to fall sick is to suffer"; while François Villon, the strolling minstrel, exclaimed: "Whom death strikes down, must die in pain."

The forces of the outer world are in league with those of the living body; natural catastrophes, earth and sky, weather and war, dead matter and our fellow creatures, all, all can wound us, can sow the seeds of pain.

At length to the pains which spontaneously arise within the body and to those which invade it from without, endangering life and threatening death or disaster, is superadded the pain caused by attempts to counteract the forces of destruction, the pain of the surgeon's knife.

We know not who taught man to use the knife in search of the evils that lurk in the body. Was it a god, an omniscient beast of fable or man's own invincible healing instinct? However that may be, the story of surgery is coeval with the dawn of history.

Homer tells us that the art of surgery was the gift of Chiron, wisest of the centaurs, son of Cronus and Philyra. Hammurabi, first king of Babylonia, was master of the surgeon's bronze bistoury as well as wielder of the scepter, himself operating for cataract and opening abscesses of the liver. On the walls of Assyrian palaces are numerous reliefs displaying "the triumphs of the knife." To the Hindus of the days of the Mahabharata surgery seemed so important that Susruta spoke of a physician who could not operate as "a bird with only one wing"; while the mythical first operative surgeon of China was god, emperor and chirurgeon rolled into one.

Yet with surgery began a new torture, the fearful torture of the knife. "Resolved to heal the sufferer entrusted to his care, the surgeon must ignore cries and pleadings, and do his work regardless of complaints." Such were the words in which Celsus, physician-in-ordinary to the Emperor, described the surgeon's pitiless duty.

Reports of operations performed in classical times, accounts of those of the barber-surgeons of the Middle Ages, and the records of modern hospitals before the middle of the nineteenth century, conjure up scenes of horror. The patient, yelling with fear, was dragged to the operating table, was firmly held by as many as half a dozen stalwarts, feet and hands were tied. Then the surgeon could begin his cruel task, burning with a red-hot iron or cutting into the quivering flesh. The fully conscious patient watched the instruments in the hands of the tormentor, heard the instructions which the surgeon gave to the assistants, each order meaning fresh and yet more intolerable suffering. If the poor wretch could no longer endure this martyrdom, and tried to break away, the assistants would look to the security of the bonds and would hold him down yet more firmly with their restraining hands.

Even such "minor surgery" as tooth extraction was so excruciatingly painful that again and again in history teeth were deliberately pulled as a form of torture or of punishment. At Alexandria, during the Decian persecution, St. Apollonia and Blasius the Blessed were tied to pillars while their teeth were extracted, in the attempt to make them abjure Christianity. A thousand years later King John of England used the drawing of teeth as a means of extortion. Wanting to get ten thousand ducats from a wealthy citizen of Bristol, the tyrant had the man brought to his palace and with his own royal hands extracted a tooth day after day for a week, until at length resistance was broken.

For thousands of years operations were dreaded more than hell, the black death or purgatory, so that one might have fancied the willful human spirit, dissatisfied with the quantum of pain so freely dispensed by bountiful nature, to have decided upon supplementing it with the artificial agonies of surgery.

"Were we to imagine ourselves," wrote the French surgeon Daetigues, "suspended in timeless space over an abyss out of which the sounds of the revolving earth rose to our ears, we should hear naught but an elemental roar of pain, uttered as with one voice by suffering mankind."

But where, in what epoch, at what stage of being, did pain begin? What creature first became conscious of it?

Myth tells us that pain began in the timeless world of the gods. In their immortal frames destruction was at work before it attacked our perishable ones. The sun-god suffered from the infirmities of old age; Isis had had an inflammation of the breast; Horus was stung by a scorpion and was also attacked by ophthalmia; Dionysus and Æsculapius could not be born by the natural passage, and had to be cut out of their divine mothers' living bodies. Even the gods, then, lords of the human race, were thralls to pain.

Some years ago Sir Jagadis Chandra Bose, Indian physicist and biologist, studied the reactions of plants to stimuli, taking graphs with delicate recording apparatus. He came to the conclusion that "a plant feels pain, just as does man and as do the lower animals." He was even able to prove that, like other living creatures, plants can be rendered insensitive to pain by chloroform. Whereas myth had referred the origin of pain to the supramundane territories of the gods, Bose found its beginnings here below, among the plants. But perhaps gods and mortals alike, from the highest denizen of heaven to the lowest terrestrial plants, are all caught up in the dance of pain.

Botany, zo-ology and comparative psychology have shown that, as evolution advances from plants to animals and man, the intensity of painful sensation increases. The privilege of consciousness is counterbalanced by the dubious advantage of becoming aware of pain. As if preserved in a receptacle handed down by parents to children, generation after generation, the possibilities of pain are unceasingly renewed. Pain, at least, is immortal.

In the Book of Genesis we read that pain came to the first human pair through the Fall.

The men of the nineteenth century, however, freed from the bonds of the suprasensual, devoted themselves to the scientific study of human origins. In Gibraltar, at Liége in Belgium, in the Neanderthal remains between Elberfeld and Düsseldorf, in China, Java and elsewhere, prehistoric human skeletons have been unearthed— Homo neanderthalensis, Pithecanthropus erectus, the cave men, and others. To man's recorded history of no more than a few thousand revolutions round the sun it was now possible to add a much longer phase of pre-history, running into millions of years. At the same

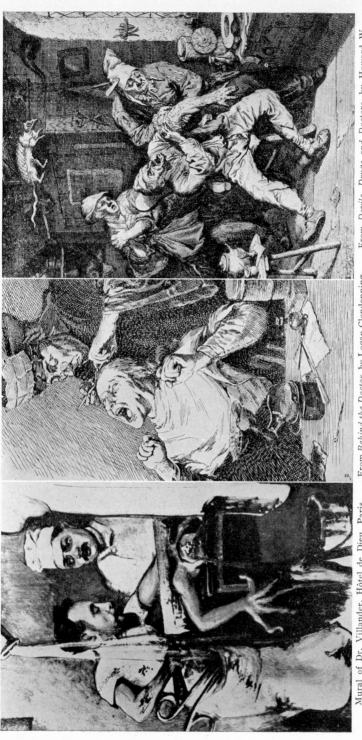

Mural of Dr. Villander, Hôtel de Dieu, Paris.   From *Behind the Doctor*, by Logan Clendenning,   From *Devils, Drugs and Doctors*, by Howard W.

A   published by Alfred A. Knopf.   Haggard, M.D., published by Harper and Brothers.

B   C

PICTORIAL RECORDS OF THE AGONY ENDURED IN OPERATIONS BEFORE THE ADVENT OF ANESTHESIA

A. A surgeon cutting with his big saw.
B. A very painful operation of the seventeenth century.
C. A surgeon torturing his patient.

Miniature, Apollonius de Kition.

Piero Giacosa.

MEDIEVAL TORTURE CHAMBERS

(Above) Two medieval surgeons working on a patient with a broken spine.

(Below) A thirteenth-century operation.

time our knowledge of pain was thrust back into the æons, for all these old bones were indelibly stamped with its sign manual.

In modern laboratories, physicians and anthropologists, chemists and physicists, got to work upon skulls and other bones, upon artifacts from the Ice Age, the Stone Age, the Bronze Age and the Iron Age. Pooling their discoveries, they held conferences. Expert pathologists, aided by the latest resources of microscopical chemistry and comparative anatomy, studied the diseases to which the bones of the men who had lived hundreds of thousands of years ago testified. They found that our primitive ancestors suffered from gout and other forms of arthritis, intracranial disease which probably caused convulsions, caries of the jaws and of the teeth, fractures and tumors of the bones. Hence they must have been plagued by multifarious pains. In many of the barrows were skulls with round holes produced by the trephine; and among the arrowheads were knives, saws and lancets—showing that our forefathers also knew the agony of "curative surgery."

Henceforward the heartfelt cry of that old-time princess of Babylon was echoed by the mute tidings of these far more ancient witnesses to pain. Skeletal fragments of men and women who lived before the dawn of history thus reinforced our conviction as to how early were the beginnings of man's via dolorosa.

While myths, skeletal remains, votive offerings and clay tablets stamped with cuneiform inscriptions thus strengthen one another's testimony as to the eternity and ubiquity of pain, art chimes in with its strong representative power. On the walls of Assyrian and Egyptian temples and tombs, in Etruscan vases and mural decorations like those of Pompeii, and in the sculptures of ancient days, are depictions of eyes blinded, bodies deformed, mouths distorted by pain. We see Polyphemus the Cyclops having a solitary orb destroyed by "Nobody" and his companions; the unhappy Philoctetes, marooned on the coast of Lemnos; Adonis torn by the boar's tusks; the dying Dirce, as shown in a group of statuary called "The Farnese Bull"; the Niobids being slaughtered by the arrows of Apollo and Artemis; Laocoön and his sons in the grip of the serpents. All these are classical tributes to the might of pain.

The core of medieval faith was the Passion of Jesus, and the artists of those days were never weary of displaying Him crowned with thorns, scourged, crucified, wounded in the side, as a theme for woodcuts, paintings, sculptures, rood screens and altarpieces. Though He had perished on the Cross, the Christ lived on in the popular imagination as the Man of Sorrows. Thus the Saviour appears on the title page of Dürer's "The Greater Passion" and in a thousand specimens of Gothic and baroque art.

The Flemish and Dutch painters Frans Hals, Adrian Brouwer, Pieter Breughel and Jan van Hemessen show the manners and customs of their time: booths of barber-surgeons, tents of wandering masons, offices of strolling dentists. With the rough humor of realists they perpetuate pain-racked countenances, eyes starting from orbits, distorted jaws and yelling mouths of suffering patients.

Yet all that historians and artists have handed down to us concerning the omnipotence and omnipresence of pain fades when compared with the unwritten, unvoiced and unlimned knowledge that comes to each one of us in bitter experience ever and ever again renewed. For the uniqueness of the human, all-too-human, tragedy that we denote by the simple monosyllable "pain" can be fully revealed to each one of us only as he suffers. What we ourselves suffer gives us our only adequate knowledge of pain as our constant companion, inseparable, born into the world with the first living creature and to die only with the last. "I have lived" means "I have suffered."

CHAPTER TWO

Shamans, Saints and Alchemists

W ITH CHANGE of times and nations, the conception of pain and the means of resisting it change likewise. In early days man regarded pain as the work of demons, and as such do surviving primitives regard it. Man believed himself born into a hostile environment. He perceived with his own senses that the animals and the elements could do him wrong. These were enemies he could understand, and with which he could cope. But at the first twinge of pain something invisible, unfathomable, disturbed the intelligibility of the visible world. What else than an unknown power, mightier than himself, could be thus capable of afflicting with illness and pain one who had hitherto been hale, upstanding and strong?

Primitive thought was, and is, pictorial. Everything in nature is alive, has a soul, is personified; and consequently the unseen powers become creatures each of which has faculties of its own. The formative imagination transmutes the prepotent causes of pain into demons, which are the hybrid offspring of visible and invisible components, bearing the image and superscription of the embodied torment which created them. The demon of earache, therefore, has gigantic ears; the demon of gout is a huge and hideous incorporeal spider; the malicious demon of toothache, a gnawing worm; and there is an "evil bird" with a sharp beak pecking incessantly at places that hurt in head, neck, bowels or limbs. Some of these demons have human form, others are like animals and yet others can change their shape at will. They inhabit trees or bushes, are carried hither and thither by the wind, sink to earth when the rain falls, creep by night into the caves of the unsuspecting, or in the daytime take people unawares from behind and hurl them into the abodes of pain.

"Clutcher," "Catcher," "Watcher," "Oppressor," "Overpowerer," are among the names given to these demons by those gripped by pain. "Pain attacks a man, clutches him, seizes him, flings him down, strikes him, shakes him, tears at his vitals, masters and slays him—or, after seizing him, may let go." In all the expressions with which man describes his feeling when pain befalls him, there dominates to this day the notion of the clutching demon.

Millenniums have passed; the aspect of the world has changed; where bush and prairie used to be, towns have been built; caves have become palaces—but the demons which man fashioned still seize him unawares. It was a demon who sent pain to the King of Ur to lay him low; and long, long afterward, in medieval Würzburg, three hundred and ninety-nine demons were supposed to have taken possession of the body of a pain-afflicted girl.

Such authorities on myth, religion and folk psychology as Tylor, Frazer, Lévy-Bruhl, Daques, Preiss, Vierkandt and the American Irving King have tried to explain why, in the "Stone Age of the Human Mind," the invisible assumed the form of demons. But the origin of that world which the human imagination created remains no less a mystery than is the creation of the material cosmos.

Touching in its inefficiency is the device first employed by man seized with pain to rid himself of the malevolent demon. He tries to shoo it away, to scare it as he might a bird or any other bodily organism.

The clay heads of tutelary spirits surround the seat of pain. A smoky fire of henbane and other potent herbs is lighted beside the lying-in woman to keep the labor pains away. Rings are worn in the ears or the nose; the skin is tatooed with exorcist signs; whole animals or their parts, plants and stones, tigers' claws, talismans and amulets, are worn to avert evil spirits. Above all, words of might are used, conjurations and spells which enable man, as magician, to control elementals, and put demons to flight. The lower animals, elementals and evil spirits do not share man's wonderful powers of speech. With words he can become their master, compel them to obey, banish them to the place whence they came. "Keep away, pain of the head! Keep away, pain of the teeth! Keep away, pain of the heart!" Thus he admonishes the torturing fiends.

Whenever a pain is supposed to be the outcome of demoniacal possession, you must choose as healer the person best fitted to act as exorcist. In the early stages of civilization this office, like most others, was assigned to woman. The head of the primitive family was the Great Mother, who was priestess and sorceress in one. She was the foundress of the healing art.

From the darkness of the mother's womb sprang new life. This was the first miracle of which man became aware. In woman's life-giving body, the primal forces of nature were at work. Evidently she was a great magician, and therefore she must be able to put pain to flight. In her, fertility made headway against the forces of destruction. The maternal instinct must make her better acquainted than anyone else with the charms and incantations necessary to protect the life she had given from the demons which were striving to kill.

In later phases of civilization, when woman had become subordinate to man, she still remained pre-eminent as healer. The blonde Agamede of the Greeks, the Meglanda of the Elder Edda, the "wild wives" of the Lay of Gudrun, the sibyls and pythonesses of the ancients, wielded exclusive power of exorcising the demons of illness and thus banishing pain.

Among primitives to this day it is the women who have charge of the ritual proceedings against pain. They utter spells and administer magic potions, while making use of a secret language unintelligible to men. The Slavs call these beneficent sorceresses "healing fairies." They are of the same genus as the "white witches" that existed on into our own time in remote parts of rural England. Christianity and modern civilization have driven the "healing fairies" into distant villages of the mountain and forest regions where they still practice their traditional arts.

But in general the sometime sorceress has become a mere midwife, though as such the common folk still rely on her, for is she not mistress of the labor pains, is it not she who evokes from the newborn babe the first reassuring cry, and does she not know best how to deal with the mysterious fruit called the afterbirth? She still retains some of the magical sheen which used to attach to the primal mother in days of old.

But among modern primitives, side by side with the healing mother, and in great measure replacing her, stands the medicine man, the conjurer, the shaman.

The mother had merely to look within, to consult the dark depths of her own nature, which would tell her how to exorcise the demons. The medicine man, having no maternal instinct, is thrust back upon the deliberate arts of the conjurer. The shaman, having as man the same shape as all other men in the village, must change it, must dress up as an anti-demon, must throw his profane body into a state of "sacred intoxication" enabling him to make his way into the realm of spirits and there learn which evil demons have entered into possession of the sick man. In a "medicine lodge" he has been initiated into the secret rites of his craft, and he carries the necessary charms in a "medicine bag." These charms are: a horse's tooth; parts of a weasel's skeleton; a lynx's hide; a serpent's tail; a twig of mountain ash; a bird's windpipe; and a few smoothly rounded pebbles. Living in a hut much like that of the other villagers, but set apart from them by his magical skill, and not mingling too freely lest custom should stale his repute, the shaman practices his craft. The sick come to consult him, or he is called to them if they are too ill to move; and only at the shaman's command will the pain-demons relinquish their grip.

Girdled by a brightly colored blanket, wearing his hair long and crowning it with a headdress of clattering laths, behung with knots of ribbon and bundles of brushwood, the medicine man comes to the patient's hovel. He crouches beside the fire and begins to intone the words of the ritual, while striking his magic drum, bending his body convulsively this way and that and dancing wildly until—dervish-like—he is completely "beside himself." The whole population of the village sits round in a circle, keeping time to the shaman's movements by rhythmical swayings of the body and loud clapping of the hands until the ecstatic passes into a trance-state which is supposed to make him clairaudient to the voice of the demon (inaudible, of course, to the others who are present); and he is believed to be clairvoyant as well, so that he can watch the doings of the invisible spirit. Now he puts his head close to the drum, out of which the demon states terms.

In a way which varies with the reputed powers of the fiend, the conjurer tries to cajole it and to induce it to leave its prey, using as exorcisms potent and noisy songs while he makes orgiastic dance movements, asks for the aid of the spirits of the patient's ancestors and of the sick man's totem, and swings his medicine bag toward the unseen adversary. Should these measures prove ineffective, the shaman begins to rail, curse and threaten, and then to wrestle with the adversary. During this hand-to-hand struggle he utters bloodcurdling cries, thrashes with his fists and belabors the fiend (really the unfortunate patient) with a stick. The assembled relatives and villagers join in the fray, all cudgeling the "possessed" invalid with the utmost fervor. Of course the invisible ancestors and totem which have been conjured up by the medicine man are supposed to fight likewise with the obstinate demon.

A different method is used by the shaman when the demon has carried off the patient's soul to hide it in a hollow tree or a rocky crevice—this withdrawal of the soul being the cause of the pain. In such cases the medicine man's ecstasy continues until he has divorced his own soul from his body, and can then track the demon to its lair. Hasting through the forest, he speeds from tree to tree and from rock to rock till he has found the hiding place. Then the conjurer's soul returns to the conjurer's body, bringing in triumph the stolen spirit of the invalid. A magic pass is made, a spell is uttered, and in a trice the spirit is back in its proper place and the pain is relieved.

When the demons abandoned the hollow trees and rock-crannies they haunted, to ascend into heaven and become gods, man's idea of the cause of pain underwent a change. What had been the unmeaning sport of evil spirits became punishment inflicted by a righteously offended deity.

One who infringed a divine prohibition or neglected a prescribed sacrifice, and thus incurred the wrath of a god, was smitten with pain and affliction by the deity he had enraged. Infuriated by Prometheus' theft of fire from Olympus, Zeus sent Pandora, the All-Gifted, to earth. Each of the gods had fashioned an evil gift to pester mankind, hence her name. Having become the wife of Epimetheus, she opened the box in which she had brought these gifts, and they were scattered abroad over the world. Pain was the vengeance of the gods.

Now the shaman, "lord and master of the troop of winged and crawling demons," was replaced by the priest, trusty servant of the gods. The healing art was in the hands of priests who frequented the temples of the pagan cults. Clad in flowing robes they worshiped the deities to placate these mighty ones, and directed the sacrificial observances which could relieve pain. This early religion was still interspersed with sorcery. In a holy ecstasy, the priests and priestesses of Baal and Ashtoreth besought the god or the goddess to enlighten them as to the offense for which a man or a woman had been smitten with a painful illness. Charms were used, as well as sacrifices, to propitiate the immortals. By degrees, however, magic was replaced by prayer, a gracious answer being left to the better judgment of a higher power.

Under all skies, there presided over the shrines appeasable, potentially helpful, deities—whether these shrines were the pillared temples of Athens, the pyramids of the Pharaohs, the ziggurats of the Assyrians, or the graded teocallis of the Aztecs. The god Ea deigned to come down in person to the town of Ur, to destroy the worm that was gnawing at the root of a sufferer's tooth; in Hindustan the asvidas, the roseate heavenly physicians, drove earthward in their golden three-wheeled chariots to free mortals from pain, and Rudra the Terrible, god of storms, carried in his left hand the panacea kuhurin; Wotan, the All-Father, amid portents of lightning, thunder and flame, sent flights of birds to tell his priests how to heal the sick. There were several divine healers in Olympus. Apollo, Poseidon, Hermes and Artemis were ready, at times, when sacrifices had been duly made, to listen to the supplications of the priests and to grant the benison of healing. The Roman priests knew to which god they should appeal for each ailment. *Divinum*

est opus cedere dolorum—it is a god's gracious task to relieve pain
—such was the guiding principle of classical medicine.

The Christian view is that God sent His Son to the world as
its Redeemer. Standing thus as mediator between God and man,
He exerted an incomparable healing influence. Thanks to His
divine origin, He could cure suffering human creatures, bring relief to those who were moaning with pain. After His death upon
the cross, burial, resurrection and ascent into heaven, His healing
faculty passed to the Church, which remained as His earthly body
here below. By prayer, and by calling on the name of Jesus, in
virtue of the power which could work the miracle of transubstan-
tiation, the Church could cure disease and therefore relieve pain.

Attached to this ecclesiastical healing institution were saints and
priests, monks and nuns, pious men and women who followed in
the footsteps of the Founder and, as part of the imitation of Christ,
recapitulated His Passion in their own fancy. After the resurrection and before the ascent into heaven, He expressly granted this
faculty of healing to the apostles and to all the faithful, for we read
in the last chapter of the Gospel according to St. Mark, the eighteenth verse: "They shall lay hands on the sick, and they shall recover." In this way did the apostles and the other early Christians
heal the sick, as did, after them, saints and martyrs.

But toward the year 900 A.D. the power of cure by the laying on
of hands was reserved for royalty. The King received this privilege
when crowned by the Pope, who was God's vicegerent on earth.
Even as, long before, in the temple of Serapis at Memphis, Vespasian, darling of the gods, was able to cure by "touching," so now
was this power revived by Christian monarchs in their threefold
function of king, saint and physician.

St. Olaf of Norway who introduced Christianity into his kingdom, Edward the Confessor, Philip I of France, Anne of England
—all were successful healers, who had merely to lay on hands to
bring about relief of sickness and pain. By Queen Anne's date,
however, skepticism had made considerable headway in England,
and "touching" was reserved for one malady, scrofula, specifically
named the "king's evil." Touching for the king's evil reached its
maximum in the ultra-loyal days of the Restoration, when we are

told that 92,107 persons were touched. In 1714, when George I, founder of the Hanoverian dynasty, came to the throne, he discontinued the practice, and in 1719 the office for the ceremony was expunged from the liturgy. But Charles Edward, the Young Pretender, touched a child for the king's evil at Holyrood in 1745. The method lingered in France, where in 1775 Louis XVI touched 2400 people for the disease—and, it was alleged, successfully. Two centuries earlier, when Henry of Navarre made his triumphal entry into Paris, faith had been more comprehensive. The sick lined the streets on the way to the palace—sufferers from gout, scrofula and various other painful diseases. Getting out of his carriage, Henry went from one to another and moved thumb and forefinger twice over the sore spot, thus making the sign of the cross, while he said, the first time, "the King touches thee," and the second, "God heals thee."

The bodies of pious kings, like those of saints and martyrs, were of perishable matter, and their assuaging hands stiffened in death. But those who had been orphaned while in the throes of pain could not believe that the healing virtue had died with the death of the healer. Faith would have it that the power once attaching to the live body must have been transferred to all things which had ever come into contact with it. Enough for the sick to call upon the holy name, to visit the places where healing miracles had been worked, to spend a little while near the tomb, to touch such relics as clothing or utensils or a dried fragment of a limb—and a cure would result.

In the Middle Ages faith in relics became so well established that a lively trade in them ensued. Ashes, fragments of bone, teeth, hands or fingers said to have belonged to saints or martyrs were in great request. When the Church set its face against this traffic on the ground that so many of the relics were spurious, the distracted sick did not shrink from stealing those which were reputed genuine. The mortal remains of St. Margaret the Virgin (martyred at Antioch in 303) were handed on like crown jewels from one French queen to another, and when the "heavy hour" of the incumbent was approaching they were brought into the lying-in chamber that the heir to the throne might be born safely, speedily and painlessly.

Faith could turn every thing and every action into a remedy. The Schoolmen held that the body was safeguarded against pain merely by allowing the mind to dwell upon the thought of God. Thomas Aquinas writes: "The blessed delight which comes from the contemplation of divine things suffices to reduce bodily pain." To the Reformers, Scripture was a medicament. One who read the Holy Book in the right spirit could not fail to get well. The Prophet tells the faithful of Islam that the Koran is a sure remedy for illness and pain. "When anyone suffers from toothache, let him lay a finger upon the sore spot and recite the ninety-eighth verse of the sixth sura."

Faith, in its infinite mercy, was lavish of its gifts, but sufferers were insatiable in their demands, so, for solace, they added superstition to belief. Women of the people would go into the forest and bind the painful part to a tree, that the ache might be absorbed by the vigorous stem. Others would thrust a wooden skewer into the affected region, and then bury the skewer (therewith burying the pain) in a deep hole dug in the cellar where neither sun nor moon could penetrate. Others, again, would feed the pain to their cattle, burn it in the fire, drown it in water, bake it into gingerbread, hide it in some object which they would palm off on an unsuspecting beggar.

Whenever thought freed itself from the trammels of faith and the snares of superstition, and was replaced by a freethinking philosophy, the attempt was made to get the better of pain by the force of reason. The Stoics believed that this could be effected by the "rational repudiation" of pain. When Poseidonius, a noted Stoic, suffering at the time from a violent attack of gout, was visited by Pompey at Rhodes, he was able, regardless of the pain, to entertain his distinguished guest in a fitting manner. Coming to modern times, we find both Descartes and Spinoza recommending that pain should be overcome through its "permeation" by reason. Blaise Pascal, when suffering severely, tried to ignore his troubles by immersion in philosophical and mathematical problems.

Immanuel Kant, the philosopher of Königsberg, devoted his life to profound thinking. This discipline, which enabled him to create the greatest intellectual system ever known, had also the power of assuaging pain. When the disabilities and infirmities of old age were increasing, Kant had recourse to "the healing power of intention." In his last work, entitled *Von der Macht des Gemütes durch den blossen Vorsatz seiner krankhaften Gefühle Meister zu sein* (Concerning the Power of the Mind To Master Morbid Feelings by Simple Intention), he writes: "For a year I have been troubled by morbid inclinations and very painful stimuli which from others' description of such symptoms I believe to be gout, so that I had to call in a doctor. One night, however, impatient at being kept awake by pain, I availed myself of the stoical means of concentration upon some indifferent object of thought, such for instance as the name of 'Cicero' with its multifarious associations; in this way I found it possible to divert my attention, so that the pain was soon dulled. . . . Whenever the attacks recur and disturb my sleep, I find this remedy most useful."

When the demons had fled, magic and spells lost their power; and with the coming of the twilight of the gods, sacrifices and priestly ritual no longer had any effect. Only when, by a quasi-magical self-deception, wishes brought their own fulfilment, did trees, water or fire relieve human beings of pain; and the healing influence of relics, texts from the Bible or verses of the Koran could be obtained only so long as people continued to believe in them. None but persons like St. Thomas, who by divine grace was endowed with special power so that he saw everything in a divine light, could dispel pain by such a method as his; while the practice of stoical equanimity, the power of knowledge, the healing thought of intention, could not drive away suffering except for those who had a peculiar talent.

When souls and spirits gained a victory over the elemental might of pain, there was always something uniquely wonderful about the matter: charms, hocus-pocus, a conjuring trick with ideas; or else the miracle of faith. Those who, in later days when the senses had been rationalized and faith had grown cold, tried to recover the lost treasure of their forefathers, could find nothing but incomprehensible words and signs which no longer worked because they had lost content.

One of the mysteries of life is that what the waking mind, the highly tensed spirit, cannot achieve, becomes possible to man in a state of trance.

When consciousness lapsed into artificial sleep, and when the body became inactive, the power of pain was broken. It vanished when consciousness ceased, going to sleep with the body which passed into the death-like sleep of trance.

The same end could be reached by the use of drugs. In the "great chemical workshop of nature," where medicines of elemental power are produced in roots, bark, herbs and blossoms, man could likewise find that most wonderful of all the means for allaying pain —artificial sleep. Associated with the scent of flowers, encapsuled in seeds, as the sap which flowed from incisions made into certain plants, in poppy, mandragora, Indian hemp and other "drowsy syrups," man could find the great gift of artificial sleep.

On Mount Ida the goddess Aphrodite, and in the Nile valley a legendary Egyptian prince, found relief from pain by sleeping upon a bed of red poppies. The Egyptian sun-god Ra is said to have been the first to administer mandragora as a soporific. From the Egyptian Polydamna, wife of Thon, Helen of Troy is said to have learned how to prepare herbal remedies which would "expunge sorrow from the memory." When the hero Rustam, son of Zâl and Rudâbah, was being born, an eagle soared round the bed of the lying-in woman and dropped a remedy which made it possible for the babe to be cut out of his mother's body painlessly. Gods that strayed to earth, kindred of the Scythian nomads, secured during their raids the sleep that is hidden in Indian hemp.

"Such herbs," we are told in the Rig-Veda, "come down to us from the most ancient times, three eras before the gods were born." Healing plants were growing upon the land where the first human habitation was built. Of old an archetypal pharmacist learned their use—a magician whose name has not survived. In a way known only to himself, he discovered how to extract from herbs their juices containing poison and remedy strangely mingled—much of the former and little of the latter. Only a few learned from him how to separate the poison from the remedy, so that the latter could be obtained in quantities sufficient to bring about artificial sleep.

Down through the ages, Indian hemp spread from land to land.

In China it was during the Wei dynasty that the famous physician Hoa Tho was able to prepare from it the sedative "mario" which could very quickly throw the patient into so profound a sleep that it was "as if he had drunk himself to death." In Cilicia, Dioscorides was able to spice wine with mandragora in so cunning a fashion that a draught of it would prevent a patient from feeling the smart of the knife. At the court of the Hindu king Bhoja the doctors were able to put their ruler to sleep with the fumes of sammojini before they trephined his skull. During the Middle Ages certain monks knew how to prepare "sleep-sponges" or pillows impregnated with mandragora, and candles in whose composition the same remedy had been mingled, and by these means to safeguard the slumbers of many distinguished sufferers. No less a man than St. Benedict, we are told, being about to amputate a leg of Emperor Henry II, put the patient to sleep upon a mandragora pillow so that the operation could be performed without causing pain.

But if such remedies were successfully used to prevent pain, whether by Chinese sage, Hindu pundit, Greek physician or medieval saint, it was only in isolated cases. The method never became general.

These herbal drugs were too incalculable in their effects ever to become part of the ordinary medical armamentarium. Barber-surgeons, army medicos and hospital doctors who had to treat the masses never became fully acquainted with the application of such methods. Often enough, in their unskilled hands, the blessing became a curse, for not infrequently the drugged sleep passed on into death. Hence these medicaments were shunned, the patients no less than the doctors having become mistrustful, thinking it better that pain, however terrible, should be endured rather than life be put in peril.

When, in the seventeenth century, Bailly, a barber-surgeon of Troyes, put one of his patients to sleep with a herbal syrup before an operation, this bold venture aroused widespread consternation. Gui Patin, a doctor and renowned man of letters attached to the University of Paris, raised his voice in condemnation of the audacious barber and addressed a protest to the medical faculty of Troyes in which we read: "If Bailly really uses narcotic plants in this way, you had better take him soundly to task. Herbal poisons have worked mischief in more skillful hands than his. See to it that these practices are not allowed, and do not let him go unpunished. The impudent barber should not be able to boast of having done such things with impunity." The case came before the courts. Bailly had to pay a heavy fine, and the stupefaction of patients before operations by giving them herbal remedies was forbidden under a heavy penalty.

The alchemists were the first to recognize that in natural conditions medicines were provided only in an imperfect state, and that special skill would be needed to separate the essential from the accidental and to win the trustworthy out of the incalculable. The "royal art" of the alchemist was perhaps the first attempt to introduce order into the untidy treasure chamber of the organic and inorganic substances: to get the effective out of the husk of the ineffective, to separate the useful from the harmful and to extract the pure, wholesome quintessence out of a jumble of impure substances.

But alchemy was still so much interwoven with magic, so extensively dependent upon the constellations, so ardently directed toward a mystical goal, that the pure active principle seemed an elusive ether, an *anima* which, in its hermetic potency, would be subject to the ascendance of particular stars. Thus in their excursions into medicine the alchemists were guided by their thirst for gold, which belonged to the house of the sun. In this "metal of light" they believed that they would find the panacea, the cure-all, which would be the remedy for every disease and would provide relief for every pain. Throughout the centuries they were continually on the search for the philosopher's stone, for the *spiritus catholicus* which would liberate from gold its sunlike *anima* converting this precious metal into *aurum potabile*—gold that could be consumed as a liquid medicine.

In their search for a panacea, the alchemists found many valuable substances, a number of useful chemical compounds. But since they kept their eyes directed toward the sun, and were dazzled by the sheen of gold, they paid little heed to anything that lay beside their path. They labeled their casual discoveries with this or that high-sounding name, and left the fluid unused in a phial, the powder unexamined in a saucer—mere accessories of which they made no further use.

In the thirteenth century Raymond Lully, the *doctor illuminatus* round whom so many legends have gathered, discovered in his alchemical laboratory a "white fluid" which he called "sweet vitriol." But two more centuries were to pass before the analgesic, the pain-allaying, properties of this "sweet vitriol" were to be recognized.

During these two centuries the Middle Ages, paralyzed by a belief in fiction, had given place to the eager and fruitful life of the Renaissance. Instead of the old-time alchemist devoting his energies to a futile search for the transmutation of metals, there came into being men with a spirit much more akin to that of modern science. Emerging from the alchemist's laboratory they smelled the reek of earth, put their fingers into wounds, studied pain, became acquainted with life. Theophrastus Bombastus Paracelsus von Hohenheim spent his days as a migratory physician wandering from country to country, seeing with his own eyes what his fellow men had to endure, and "taught the healing art by the greatest of teachers, experience." He had carried out diligent investigations "in all the ends of the earth"; had learned from herdsmen, bath-attendants and old women how to knead, rub and massage parts of the body stricken with pain; had crossed the mountains and roamed along the valleys to ask nature herself to disclose her analgesic herbs. No natural product which was capable of relieving pain could escape his eager attention, for he explored "all three realms of nature," the animal, the vegetable, and the mineral world. Having recognized with his own eyes and learned by his own intelligence the multifariousness of sickness and pain, and knowing how scanty was the supply of unmodified natural remedies, he returned to the alchemist's laboratory in order to perfect what was so imperfectly given us by nature, having recourse to the "royal art" of distillation, purification and extraction.

One day, having mixed sulphuric acid with alcohol, heated

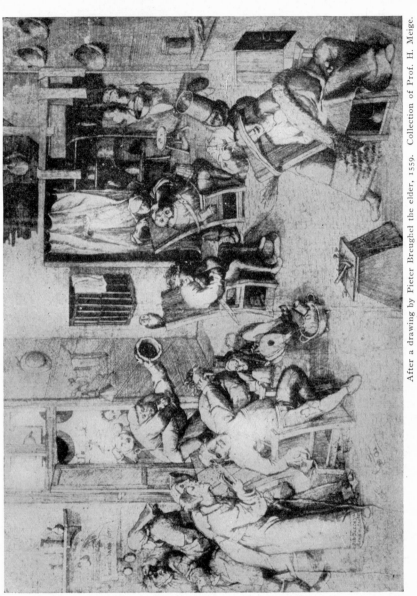

After a drawing by Pieter Breughel the elder, 1559. Collection of Prof. H. Meige.

A head operation.

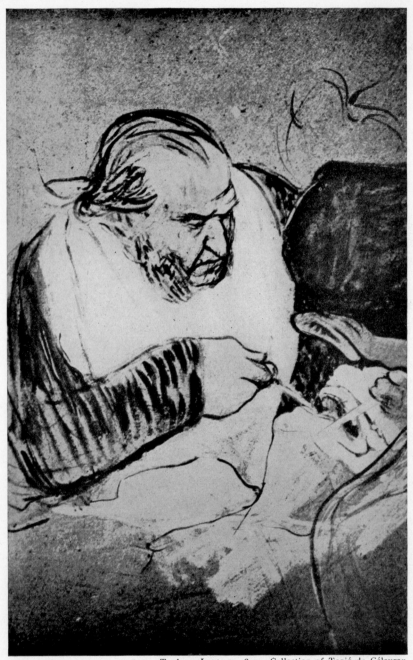

Toulouse-Lautrec, 1891.   Collection of Topié de Céleyran.

An operation by Péan.

the mixture and condensed the steam to form a liquid, he rediscovered the "white fluid" first found long before him by Raymond Lully. Trying this fluid upon chickens, he made an observation which almost entitled him to be called the founder of anesthesia.

"With respect to this peculiar vitriol, we must take a certain circumstance into account," he writes, describing his experiment. "Of all the extracts of vitriol, this particular one is the most important, being stable. Furthermore, it has an agreeable taste, so that even chickens take it gladly, and thereafter fall asleep for a long time, awaking undamaged. In view of the effect of this vitriol, I think it especially noteworthy that its use may be recommended for painful illnesses, and that it will mitigate the disagreeable complications of these."

This "sweet vitriol" with which Paracelsus put chickens to sleep was nothing other than what we now know as sulphuric ether.

A young man, Valerius Cordus by name, was at this time acting as apprentice to his uncle, the traveling apothecary Joachim Ralla. Cordus carefully noted anything he came across in the way of new drugs. Indeed, his hobby took the form of collecting a complete record of all extant medicaments.

In the course of his wanderings, Cordus encountered another wanderer, Theophrastus Bombastus Paracelsus von Hohenheim. Like all who came within Paracelsus' range, he promptly succumbed to the spell of this great physician. For months he dogged the Master's footsteps, digging with him for herbal roots and accompanying him to the bedsides of patients, where he listened attentively to the great man's utterances, jotting down every prescription.

Much that has come down to us concerning the remedies used by Paracelsus we owe to the industry of this apothecary's apprentice smitten with the note-taking fever; and among them a precise description of ether.

In 1542, a year after the death of Paracelsus, Cordus, visiting the town of Nuremberg, proudly showed the physicians there his long list of then known remedies. These medical worthies were greatly surprised, for not one of them had ever seen or even heard of half the number. The Senate of Nuremberg was induced by Valerius Cordus, for the greater glory of the town and for the welfare of mankind, to purchase his collection of notes. A deputation came to the young man's hostelry, offering to pay his bill there and to give him in addition a fee of one hundred gold ducats if he would make over the notebooks. Cordus jumped at the offer and handed his manuscripts to the learned committee of Nuremberg doctors.

Thus was the "sweet vitriol" which had been discovered by Raymond Lully two hundred years before, retrieved from the waters of oblivion. Paracelsus learned its analgesic properties, and Cordus made a record of the preparation and effect of the remedy. Anyone, now, could read about ether, but for centuries more no one troubled to do so. *"Habent sua fata libelli."* Like books, discoveries and substances have their own laws, their own destinies. The knowledge of "sweet vitriol" remained a dead letter in a dusty pharmacopœia at Nuremberg.

When, more than a hundred years later, Sir Isaac Newton and the chemists Godfrey and Boyle made renewed references to "sweet vitriol," this was of little avail, for soon afterward it was again forgotten. In the year 1792, the German apothecary Frobenius brought it to light once more and, in reminiscence of its alchemist origin, gave it the pompous name of *ether*. By degrees thereafter the remedy came into use for the treatment of asthma and other respiratory diseases. But it was not until another half-century had elapsed that doctors turned to practical account the analgesic or anesthetic potentialities discovered three centuries earlier by Paracelsus.

CHAPTER THREE

The Last of the Magicians

FAITH, USED by our forefathers as a remedy for pain, had been robbed of its efficacy by the Enlightenment. Narcotics, derived from the plant world, were proving untrustworthy. Alchemy tried to correct and improve upon nature but, being entangled in its own speculations, never realized what it had brought to light in the way of a pure and potent preventive of pain.

Now a new spirit was arising, one which led people to study the laws of material nature. The sciences of chemistry and medicine with their ancillary disciplines issuing from this new spirit gave hope of fulfilling the promise that suffering man could be helped by science and art better than he had been helped by herbal remedies or by alchemy.

But before chemistry and medicine could attain that scientific freedom from prejudice which enabled physicians to understand the true nature of the sensitive body and the true composition of the remedies for pain, they had to pass through the erroneous ways of such materialistic speculations as iatrophysics and iatrochemistry and, having come out on the other side, create precise methods of scientific research.

Pain, however, continued without cessation. All those who suffered craved for relief. Of what avail to them was the new spirit, the new science, which had discredited the old remedies and was only beginning to hold out hope of the new? The healer, in whose ears rang the moans of the suffering, and to whose eyes their pain-racked faces were a distress, was one of the first to desert the colors of the Enlightenment to become the pioneer of a new faith in miracles.

In the eighteenth century it was no longer possible to return to a simple faith in magic or in religion. In salons and cafés, discussion was rife concerning the advance of science, which was now a power and, more than that, had become the fashion. If miracles were to be resurrected, they must woo the favor of science, speak the tongue of science and make terms with the new outlook.

The new doctrine of a healing vitalism, which recognized the intense vitality of pain, therefore came into being as a compost of science and miracle. From this outlook, the cosmos was regarded as interpenetrated with vital forces, of which man himself was a part. In man worked the magnetic fluid which kept the cosmos going. The healer could do all that was necessary if he stored up this magnetic fluid in himself and then passed it on to his patients. To the apostles of the new doctrine, the wonder-working powers of the new medicine were instinct in man himself, in his magnetic vital force.

A man was needed who would weave all these ideas into a system, and was bold enough to say: "I am one through whom the universal healing fluid becomes effective. These cosmic energies which can heal every disease, mitigate every pain, radiate from my hands and from my words."

The man who claimed the power of working miracles with his "vital energy" was Anton Mesmer, sometime student of divinity, sometime student of law, then a student of medicine in Vienna, where he took his degree in 1766. He was an adept of the "science of the stars." Short and stout, he had a double chin and a friendly manner, a taste for music, and was a performer on the glass harmonica—enough of a musician to win the esteem of Mozart, Gluck and Haydn.

As soon as he announced his new revelation, almost everyone was ready to believe it. Sufferers streamed to him in enormous numbers, eager for him to use his "vital fluid" for the relief of their pains.

This was in Paris, just before the great French Revolution which, in the name of the Enlightenment, was to make Reason the State religion.

Like the herbalist empirics who hoped to relieve pain by the artificial induction of sleep, this apostle of "magnetism" believed himself able to relieve pain by putting his patients to sleep. But before this magnetic sphere could be fully developed, Mesmer's doctrine was to undergo many transformations.

The magnet used by Mesmer in his first experiments had long been part of a magician's armamentarium. Since Paracelsus first administered magnetic iron as a remedy, many attempts had been made to use its strange attractive force in the sphere of disease. Shortly before Mesmer, Hell the Jesuit father and astronomer recommended the magnet as remedy; but Mesmer was the first to make it a symbol of the theory of a healing fluid. In magnets, he declared, this mysterious cosmic energy was most plainly manifested, the energy which pervaded and maintained the harmony of the universe. All that he held necessary was to place two magnets in contact with the body of an afflicted person. Then the healing fluid would flow through the disordered body and restore it to harmony with the universe.

In an age which had begun to grow weary of inefficacious rationalist methods of cure, the new medical mysticism secured ready acceptance. As soon as Mesmer applied his magnets the patient felt better, and could plainly sense the healing current flowing through his body and putting pain to flight. Not one patient only, but hundreds upon hundreds, experienced the same thing; and the afflux of the sick, the halt and the maimed was soon so great that Mesmer found it impossible to treat them all individually, or indeed to do justice in this way to more than a handful of those who sought relief. Then a fruitful idea occurred to him. Taking a wooden rod, he made passes over it and thus invested it with his own magnetic energy. By pointing this rod at his patients from a little distance, he could set the magnetic forces at work upon from thirty to a hundred of them simultaneously.

You can picture Mesmer in a long violet-silk robe. He held the magnetized staff in his hand. But a staff or rod has always been the first requisite of a magician, arousing a predisposition to believe. Mesmer's patients were absolutely convinced that they could feel the magnetic wand drawing the pain out of their bodies.

At the climax of his successes, a yet more remarkable secret was revealed to Mesmer. He discovered something more vital than anything which could be hidden away in the dead matter of the magnetic wand, namely, that it was not this which he held in his hand but the hand itself from which the healing force emanated. If he merely touched the patients, or made passes with his fingers above their shoulders and down the arms, repeating the movements twice or thrice and then touching the seat of pain with his hands, lo and behold, the pain and discomfort vanished.

The healing power of touch, as exercised of old by Vespasian and the monarchs of former days, had been resurrected in mesmerism, but it was now given a name derived from the terminology of the new doctrine of vitalism. There was diffused from Mesmer's hands a force akin to metallic magnetism, and it was therefore styled "animal magnetism."

Subsequently it was found that even the mesmerizer's touch was superfluous. He need merely bring his will into operation, and the healing fluid did its work upon the sick. Thus, in this third phase of mesmerism, the magic word, the "open sesame" of the shamans, achieved honor once more. Enough for the conjurer to say, to will, "go away, pain," and pain went.

From near and from far, those who were afflicted with pain flocked to Mesmer's house in the rue Montmartre. Early or late, they awaited his coming, and when he at length appeared in the street the patients ran to meet him, hoping to touch his garments and thus come into contact with the healing emanations.

The Paris court idolized the wonder-working physician. Marie Antoinette, the Duke of Bourbon, the Prince of Condé and Lafayette became his close friends. Other persons bearing the most famous names of the epoch were among his patients, and princesses besought the favor of being admitted to his presence.

So great was the afflux that even the energies of a man who could make magical passes, use a magician's wand and utter words of power were insufficient to cope with the multitudes. Mesmer had to discover an expedient which would enable him to meet the demand, without forfeiting the nimbus of his miraculous personality. He also declared that, although the magnetic force was present in everyone, this was in varying strength, so that only in elect personalities did it "accumulate" to operate as a healing fluid. But these elect, these "magnetic personalities," were able to transfer their fluid to all kinds of objects, which would then become instinct with the power of healing.

Here, once more, with his "new doctrine," Mesmer was reviving the old and tried faith in magic. Had not the saints been able to transfer their healing virtue to inanimate objects? Relics, including whatever the saints had touched when alive, acted in this way.

By this device, while remaining in the eyes of the faithful the supreme source of the miraculous healing fluid, Mesmer, by transferring it to inanimate objects, found he was able to multiply its fabulous magical virtues a thousandfold, so that a thousand things in a thousand places could function simultaneously in the absence of the magician. In that way it was possible to provide for the needs of a vast multitude.

The first object to be used in this way to work miracles in the absence of the magician was a great wooden tub or vat in Mesmer's house—the so-called *baquet*. This *baquet* contained a double series of bottles which he charged with animal magnetism. The bottles converged upon a steel rod from which conductors issued to the painful spots in the bodies of the various patients.

Finger tips touching one another, the patients sat in reverent silence round the magnetic *baquet* as if before an altar. Not a sound disturbed the oscillations in the room. Thus for an hour the body of each was charged with magnetic energy. Then began the "crisis" in which pain and sickness vanished to the accompaniment of convulsive twitchings. As soon as the convulsions were over, the patients fell into a healing trance, from which they awakened free from all their troubles.

These cures at Mesmer's *baquet* became so popular that the Parisians had to reserve a place many days in advance to get their dose of the healing fluid. The wealthy and the nobles would invite their friends to a seat at Mesmer's, even as aforetime to a seat in a private box at the Comédie Française.

Once more demand exceeded supply, so Mesmer went a stage further, making mesmerized pocket *baquets* which were sold for home use. His inventive faculty enabled him to find various other objects which would serve his purpose. He magnetized water-basins in which, by hundreds, the sick could wash away their ailments; he magnetized mirrors before which the patients filed in a queue, each in turn contemplating his image and "looking himself well."

Other methods of mass healing were the use of magnetized musical instruments such as harpsichords and glass harmonicas. As soon as the notes were sounded, the pain of persons within hearing was stilled.

Since, ere long, the space in any house grew too small to accommodate those who craved healing, Mesmer went on to transfer his powers to the open country. He magnetized gardens, parks, shrubs, bushes, whole forests. The sick tied themselves with ropes to the trees charged with fluid. In the rue Bondi, day after day, hundreds of persons flocked round an oak tree magnetized by Mesmer, awaiting there the relief of pain. In this way Mesmer's cures were effected against a background more colorful than that made available by any magician of former days.

France, believing Mesmer to be the most precious force then alive in any part of the world, was much concerned to know what would happen when he went the way of all flesh. The *baquets,* the pocket instruments of the same kind, the mirrors, the harpsichords and the trees must, from time to time, be re-charged with magnetic energy, since their power slowly evaporated. What would happen when Mesmer had departed this life forever? Louder and louder grew the demand that, of course for a suitable consideration, the wonder-worker should pass on his powers to disciples, so that the healing force of animal magnetism might remain available for mankind throughout the ages.

The State was eager to monopolize these powers, so the government offered Mesmer a pension of forty thousand livres, and was prepared to build him an Institute were he willing to transfer his powers to certain persons nominated by the State. Mesmer was disposed to agree, but made a condition. The government must provide something which the healer had not yet been able to secure —official scientific recognition of his discovery.

But though quite a number of doctors, such as d'Eslon, physician-in-ordinary to Count Artois, and various scientists such as Constantin de Gebelin, president of the Paris Museum, were faithful adherents of Mesmer, most physicians of the day regarded his healings with outspoken contempt. The government approached the Academy of the Sciences, but these learned men, who had long since expressed their devotion to the Enlightenment, refused to renounce it in favor of the modern miracle-worker. Nothing would induce Mesmer to abandon his demand. He continued to declare: "I cannot accept any pension from France until the Academy recognizes my discovery." Again: "The honor and glory of having bestowed upon mankind this most important source of healing is worth more to me than estates or money."

At length King Louis XVI intervened, and persuaded the Medical Society to hold an inquiry into the effects of animal magnetism. The committee of eminent physicians and scientists nominated by His Majesty to study this question contained some of the most famous men of the day: Dr. Guillotin, who was later to invent the guillotine as a humane killer; Benjamin Franklin, discoverer of the lightning-conductor; Lavoisier, one of the founders of modern chemistry; and Jussieux, the botanist.

The members of this commission got seriously to work. Some of them even consented to be magnetized, that they might have personal experience of the effects of mesmerism. At its last sitting, the commission drafted a resolution to the effect that, although Mesmer's activities certainly involved something unexplained and for the time being inexplicable, and was not devoid of value, science was not in a position to approve what it could not explain.

Mortified by this decision, Mesmer decided to leave Paris. The Queen was in despair, and persuaded Maurepas, minister of State, to intercede with Mesmer. Maurepas, complying with Marie Antoinette's wishes, proffered all conceivable honors and a large sum of money as compensation for the "incredibly foolish" verdict of the commission. But Mesmer remained stubborn and said he was determined to shake the dust of the metropolis from his feet.

Still the devotees plied him with further requests, which were conveyed to him privately. Some of them had founded a body called the Société Harmonique. Its members called upon Mesmer and declared themselves ready to raise a sum of money with which he could form an Academy of his own in opposition to the official Academy of the Sciences. In return for this, Mesmer was requested to place at the disposal of the Société a number of mesmerized apparatus, and to instruct the members in his magnetic methods. He was solemnly assured that the secret of these would be faithfully guarded by his disciples. To finance the scheme, the Société Harmonique issued shares of one hundred louis each, and these shares had all been oversubscribed before issue.

Among those who took out shares was no less notable a person than Madame Dubarry, the late King's mistress, who had a private Mesmer apparatus at her bedside, using it as a remedy whenever she suffered from any ailment. In her memoirs, Madame Dubarry records indignation that Mesmer should have asked so large a sum for imparting his wonderful secret. "The fee demanded by this doctor for explaining the use of his magnetic apparatus was no less than one hundred louis, and it surprised me, nay, shook my faith, that the man who declared his sole object was to serve humanity should have expected so vast a sum from his supporters." From what she goes on to write it is plain that she had begun to share the growing disillusionment of the Parisians. "His lectures were extraordinarily well attended, but whereas many of the audience gathered the impression that one who could work such miracles must be possessed of superhuman powers, others opined that he must have received these powers direct from Lucifer."

The dispute about Mesmer, the struggle between mystical credulity and scientific skepticism, between excessive admiration and suspicious reserve, became gradually intensified until brought to a close by the outbreak of the Revolution.

Most of Mesmer's distinguished patients died under the guillotine. He himself, being a favorite with the court and the nobility, was suspect and had to flee hotfoot from the town of his triumphs, abandoning apparatus, manuscripts and property.

He naturally made for Vienna, to find that the authorities there regarded him as a masked Jacobin, as a secret agent of the French Revolution, and believed that he had come to the Austrian capital only in order to prepare a coup against the monarchy. He was therefore arrested, and spent two months in jail. Having at length managed to secure release, Mesmer turned his back upon a world gone crazy about politics and retired to his birthplace, Meersburg, on the Lake of Constance.

In Europe, during these later years, one notable historical event followed hard upon the heels of another. Napoleon issued from the French Revolution and pursued his plans for world conquest; Prussia at length revolted against the Emperor's dominion; revolution broke out in Spain; in Austria, Andreas Hofer became the head of the Tyrolese insurrection and champion of a war of liberation; Europe was in the throes of reconstruction.

During the twenty years which elapsed between his retirement and his death in 1815, Mesmer the wonder-worker passed into complete oblivion. Before the fascination exerted by the march of history during the close of the eighteenth and the opening of the nineteenth century, that of even so remarkable a person as Anton Mesmer paled.

It was natural enough that those who were engrossed in great affairs should forget this remarkable man, but Pain itself, the body's everlasting associate, continued to cherish the memory of the "caressing hand" which had once brought relief. When the hermit of the Lake of Constance had passed away, the charm of his "magnetic fingers" lived on in some of his disciples, who rescued it for future ages despite the world-shaking events that were going on.

One of these disciples, who had paid the Master four hundred louis for instruction in magnetism, was Count Maxime de Puységur of Busancy. Like most of Mesmer's titled adherents, in his park he had a magnetized lime tree, to which, when they were ill, the peasants came in crowds as pilgrims, hoping to be cured with the aid of their aristocratic landlord.

One day a shepherd named Victor, a man of three-and-twenty, stood beneath the tree to which he had been tied. The Count made passes over his body to increase the magnetic influence. But at the moment when, according to the normal course of the treatment, the crisis ought to have taken place, the shepherd fell into a profound sleep. The Count ordered him to awake and to untie himself from the tree. The young man nimbly freed himself from his bonds and, with eyes closed, walked across the park. He spoke like one in a dream, but promptly obeyed all commands uttered by the Count.

Something incomprehensible had occurred. By the power of "animal magnetism" a mesmerist could induce an artificial trance, a profound sleep which had hitherto been exclusively ascribed to the virtues of herbal narcotics.

At first Puységur himself was so much surprised by this unexpected onset of a trance that he did not venture to make his discovery public. Only after he had gone on experimenting for some time, and had obtained the same result in numberless cases, did he promulgate the new doctrine of somnambulism.

Then the tidings of Puységur's successes spread rapidly from Busancy throughout France and beyond into Germany, where it aroused much excitement. Some of the most notable exponents of the German romanticist revival, such as Heinrich von Kleist, E. T. H. Hoffmann, Clemens von Brentano, Ludwig Tieck, Schelling and Fichte were among the most zealous advocates and disseminators of the new doctrine. Even Hufeland, court physician and president of the Prussian Academy of the Sciences, who had dismissed Mesmer as a "dreamer," voted for the acceptance of Puységur's somnambulism as one of the officially recognized methods of cure.

Soon other doctors were found to use and recommend this artificial sleep induced by "animal magnetism" as a means for allaying pain. It was impossible that the surgeons should remain blind to the method. One of the first to adopt it was Baron de Potel who, influenced by Puységur, tried somnambulism to render operations painless. His example was followed in France by Récamier, an authority on cancer, and by Jules Cloquet, professor of surgery.

But Edinburgh became the acropolis of somnambulist operative surgery. In that city were trained the two most famous apostles of Puységur's method of artificial sleep: John Elliotson and James Esdaile.

Dr. Elliotson, a friend of the novelist Thackeray, declared that God, in His infinite mercy, had implanted in the human body the healing power of animal magnetism. Somnambulism was the quickest and best way of relieving pain, being more effective than any narcotics hitherto employed.

Elliotson introduced his own method of putting patients to sleep. Having allowed the subject to rest for a while in a darkened room, with his eyes closed, he then, without actual contact, made passes over the body, breathed on the vertex and had, within about an hour, induced such a sound sleep that the operation could be begun. Elliotson was so firmly convinced that this development of mesmerism would prove an infallible means for painless surgery that he resigned his position at University College Hospital and then, undismayed by scorn and persecution of his colleagues, he devoted himself exclusively to the task of applying in the field of operative surgery the sleep induced by animal magnetism.

The other Edinburgh student, James Esdaile, went to India, determined to pursue his experiments with somnambulism far from the disturbing influence of his colleagues' skepticism. Hindustan proved to be a favorable place for such work. Certain castes and families had known of the method for ages, being familiar with a physiological state akin to somnambulism and known as "Yar-Phoonk," so that they were naturally ready to receive the physiological doctrine which was new in Europe.

In India scrotal tumors were common among the natives, and most surgeons hesitated to remove them because of the danger of the operation. Helped by his faith in mesmerism, however, Esdaile ventured to deal with such cases by the use of the knife, and those who were operated upon were unanimous in declaring that they had not felt a trace of pain. Since Esdaile made a method hitherto reserved for the higher castes available for the lower orders of the Hindu population, he was acclaimed by them as a saint. Patients

came in large numbers, and were operated upon while in the trance
induced by this wonder-working British doctor.

Esdaile was able to persuade the authorities to support him.
A hospital was placed at his disposal, and in the report of this Calcutta institution we read of cases in which, besides scrotal tumors,
legs and arms were removed, and various other major operations
performed without pain, under somnambulism.

Even in its new dress, mesmerism was regarded by official
medicine with hostility and suspicion. Very few doctors had
hitherto been willing to follow the examples of Récamier, Potel
and Cloquet. But when these amazing reports came from Calcutta,
the faculty felt that it was necessary at least to make a trial of the
new method. The result was that the miracles which had been
successfully worked in India could not be reproduced in Europe.
Somnambulism failed to prevent pain during operations performed
in Vienna by Strohmeyer, in France by Auguste Nélaton and at the
Massachusetts General Hospital in Boston by Professor John Collins
Warren. The verdict of western science was unfavorable. The
anesthesia was insufficient to prevent the patient's feeling the pain
of the incision.

Before the long-lasting dispute between the upholders of mesmerism and those of official medicine came to an end, there had
to be a dramatic struggle between credulity and skepticism.

Under pressure from the official faculty, the British government in India had withdrawn support from Esdaile's hospital in
Calcutta. Orders went forth that it was to be closed. Thereupon
the Hindus who had been treated by Esdaile set themselves in
motion. Three hundred natives rose in revolt against the dogma-
tists of science. After the government, ignoring their petition, had
closed the "redeemer's" hospital, the Hindus held a meeting at
which money was subscribed to enable Esdaile to start a hospital
of his own.

The medical newspapers had long since dismissed Esdaile as a
"cheat," a "lunatic" or a "quack." When the Hindu masses now
loudly trumpeted their savior's successes, thus threatening the supremacy of official science, the faculty felt called upon to set its
artillery in motion against Esdaile's patients. Like Esdaile himself,
they were branded as lunatics and cheats who had been doped with

hashish and other narcotics to induce an artificial insensibility to pain and thus array them against science.

When Lafayette went to America during the earlier days of Mesmer's stay in Paris, he informed Washington that, besides munitions of war, he was bringing the United States a most important gift known as mesmerism, "a marvelous weapon against illness and pain." But now, when the medical faculty believed itself to have fully "exposed" somnambulist surgery, it threw the whole mesmeric apparatus overboard as well. Wakley's paper, the *Lancet,* which had become the most influential medical weekly in the world, declared mesmerism and its varieties to be such preposterous humbug that no one could take it seriously, and demanded that all representatives of mesmerism should be expelled from the profession as quacks and swindlers.

After priestly medicines, mandragora, alchemists' brews, the sign of the cross and empiricism had failed to overthrow the dominion of pain, man fancied that the long-sought panacea had been discovered in Mesmer's and Esdaile's vital fluid. Now this hope, too, was dashed.

Before the French Revolution, when Mesmer first came forward with "animal magnetism," science was still in the nursery. The actual achievements of research were scanty and the medical message of youthful natural science, then only in its childhood, consisted mainly of the catchwords of the Enlightenment and of confused theories of the iatrochemists and the iatrophysicists. While medical men were still groping in the dark, they could easily be defeated by Mesmer's unscientific faith in miracles.

But the turn of the century was to prove of the utmost importance to the growth of the exact sciences. One experiment after another succeeded, each of them being a fresh triumph for the cause of science. When the official medical world took the field against Esdaile's somnambulism it had already outgrown the purely meditative and critical phase. Being founded upon an elaborate system of pharmaceutical chemistry, it secured an easy victory. An indisputably trustworthy means of preventing pain, such as mankind had long looked for from various practitioners of the healing art, was now to be provided by exact science.

CHAPTER FOUR

God Speaks from the Lees

THE MEANS for bringing about a dependable artificial sleep, a sleep so profound that the sleeper would be fully guaranteed against feeling the cut of a knife, did not exist ready-made in nature, either in herbs, in dead metal or in the living natural energies of any animal fluid. It was hidden away in a sphere which the bold and inventive human spirit would have to make for itself, in the world of synthetic chemistry.

There—where "Promethean science," godlike and autocratic, was to intervene in the realm of nature and produce a second and artificial realm with the aid of man's creative imagination—was the means to be discovered whereby medicine would be able to conquer pain effectively.

Modern chemistry, synthetic chemistry, which was to produce materials that do not exist in the natural world, could alone provide what was wanted.

It was the human mind which conceived for itself this sort of artificial intervention, having realized that the remedy which was wanted to dull pain by profound artificial sleep must itself be an artifact. Thus was closed the circle of an artificial world.

The first trustworthy pain-controller was secured from the invisible world of the gases.

The man who was to march boldly as pioneer into this world of gases, the discoverer of oxygen, many other substances of the kind, and among them (in the year 1773) the pain-controlling

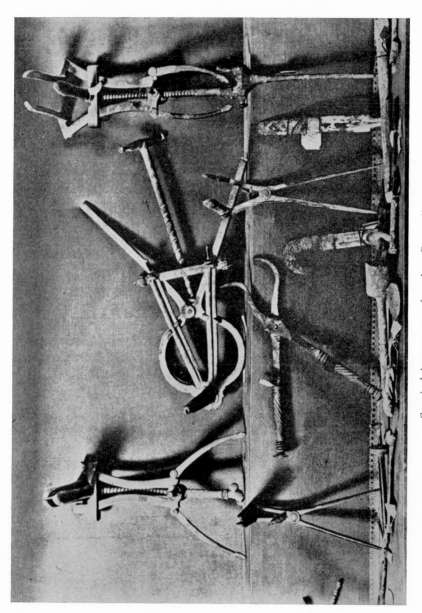

Surgical instruments found at Pompeii.

An eighteenth-century caricaturist portrays an amputation of the period.

Rowlandson, 1785.

nitrous oxide, was Joseph Priestley, the son of a nonconformist cloth-dresser, born near Leeds in 1733, and for a time, in youth, schoolmaster and divine.

On Sundays he fervently read the lessons and preached sermons; occasionally he conducted the wedding service, he presided over baptisms or funerals, taught the catechism and conscientiously performed all the duties of his office.

Near the minister's dwelling was the brewery of Jacks and Nell. When Joseph Priestley had an hour or two to spare, he would go to this brewery and watch little bubbles of air rise to the surface of the fermenting beer. Every brewer was familiar with the process and thought no more about the matter. That was what happened when fermentation took place and beer was being made.

Why this dissenting minister was not satisfied to take the facts as he found them, why he pored over chemical books to find out what these idle bubbles of vapor could mean, why he would not accept the explanation put forward by his contemporary Dr. Black, a chemist, who said that they were nothing more than "fixed air," and why he went on worrying about the matter until he unraveled the nature of fermentation—that is one of those eternal mysteries which will be solved only when we know why God made the minds of inventors and discoverers of so restless and inquisitive a pattern.

Priestley was driven onward by the insatiable craving for knowledge which is the motive force of the discoverer, and he could not rest until he had answered the questions he set himself. Primarily, no doubt, he was instigated by a religious motive. All natural phenomena were revelations of the glory of God. One who could elucidate them was learning to read the secret characters in which God had written His name in nature. For Priestley, a child of the eighteenth century, the study of nature was the same thing as serving God. Jacks and Nell's brewery was a sacred place, for God spoke to him out of the frothing beer.

The simple dicta of faith were not sufficient to enable anyone to understand the laws and revelations as conveyed in the fermenting fluid. In the eighteenth century, by the dispensation of Providence, man had been given a glimpse into a new, a second, creation, into the world of artificially produced chemical substances, and had shown a chosen few how to master this untrodden road. The new age set new problems to those who earnestly wished to serve God.

Joseph Priestley was convinced that he was one of these chosen few. It did not suffice him, therefore, to fulfill his aforesaid part as minister of religion. God had appointed him, Joseph Priestley, to guide mankind into unexplored paths, those leading into the domain of chemistry.

When the Almighty put these thoughts into his mind, it was also made plain to him that he would need special tools. Priestley found what he wanted in this respect among the most inconspicuous utensils of the brewery. His peculiar faculties as an inventor soon made it plain to him how to use the available apparatus and modify it to suit his purposes. With the aid of the instruments he fashioned, he was soon able to collect and store the rising bubbles, to study their composition, to carry on his researches upon the "different kinds of air" until much of their mystery was fathomed.

His powers developed by using them, and he was soon able so to perfect his apparatus that he could isolate the various gases in a pure state.

Joseph Priestley spent most of his stipend upon chemical apparatus, and it was not long before he had succeeded in isolating carbonic acid gas.

Since it was by the will of the Lord that he had become a discoverer, things went smoothly. Lord Shelburn, secretary of state (afterward the Marquis of Lansdowne), chose him as literary companion. It is doubtful whether the noble Earl was moved by any better motive than vanity. Having heard of Priestley's strange apparatus and remarkable experiments, he wanted to show off the budding scientist and the researches into the different kinds of air as curiosities to the guests at Calne, his country mansion near Bath.

God works in a mysterious way, often making unworthy purposes turn out for good. Sometimes the will of the Lord will place a man in degrading situations that in the end good may come for himself and for the race.

Priestley knew how important his experiments were for the advancement of science, and he therefore possessed his soul in patience while demonstrating his results for the idle amusement of Lord Shelburn's guests. God rewarded him abundantly. Shelburn was for the most part busied upon his duties as secretary of state, which left the literary companion free to get on with his own work. Nor was there any shortage of funds at Calne: Priestley was able to purchase expensive apparatus and to continue his studies under the most favorable conditions.

Thus he successively discovered oxygen (which he called dephlogisticated air), sulphurous oxide, ammonia and fluorine. One day, treating damped iron filings with nitric acid and heating the mixture, he hit upon nitrous oxide, which was later to be used as the first gaseous anesthetic.

Accompanying Lord Shelburn, he visited Holland, Germany and France, becoming acquainted in these countries with the most noted chemists of the day.

What Priestley discovered at the brewery, and subsequently during the seven years when he was kept in funds by his noble patron, formed the foundation of our modern knowledge of the chemistry of gases; and, in addition, Priestley's work at Calne was the groundwork for much subsequent advance in modern chemical knowledge.

He was also a pioneer in physiology. In his book *Experiments and Observations Concerning the Different Kinds of Air* he tells us how he hit upon the idea of trying the effect of oxygen upon the human organism:

"From the greater strength and vivacity of the flame of a candle in this pure air, it may be conjectured that it might be peculiarly salutary to the lungs in certain morbid cases. I had a fancy for trying its effect upon myself, and inhaled a considerable quantity of it through a tube. This gave me a remarkable sense of freedom and lightness in the chest. Who can tell but that, in time, this pure air may become a fashionable article of luxury? Hitherto only two mice and myself have had the privilege of breathing it."

These first experiments with the inhalation of oxygen were to become of great importance for the art of medicine. Before the days of Priestley, doctors had administered only solid or liquid medicaments, which had to find their way in through the stomach. The effect of such remedies was slowly produced, and once the patient had swallowed them the doctor knew no way of influencing the process of absorption.

There were various remedies which had a beneficial effect in small doses but in larger doses produced symptoms of poisoning and did serious harm. As long as the only way into the body was through the mouth and the stomach, the physician had very little power of measuring the strength, duration and effect of his remedies, and it sometimes happened that an unduly concentrated and poisonous dose found its way into the blood.

But Priestley's experiment upon himself with oxygen did not merely provide medical science with a new remedy but disclosed a new way of administering remedies in general. The lungs, whose alveoli have a very extensive surface, proved to be the quickest possible way of getting certain substances into the blood stream. Since these substances were absorbed and eliminated by the breath, dosage could be controlled easily. Thus did the doctors master the strength and the time limits of the action of these volatile substances administered by way of the lungs.

From his experiments on oxygen, Priestley went on to further experiments with the other gases he had discovered, and was making his first trials of nitrous oxide upon the lower animals when God summoned him once more to his position in the pulpit, that he might fight in the cause of the true faith.

For the beginning of a new era was being revealed in various other domains as well as in that of science. Industry was on the march. Adam Smith had just published his *Wealth of Nations*— the bible of free trade—in Edinburgh. In the political field, dissent was gaining power, and was wrestling for the Rights of Man; Parliament was discussing the younger Pitt's schemes of reform; in the oratorical duels between Fox and Burke, liberalism and conservatism were fighting for supremacy. Across the Channel, in France, the great Revolution was developing, and Britain was taking time by the forelock with her advance along the liberal path.

So notable a revolution, transforming political and social life, could not leave Christianity fixed in orthodox rigidity. The spirit of liberalism made its way into the houses of the clergy, especially those of the nonconformists, separating divines into two camps, those who clung to the traditional faith, and the Unitarians who regarded liberal ideas and the Rights of Man as a new revelation.

Joseph Priestley, the renovator of chemistry, was wholly on the side of the Unitarians. For him, who in the depths of his own soul had experienced the working of the *Zeitgeist* on behalf of new creations, for him whom God had commissioned to reconstruct the extant views of the universe, for him there could be no doubt that the new, the coming, expressed the will of the Lord.

How was it possible to suppose that the Church, God's earthly habitation, would retain the obsolete forms which had come down through the ages? Another day had dawned, the Church was not to remain a mere museum of contemplation; it must be infused with the spirit of liberalism; evolution must play its part in shaping the new life.

Joseph Priestley was at work in his laboratory when the dispute between the orthodox and the Unitarians began to disintegrate the churches. He abandoned his researches, for the Lord had summoned him to play a part in bringing about the new dispensation. He was the apostle of progress. Thenceforward this religious struggle was to dominate Priestley's life and determine his destinies.

Priestley resigned his post as literary companion to Lord Shelburn and accepted a call to a dissenting pulpit in Birmingham. A number of noted men were then living in that Midland city, and Priestley joined their circle. He became a member of the Lunar Society, a friend of Erasmus Darwin, poet and scientist, grandfather of the famous Charles Darwin; of James Watt, the manufacturer of steam engines; of William Murdock, the discoverer of gaslighting; and of Richard L. Edgeworth, who was working at optical telegraphs.

His close association with these distinguished men made Priestley's life in Birmingham very agreeable. The only thing that troubled the harmony of his existence was that he became more and more immersed in theological disputes, and that his sympathies with revolutionary France aroused a great deal of enmity.

After the taking of the Bastille, a reaction against the ideas of the French Revolution had begun. Burke's policy gained the victory over that of Fox, and in the churches the orthodox got the upper hand. To these latter the Unitarian minister Joseph Priestley, who was also infected with liberal ideas, was a Son of Belial, against whom everyone must be warned, were it only for his soul's salvation.

Priestley regularly mounted the steps of his pulpit, but the pews were empty. Numbers of his congregation were married, children were born to them, deaths took place, but no one would have anything to do with the ill-famed minister. When he met any of his people in the street and said "good morning" to them, they gave him the cut direct. Street arabs ran after him shouting: "Priestley be damned, damned, damned forever, forever!"

Why should he stick any longer to his cure? The sidesmen refused to obey the heretic any longer, and threw up their jobs. His neighbors drew away from contact with this Son of Belial; they moved to other houses, in less "infected quarters."

As obstinate as they, he sat alone in his forsaken dwelling, shunned by all. But now, when Priestley could no longer do his work as minister of the Gospel, he returned to the experiments on which he had been engaged at Calne, and to the records of them he had been writing when on his travels with Lord Shelburn. Was it not possible that God's inscrutable will had only involved him in this dispute that he might have time to learn more about nitrous oxide, to make further experiments upon it and to convince a refractory age of the reality of progress by presenting it with irrefutable chemical formulae?

Priestley had tied one of the animals upon which he was experimenting to the laboratory table, and was preparing the nitrous oxide which he intended to administer by inhalation, when there came a knock at the door. A friend, the only one who still had courage to visit the discredited house, came breathless to inform Priestley that the mob was approaching to set the place on fire, and that the experimenter's only chance of escaping death in the conflagration was to flee with the utmost speed. He would gladly have saved the apparatus so laboriously constructed, the manuscript books filled with notes in which years of work were recorded. Impossible, it was too late. The raging mob rounded the corner and a crowd was already storming the house. The investigator had barely time to escape by the back door before the place was in flames, the notebooks had been reduced to ashes and the laboratory (the first chemical laboratory to be well equipped with modern apparatus) lay in ruins.

The fugitive attempted to reorganize a new laboratory at Hackney, then on the outskirts of London, and to start life afresh there. The plan miscarried, for feeling ran high against him: in various localities he was burned in effigy as a revolutionist. One day leaflets were showered into the streets denouncing him as an enemy of King and State. France, meanwhile, offered to build him a laboratory in Paris, hailed him as a "knight of progress" and appointed him a *citoyen de la République*. As soon as this news reached England, everyone began to howl for Priestley's trial and execution as a traitor.

There was nothing left for him to do but flee like a hunted beast. He decided to cross the Atlantic, and found repose at length on American soil. The liberal United States made this distinguished man of science welcome. A delegation called on him in New York; Philadelphia offered him a professorship, but the exhausted Priestley declined the honor.

For a time the experimenter went on with his work, his last discovery being carbonic oxide, and he also wrote a few theological pamphlets; but by this time the zealous theologian and the protagonist of modern science was a weary and a broken man. He lingered ten years, dying in 1804 at the age of 71, his declining days being passed in retirement as a farmer at the confluence of the northeast and west branches of the Susquehanna, in Northumberland, Pennsylvania.

Toward the close of the eighteenth century there were several distinguished men whose task it was to guide the footsteps of an old time on its path toward the new. In the field of chemistry,

Cavendish, Black and Lavoisier, and with them in the first rank Priestley, took part in this transformation. In every era of change, notes of the old music sound on into the new times. Priestley's thoughts, his activities and his life, therefore, show a mingling of the old and the new, and it was inevitable that the chemical views of this great innovator should be influenced by many errors of the past, should bear traces of the inadequacy of earlier theories.

Eighteenth-century chemistry still smacked of the phlogiston theory, which dated back to the time of Plato but had been renovated by Stahl. According to this theory, in every kind of combustion, whether metallic or non-metallic matter was committed to the flames, the burning bodies gave off a hypothetical substance to which Stahl gave the name of phlogiston.

Priestley's discoveries of oxygen and other gases rang the knell of this theory, but he himself never realized the full import of his researches, and to the day of his death he clung obstinately to the conception of phlogiston. He even attempted to force the whole complex of his revolutionary discoveries into the antiquated framework of the phlogiston chemistry. Oxygen, for him, was "dephlogisticated air," and nitrogen was air saturated with phlogiston, or "phlogisticated air." Even when other chemists convicted the phlogiston theory of error, Priestley continued passionately to defend the cherished doctrine, and he stuck to it with inviolable loyalty to the last. During his stay in America, as late as the period 1796–1800, he wrote polemics in defense of phlogiston. He had created the new, but failed to draw the proper conclusions from his experiments and thus, though one of the most notable founders of modern chemistry, was unable to grasp the significance of his own discoveries.

All the same, in the writings of this fanatical divine who spent so much of his life in struggles for what he regarded as the true faith, we can glimpse the first outlines of modern chemistry; and even though he was entangled in the errors of the phlogiston theory, his chemical researches were guided by the new methods of precise experimental study—the methods which are still, for the most part, in use today.

It is true that since Priestley was and remained the dissenting

(Above, center) Michael Faraday, who discovered the soporific nature of ether vapor.

(Lower left) Joseph Priestley, English divine who discovered the invisible world of the gases. In 1776 he discovered nitrous oxide, first gas to be used for the alleviation of pain.

(Right) Anton Mesmer, who possessed the power of "animal magnetism."

A contemporary caricature of mesmerism, faith-healing cult which held sway just before the French Revolution.

minister, he regarded chemistry and science as pre-eminently "God's revelation"; but his method of research was entirely free from unscientific presuppositions. With a mind to which mere theorizing was alien, he was always a sober and unprejudiced investigator, guided exclusively by the considerations and comparisons of reason. The unbiased study of nature was his goal, and he considered precise observation the only acceptable method, while experiment was the touchstone of every theory.

Even though, before he died, his findings had been more correctly interpreted by others than they ever were by himself, he was indubitably one of the chief pioneers of modern chemical research. His experiments were the foundation of all those that followed, and the whole edifice of the new chemistry has been built on that foundation.

With Priestley a completely new type of savior appeared in the history of the fight against pain.

If we examine the long series of the fighters against pain, if we conjure them up from the tomb, we see shamans hung with skins; dancing, running, howling medicine men; helpful gods, demigods and saints; priests bowed over the victims of the sacrifice and robed in the vestments of ancient cults; kings in ermine; alchemists brewing tinctures, their minds stuffed with the verbiage of the Schoolmen; monkish medieval physicians dominated by their faith; collectors of herbs and roots; mixers of unguents; midwives; quacks— enchanters and themselves enchanted, one and all. The last link in this long chain of sorcerers was the man who held the world in his magnetic spell at the very time when Priestley was making his first experiments in inhalation: Franz Anton Mesmer, the revealer of the "animal fluid."

With Mesmer died the last of the great enchanters, and the path was cleared for a younger generation which began with Priestley.

How utterly different in methods, aspects and actions was Priestley, though a theologian, from all those who, before him and after him, tried to find a remedy for pain! One who, in his laboratory, began by experimenting on himself; one filled with a keen sense of responsibility, and therefore one who distrusted any experience which could not be submitted to the test of vision; one who tried all his reactions over and over again until he was sure of them—such a man was Joseph Priestley. With him opened the line of investigators, chemists, apothecaries and physicians who now took on the fight.

Now was first staged a titanic drama which took the place of attempts to "charm away" suffering—titanic alike in its greatness and in its shattering tragedy.

Science, which human reason, working creatively like God, has created, is addressing itself to the task of conquering pain. In this task it is faced by one of the mightiest of forces, the primal curse by which immediately after the Fall man was doomed to an eternity of pain.

CHAPTER FIVE

Laughing Pain Away

WHEN PRIESTLEY began his experiments upon the inhalation of oxygen and noted his first observations upon the therapeutic use of gases, chemistry was still a branch of knowledge which the medical faculty regarded with contempt, looking upon treatment by gases as an extremely venturesome innovation to which experts reacted with distrust and aversion. Before long, however, a good many doctors, following Priestley's hint, began to try the effect of gases upon their patients and to make a regular use of them; thus "pneumatic medicine" speedily became an important section of the healing art.

Gases were first employed for the treatment of disorders of the respiratory organs, inhalations being tried for the relief of asthma, catarrh, difficulty of breathing and even consumption. Subsequently the "pneumatologists" extended their method to the treatment of paralysis, scurvy, hysteria and cancer. By the time Priestley retired to his American farm, the therapeutic use of gases had become so general that Jan Ingenhousz, the Dutch physician-in-ordinary to the Imperial Austrian House, thought it expedient to warn the medical confraternity against the danger of regarding gases as a new "elixir of life."

Priestley's discovery of oxygen was soon followed by the discovery of hydrogen and nitrogen, and most of these gases were tried by the pneumatologists.

But there was one of Priestley's "different kinds of air" which no doctor was venturesome enough to give his patients to breathe, and this was nitrous oxide which Priestley had made during his experiments at Calne. It had been branded as dangerous by the American chemist and physician Dr. Lantham Mitchell who had administered it to animals, nearly killed them and come to the conclusion that it was a powerful poison. Indeed, he thought it might even be the semi-mythical *contagium* by which epidemic diseases were supposed to be spread.

Lantham Mitchell was considered an authority in the field of medical chemistry. No one challenged his opinion, and his warning was tantamount to a prohibition. Neither chemist nor doctor was courageous enough to try nitrous oxide on himself.

But in 1795, the year after Priestley went to America, Humphry Davy, then seventeen years old and apprenticed to John Bingham Borlase, a prominent surgeon of Penzance, took the risk.

Treatment by these recently discovered gases was a frequent topic of conversation with Borlase and his circle—medical colleagues and commercial travelers who visited Penzance. They discussed the use of this gas and that in various diseases. Of course many of the gases were dangerous. "For instance, Mr. Priestley's nitrous oxide," said Borlase, "which could easily cause death."

Young Humphry listened eagerly to the talk of his elders. These gases were a wonder-world with which his imagination was busied; and, of course, he was especially interested in Priestley's "dangerous gas" which none of the learned chemists and doctors dared to administer. What if, after all, Dr. Mitchell had made a mistake? It does not follow that everything a distinguished man says is true. Humphry Davy was barely seventeen, and he had scant respect for authority. He would only have been snubbed had he put in his word during the discussions in the surgery, but he made up his mind to find out for himself whether Dr. Mitchell was right. All sorts of mysteries might lie hid in this reputedly dangerous gas. Here was a chance for a lad whose dream was to do great work for science, to make himself no less famous than Mr. Priestley, the sometime nonconformist minister whom all the world admired as the discoverer of the invisible realm of gases.

The doctor's apprentice yearned to unriddle the mystery of

this "dangerous gas." Dr. Mitchell declared that anyone who inhaled it would die. Well, perhaps he, Davy, would die. Was there not fascination in running such a risk on behalf of science?

Day after day Humphry Davy stuck to his duties, helped in the compounding of medicines; he mixed ointments, weighed out powders, distinguishing himself both by modesty and by skill. When night came, since the thought of these "different kinds of air" had taken possession of him, the youth pored over the most famous chemical treatises of the day: Nicholson's *Dictionary of Chemistry;* Lavoisier's *Traité élémentaire de la chimie;* above all, Priestley's *Experiments and Observations,* which made the greatest impression on him.

He learned from Priestley how to prepare this "dangerous gas." One night while Mr. Borlase was upstairs sleeping the sleep of the just, Humphry, in the dispensary, prepared nitrous oxide, which with a lad's impatience he promptly inhaled. Drawing deep breaths of it into his lungs, he thought it likely that his last hour had come. He waited. He breathed in some more; and then a third time. Wonderful! Not only was there no sign of the sudden death prophesied by Dr. Mitchell, but something else, almost as surprising, happened. As young Humphry continued, with increasing boldness, to inhale more and more of the nitrous oxide, a strange and agreeable sense of lightness pervaded his body. His muscles relaxed; there was a pleasant sensation in the chest and in the limbs. Then the young man became aware that his hearing was unusually acute, and that the agreeable sense increased to become an unspeakable cheerfulness. He wanted to laugh; he had no choice but to laugh; and he went on laughing, in spite of himself, until he put aside the empty flask.

"So much for the famous American doctor's theory," thought Humphry Davy. "It was a good thing that I paid no heed to the warning." He had entered upon the experiment determined, at the risk of his life, to discover whether Priestley's nitrous oxide could really be the *contagium* of epidemic diseases. Instead he had learned what nobody had hitherto suspected, for he had discovered that the gas induced marked cheerfulness, evoked laughter. Perhaps in due time he would be universally acclaimed as the man who had given the world a source of artificial pleasure, a source of artificial laughter?

The son of a wood carver, Humphry Davy had become Bingham Borlase's apprentice only in the hope of making a livelihood as a doctor. But, like certain other famous scientific investigators, he had the soul of a poet. Since early childhood he had scribbled verses. At the seaside on the Cornish coast, he would stand for hours declaiming verses to drown the howling of the wind and the roaring of the waves.

The night when he discovered the pleasure-giving virtue of the new gas, he seated himself, without wasting a moment, at the laboratory table, seized pen and paper, and indited a pæan of joy, as follows:

> Not in the ideal dreams of wild desire
> Have I beheld a rapture-wakening form:
> My bosom burns with no unhallow'd fire,
> Yet is my cheek with rosy blushes warm;
> Yet are my eyes with sparkling lustre fill'd;
> Yet is my mouth replete with murmuring sound;
> Yet are my limbs with inward transport fill'd;
> And clad with new-born mightiness around.

But since young Davy was an investigator as well as a poet, he did not remain content with this outburst of poetic enthusiasm. The next night he repeated his experiment; tried it again and again on the following night; and each time the result was the same.

Soon the desire for the renewal of this feeling of delight grew so strong that he would seek it in the daytime and, while compounding medicines, would often desist from his work to enjoy the pleasurable inhalation.

Then he had a strange experience, which I will record in his actual words:

"The power of the immediate operation of the gas in removing intense physical pain, I had a very good opportunity of ascertaining. . . . In cutting the unlucky teeth called dentes sapientiae, I experienced an extensive inflammation of the

gums, accompanied with great pain. . . . On the day when
the inflammation was most troublesome, I breathed three large
doses of nitrous oxide. The pain always diminished after the
first three or four inspirations; the thrilling came on as
usual. . . ."

But if the gas could relieve pain due to inflammation round a
tooth-socket, might it not relieve other pains as well? He must
go on experimenting, must explore all the effects of the gas and
then face the learned world and the highly respected Dr. Mitchell.

Davy went on experimenting with the utmost secrecy, but was
prematurely betrayed by a puckish chance. One night a patient
suffering from intense colic was brought to Mr. Borlase by a son.
Borlase, awakened by the night-bell out of profound sleep, hastened downstairs to admit the patient. Then he called to the
apprentice, whose bedroom was behind the laboratory. Humphry
came out doubled up with laughter. Borlase, in great wrath, looked
at the young man severely, but, do what he could, the latter was
unable to control the fits of laughter which continued, peal after
peal, outrivaling the anguished cries of the patient. "Really, this is
monstrous," complained the invalid. "Surely I have enough to
suffer already, without that unmannerly young cub of yours laughing at me?" Taking his son's arm, the irate man departed before
Borlase could get him any medicine, and slammed the surgery
door behind him.

Borlase wondered what fly had bitten his usually well-bred
apprentice. He questioned Humphry sharply, loaded the young
fellow with reproaches, and at length angrily told him to go to
bed.

A few days later the same thing happened. Once more the
patient was outraged; once more the chief scolded his apprentice;
and once more Humphry continued to laugh.

On Friday, which was market day, there came a great afflux
of patients. Borlase could not cope with them all, and wanted the
assistant to help him. Since Humphry did not appear when called,
the chief went to fetch him. When Borlase opened the dispensary
door, it was to see the young man grinning like an idiot. Borlase

thought his apprentice must be going mad, but decided not to give him notice until this fit of frenzy was over. He returned to the surgery, shutting the door behind him. But his patience was at an end, and he was fully resolved to dismiss the giggling youth.

When Borlase gave young Humphry notice, he found the apprentice as cheerful as usual. Davy was laughing heartily, surrounded by a litter of apparently empty bottles, air-pumps and glass tubes, remaining quite undisturbed by the entry of his chief.

"What the devil are you up to?" asked Borlase furiously. Instead of answering, Humphry picked up an empty bottle, uncorked it, and held it out to his master. Borlase, who was just about to breathe in, involuntarily inhaled the whole contents of the bottle. Then something happened which surprised him very much. His expression of anger was replaced by a cheerful grin; and his voice, with which he had been about to scold, relaxed into uncontrollable laughter.

The surgery bell rang twice in swift succession. New patients arrived. They called impatiently for attention. Borlase and Davy went back into the surgery, both of them brimming over with hilarity, so that they could not pay serious attention to what the patients wanted. These latter were not used to being treated in such a way, and departed in a huff, leaving Borlase and his sniggering assistant.

As soon as the effect of the gas had passed off, and the surgeon, recovering as from intoxication, gradually came to himself, he asked the assistant for an explanation. Thereupon Humphry admitted that, disregarding Dr. Mitchell's warning, he had tried nitrous oxide on himself. He went on to explain all the strange sensations he had experienced after breathing in the gas, and spoke of the relief of pain the inhalation had produced when his palate was inflamed.

Borlase listened with keen interest to all the remarkable young man had to say. So this gas, which Mitchell had described as deadly, could relieve pain. He might be able to make a good use of it in his practice. He imparted this idea to Humphry, agreed to co-operate, and held out hopes of a partnership should the gas prove really effective.

But before these plans could be put into operation, rumors began to spread through the provincial town concerning "strange goings-on at Borlase's surgery." The upshot was that the worthy Borlase became suspect, was supposed to be playing tricks with a "devilish gas"; and thereupon his practice fell off. Borlase, afraid of being accused of quackery, abandoned the idea of using nitrous oxide, and ordered his assistant to have nothing more to do with it.

But Humphry was absolutely convinced that he would be able, through his experiments with this remarkable gas, to open a new and extensive field for chemical medicine. He paid no heed to Borlase's exhortations and, though he stayed on for a time as assistant, applied to Dr. Tonkin, his foster father, who had acted as guardian since the death of the elder Davy, begging for a room under Tonkin's roof. Tonkin had no objection, and Davy secretly continued his experiments in his foster parent's house.

The instruments at the young man's disposal in his new quarters were much more primitive and inadequate than those in Borlase's dispensary. The entire armamentarium consisted of no more than pots and pans, wineglasses and teacups, Mrs. Tonkin's enema syringe, some old tobacco pipes and, to conclude, a few rusty surgical instruments which a French doctor had left behind at Tonkin's. But the young man's inventive faculty enabled him to turn these miscellaneous articles into chemical apparatus. Thus equipped, in the dead of night, Humphry Davy continued to inhale the gas, carefully noting the results. Always he perceived the same sense of happiness, and after each inhalation he felt an irresistible desire to laugh. That was why he gave the new gas the name by which it was later to become known in chemistry and medicine, calling it "laughing gas."

At length, however, these nocturnal experiments at Tonkin's came to a disastrous close. One peaceful night the family was awakened from sleep by the sound of an explosion. It seemed to come from Humphry's room, so Tonkin ran thither, thrust open the door, to find his foster son with a guilty countenance, surrounded by all kinds of strange-looking apparatus. A bottle of the gas had exploded.

"This incorrigible boy will blow us to atoms with his tricks," exclaimed Tonkin, and strictly forbade the lad to make further experiments.

An end seemed to have come to Davy's plans and hopes. Then chance came to the inventor's aid. Dr. Giddy, afterward president of the Royal Society, on a visit to Penzance heard the town gossip about the "devilish gas" in Borlase's surgery, listened to the Tonkins' complaints about Humphry, and said he would be glad to meet the "incorrigible youngster." The short, slight, round-shouldered lad with a painfully shrill voice and a provincial speech was by no means prepossessing; but Giddy was quick to recognize that the apprentice entertained some very remarkable ideas, and he promised to put Humphry in a position to continue work as an experimenter.

Immediately after the interview he wrote to his friend Dr. Beddoes, head of a Pneumatic Institute at Clifton near Bristol, to say that at Penzance he had found "a treasure" in the person of a young man named Humphry Davy, who would certainly be helpful to Beddoes at Bristol. After a brief exchange of letters, Beddoes wrote to the young assistant in extremely gracious terms, offering Humphry the post of superintendent at the Institute. Humphry was overjoyed.

The term of apprenticeship with Borlase was not yet expired, but the surgeon, though he had decided to have nothing more to do with gases, was "unwilling," as he wrote in a testimonial, "to stand in the way of so promising a youth who had every chance of gaining fame and fortune." Foster-father Tonkin, however, whose only desire was to make Humphry a doctor at Penzance, was less accommodating than Borlase and when, in 1799, Humphry Davy followed the call to Clifton, Tonkin would have nothing more to do with him, and disinherited the intractable youth.

To Humphry Davy, Clifton was a paradise. Here he possessed all the requisites for the fulfilment of his dreams. In Penzance he had been forced to work with primitive and clumsy instruments of his own devising, in order to study the properties of nitrous oxide. Now, as if by a transformation scene, he was superintendent of a roomy laboratory in Dr. Beddoes' Pneumatic Institute, where the latest and most expensive apparatus were available for the continuance of his researches.

The members of his new circle shared his interests and were inspired by the same enthusiasm. Dr. Beddoes had been one of the first to devote himself to making available for use in medicine the various gases which Priestley and Priestley's successors had discovered. In collaboration with James Watt, one of Priestley's intimate friends, Beddoes had written a book entitled *Considerations Concerning the Medical Use of Gases and their Production in Large Quantities*, recording the results of various experiments with gases made by him on animals.

For the furtherance of his plans, Dr. Beddoes founded his Pneumatic Institute in Rodney Place, at Clifton Hotwells. The Institute was "for the treatment of disease by inhalation." Some of the leading spirits in England regarded Beddoes as the protagonist of a new science, and gave him active help for the realization of his plans. Thomas Wedgewood, the poet, placed the sum of £1000 at Beddoes' disposal, and James Watt gratuitously supplied him with the apparatus needed for the laboratory.

To Dr. Beddoes' chemical laboratory was attached a hospital with ten beds and an out-patients' department where there were facilities for the treatment of eighty persons. Here Beddoes applied pneumatological methods for the relief of all kinds of bodily and mental disorders. Being himself extremely obese, he hoped to get rid of superfluous fat by the inhalation of gases. But his pet scheme was to build airtight rooms where patients could spend many hours in an artificially modified atmosphere, for this, he believed, would have an extremely beneficial effect in many kinds of illness.

The gases which Beddoes had been using for treatment were oxygen, hydrogen, nitrogen and some of the still more recently discovered compounds of carbon and hydrogen. When Humphry recommended him to try nitrous oxide, he adopted the idea with enthusiasm.

The young investigator could not have dreamed of a better place to work than in the Pneumatic Institute. There was a well-equipped laboratory, and there was an abundant supply of patients.

In other respects, too, there could not possibly have been a better environment. Beddoes inspired admiration and confidence in his pupil, being not only a great chemist but a man with a philosophically trained and poetic imagination, keenly interested in the problems which concerned the welfare of humanity.

He had studied in Paris, London and Edinburgh; was a good linguist; had come into contact with Lavoisier; had gained renown at Oxford by his lectures on chemistry; entertained remarkable psychological theories about dreams and the impressions of early childhood, so that he may be regarded as a forerunner of Sigmund Freud—all these things in addition to his pioneer work upon the treatment of diseases by the inhalation of gases. With such a man, Humphry Davy could joyfully converse about the matters which interested his own poetic and scientific fancy.

In a letter to his mother, Davy writes of the chief as an elderly man (the master was only eighteen years older than the pupil) of a short and stout habit of body, and endowed with an extremely original mind. He was good, able and generous. His wide-ranging and active imagination contrasted strongly with his seeming coldness in discussion; and he was as poetical as Erasmus Darwin. His talents might make him one of the greatest philosophers of our time, and he had a keen appreciation of Davy's own ideas.

Dr. Beddoes' house was also a meeting-place for the contemporary lights of the literary world. The poets of the English Romantic movement; those of the Lake School, such as Coleridge, Wordsworth and Southey; their friend Amos Simon Cottle, bookseller, publisher and poet; Erasmus Darwin—these were among the more intimate members of Beddoes' circle. Naturally Davy the poet as well as Davy the experimenter found the atmosphere congenial and stimulating.

Mrs. Beddoes, a handsome and merry young woman, presided over these illustrious gatherings. Humphry Davy, who regarded her with reverence, also had a great liking for her, and she did her best to mother the young man. "She is one of the most charming women I have ever met," wrote Humphry to Penzance. She combined an admirable simplicity with a fine understanding and an exceptionally good heart. "We are already very great friends."

Humphry was, indeed, most enthusiastic about everything at Clifton. "This is the loveliest spot in the world. Our house is spacious and pleasant; my rooms are large, prettily decorated, and comfortable; and, above all, I have a splendid laboratory."

Before trying his "laughing gas" in the treatment of the patients at the Pneumatic Institute, Humphry wanted to recapitulate and confirm the experiments he had made at Penzance.

Again and again he tried it on himself in varying doses. His first essays were risky, because he inhaled too much of the gas, and twice nearly died. On one of these occasions he completely lost consciousness, but before doing so he had just enough strength to lay aside the mouthpiece. Next day, though considerably shaken, he made a fresh trial undismayed.

At length he prepared a gas-tank for the collection and storage of gases; and on April 11, 1799, he succeeded in producing chemically pure nitrous oxide. Now he had reached his goal, for in this form its inhalation proved free from risk. On the following day he demonstrated its effect to Dr. Beddoes and Dr. Kinglake (junior assistant at the Institute) by inhaling large doses of the gas.

Having constructed an almost impermeable silken bag, he breathed in, first three and then four quarts without any evil results. His success was loudly acclaimed.

The first persons bold enough to follow his example and try nitrous oxide on themselves were his friends Coleridge, Southey and Wedgewood. The initial reports, therefore, upon the effects of laughing gas do not read like dry scientific observations, but as the inspired words of poets.

Samuel Taylor Coleridge, after his first inhalation, wrote: "I experienced the most voluptuous sensations. The outer world grew dim, and I had the most entrancing visions. For three and a half minutes I lived in a world of new sensations." Wedgewood, in like manner, described his condition as one "marked by lovely ideas." Davy's own notes of this sitting have the same impassioned tone:

"A thrilling extending from the chest to the extremities, was almost immediately produced. I felt a sense of tangible entension highly pleasurable in every limb; my visible impressions were dazzling, and apparently magnified, I heard distinctly every sound in the room, and was perfectly aware of my situation. By degrees, as the pleasurable sensations increased, I lost all connection with external things; trains of visible images rapidly passed through my mind, and were connected with words in such a manner, as to produce perceptions perfectly novel. I existed in a world of newly connected and newly modified ideas: I theorised, I imagined that I made discoveries. When I was awakened from this semi-delirious trance by Dr. Kinglake, who took the bag from my mouth, indignation and pride were the first feelings produced by the sight of the persons about me. My emotions were enthusiastic and sublime, and for a minute I walked about the room perfectly regardless of what was said to me. As I recovered my former state of mind I felt an inclination to communicate the discoveries I had made during the experiment. I endeavoured to recall the ideas: they were feeble and indistinct; one collection of terms however presented itself; and with a most intense belief and prophetic manner, I exclaimed to Dr. Kinglake: *'Nothing exists but thoughts! The universe is composed of impressions, ideas, pleasures, and pains!'"*

Next Davy tried the gas upon some young women and girls of his acquaintance. Two ladies were thrown into a trance by the inhalation of three quarts of nitrous oxide each. They both said that they had heard roaring and drumming noises, that their perceptions had grown indistinct, this being accompanied by a sensation of warmth and an extraordinary feeling of lightness in the limbs. Their thoughts had been most impetuous and incredibly cheerful, so that they could not but laugh aloud for joy. On coming to, one of the girls said most emphatically: "I felt myself to be the tones of a harp." The other said: "Mr. Davy's silk bags hold the key to Paradise."

The tidings of these effects of nitrous oxide soon spread far beyond Clifton, attracting patients and quidnuncs from all parts to Dr. Beddoes' Institute. Asthmatics, in particular, believed that the new method would give them relief, that they would be able to "laugh away" their difficulty of breathing, and transform discomfort into comfort.

The first cures with the new gas exceeded every expectation. Asthmatics who had been struggling for breath became appeased as soon as Davy applied the mouthpiece of his sack. Their facial expression indicated immense relief, and a sense of unparalleled well-being pervaded them. Most of the patients declared that they had been "born again" by the treatment with gas.

Thus Davy's "laughing gas" was considered to be a wonder-working remedy, and the fame of the Institute grew from day to day. "My discoveries with regard to nitrous oxide, the 'pleasure-producing air,'" wrote Davy to his brother, "are attracting attention everywhere. The professors of Edinburgh University have taken up the matter with much enthusiasm, and have repeated my experiments. I have also received letters of thanks and praise from some of the most highly respected English authorities. Our patients here grow in numbers from day to day, and the Institute is regarded with respect by the great trading city of Bristol. I shall soon be able to send you proofs of the successful way in which, recently, we have been able to handle some of the most obstinate diseases. We have, indeed, found laughing gas useful in the most varied illnesses."

Encouraged by these results, Davy at length ventured to publish a newspaper article in which he took up the cudgels against Dr. Mitchell's theory of *contagium*.

In 1800, he published a book entitled *Chemical and Philosophical Researches Mainly Concerning Nitrous Oxide and Its Inhalation*. In this work he described the physiological and medical effects of the gas, and reported the experiments he had made on himself.

Notwithstanding his successes, and his enthusiasm about the gas, Davy never forgot the caution so characteristic of modern research. "Pneumatic chemistry," he wrote, "is, as far as medical applications are concerned, still in its infancy; but it has great developmental possibilities. If these possibilities are to develop they must be confirmed by additional facts, derived from additional experiments; and the caution of reasonable scepticism must dominate them throughout."

Davy's experiments and writings soon brought him fame. Count Rumford, who had married Lavoisier's widow, co-operating with other noted men of science had just founded a body for the study of natural sciences called the Royal Institution. Its headquarters were in the Albemarle; it had well-equipped laboratories of its own; and it appointed professors to give lectures upon their own researches in physics and chemistry. Davy was only twenty-two when he became assistant lecturer of chemistry and delivered his inaugural address upon laughing gas which, he said, "produces the same sort of cheerful intoxication when administered by the lungs as alcohol does when absorbed by way of the stomach."

This lecture made so strong an impression that several members of the audience expressed a wish to inhale the gas. The demonstration that followed, the laughter and cheerfulness of those who submitted themselves to the test, delighted the public. A certain Mr. Underwood was so enthusiastic about his sensations that, to the great amusement of everyone present, the mouthpiece had to be forcibly removed.

Davy's lectures speedily became the fashion in London. "The sensation created by his first course of lectures at the Royal Institution, and the enthusiastic admiration which they obtained, is scarcely to be imagined," writes a contemporary. "Men of the first rank and talent, the literary and the scientific, the practical and the theoretical, blue-stockings and women of fashion, old and young— eagerly crowded the lecture-room. Compliments, invitations, and presents were showered upon the lecturer; his society was courted by all, and all appeared proud of his acquaintance."

What now chiefly interested Davy was not so much the beneficial effects of laughing gas in diseases of the respiratory organs, but its power to relieve pain. It was in this direction, he considered, that the greatest medical possibilities were opening.

Already at Penzance he had noticed how the inhalation of laughing gas could relieve the pain that attended the cutting of a wisdom tooth. Subsequently he had a similar experience in another ailment: "I had headache from indigestion and it was immediately

From *Devils, Drugs and Doctors*, by Howard W. Haggard, M.D., published by Harper and Brothers.

The pneumatic treatment of respiratory diseases, widely used in the eighteenth century, indirectly aided the development of anesthesia.

Published by John Murray, 1870.

Thomas Beddoes, M.D., Davy's patron and co-worker.

Sir Humphry Davy, who made the first experiments with laughing gas as a pain-killer.

removed by the effects of a large dose of gas (nitrous oxide) though it afterwards returned, but with much less violence. In a second instance a slighter degree of headache was wholly removed by two doses of the gas."

While at Dr. Beddoes' Institute, he had often noted how pain could be alleviated by laughing gas. These experiences led him to suppose that the gas might be used to dull pain in patients submitted to surgical operations.

This idea is first enunciated in his book *Medical Vapours*. He writes: "As nitrous oxide, in its entensive operation, appears capable of destroying physical pain, it may be used with advantage during surgical operations in which no great effusion of blood takes place."

Thus Davy was very near becoming the discoverer of anesthesia for surgical purposes. What he did not yet know was that the transient "state of intoxication," that the "agreeable sense of well-being," which he had observed in his experiments, was not itself true anesthesia (as it later came to be called), but only an early stage of artificial anesthesia. Had he continued his experiments in this field, it is likely enough that he would have succeeded in elaborating the requisite technique and in ascertaining the proper doses for transforming a "temporary intoxication with gas" into an "artificial sleep," and thus inducing a durable narcosis. But this was rendered impossible for reasons inexplicably intertwined with the destinies of the modern movement for the prevention of pain.

After Paracelsus' experiments upon chickens, the use of chemical remedies in the fight against pain had experienced a freakish misadventure which put a barrier in the path. For reasons which are unknown to us, Paracelsus discontinued his experiments with ether. When Priestley was on the point of studying the medical effect of nitrous oxide, the mob at Birmingham stormed and destroyed his laboratory. Now Davy, at the very time when he came to recognize that laughing gas might be used to prevent pain during surgical operations, relinquished the quest when about to reach his goal.

Unfortunate circumstances brought this about. Rumors were rife that in many instances doctors who had experimented with the gas had noticed in their patients a diminished frequency of the pulse and attacks of giddiness. This led a good many physicians to discontinue the use of the new drug. The first enthusiasm for it waned, was replaced by doubt and then by positive antagonism. The "pneumatic method of treatment" was not yet sufficiently established to stand the shocks and hostilities to which every innovation is exposed. There had been a change of opinion in medical circles: "No doubt study of the nature and composition of gases paved the way for important scientific discoveries," writes a commentator. "Although the great services of chemists were undeniable, the fantasies of doctors had been dispelled. Only quacks and fee-snatchers treated credulous patients with gases."

It was not long before the advocates of "pneumatological methods of treatment" were openly denounced as charlatans, and at length the use of laughing gas by inhalation was made illegal.

Dr. Beddoes, who had been so enthusiastic a pioneer of pneumatology, was compelled to transform his Institute into a hospital where the familiar methods were employed, and to drop the adjective "Pneumatic." In 1808, on his deathbed, a disappointed man, he wrote to Davy as follows: "Greetings from Dr. Beddoes, one who has scattered abroad the Avena fatua of knowledge, from which neither branch nor blossom nor fruit has resulted."

After the many disillusionments he had sustained in the practice of pneumatology, Davy, too, was disinclined to continue the experiments upon the medical use of gases which were now universally discredited. Nay, more, he turned his back upon the healing art, to devote himself henceforward exclusively to physico-chemical researches—a field in which he made one valuable discovery after another. He was interested in the problems of electricity, in the voltaic pile, in chemical inventions for industrial purposes, in the manufacture of a new kind of gunpowder, in investigations upon chlorine. In the course of his labors he invented a lamp for miners, called after him the Davy lamp, which made it possible to work without risk of explosion in coal mines liable to an inrush of fire-damp. He had already been knighted in 1812; he invented the safety lamp in 1815, and was made a baronet in 1818. Napoleon granted him a high distinction. In

1820 he was elected president of the Royal Society, the most coveted position in the scientific world.

Amid all these successes, Davy had forgotten his experiments in "pneumatic treatment" of more than twenty years before. Thus was lost to medicine one of the most brilliant experimentalists that ever lived, a man who, under favorable circumstances, would probably have anticipated by half a century the discovery of anesthesia which made operative surgery painless.

At the time when Davy was concentrating upon chemico-technical problems, his laboratory assistant Michael Faraday made a memorandum which was in due time to become the basis of anesthesia with ether, and was therefore of even greater importance than were Davy's experiments with laughing gas.

The conditions under which Faraday secured an appointment in Davy's laboratory, where he developed to become an independent chemist of outstanding importance, form, in conjunction with the story of the relations between the two men, one of the most remarkable chapters in the history of scientific research.

Faraday sprang from an even lower grade of the population than did Davy. Thirteen years younger than his chief, he was early inspired with a craving for knowledge, and became a newspaper boy, which at least brought him into contact with the printed word. Then he got a job in a bookshop, and later earned his living as a journeyman bookbinder, having thus, at any rate, ample opportunities for reading. He made a point of trying to read the books he was called upon to bind, and it was not by choice but by accident that the works which were to exercise a great influence on his subsequent career fell into his hands.

Chance soon determined his fate. One day he was commissioned to bind a number of chemical works. That night he sat up late reading the sheets which introduced him to a world in which he was to become one of the most accomplished masters. Having a quick understanding, he was not unduly puzzled by the new terminology, and committed to memory much of what he thus read.

But the work of bookbinding was held up by the eager student. Mr. Dance, a member of the Royal Institution, the gentleman who had sent the books to be bound, became impatient and called at the bookbinder's to inquire into the cause of the delay. At first he was inclined to berate the neglectful journeyman, but was indulgent when he learned what use the young fellow had been making of the books. Indeed he was astonished at the extent of Faraday's chemical knowledge. Being a good-humored man, Dance said that young Faraday could keep one of the books for his own. The grateful youth picked out a work by Sir Humphry Davy. "All right," said Dance. "If you like, I will take you to hear one of Davy's lectures."

The very first lecture was enough to inspire Faraday with the wish to exchange his job at the bookbinder's for a post as Davy's laboratory assistant. "When I was still a journeyman bookbinder," he writes about this great turn in his career, "I was already interested in chemistry and averse from trade. Then it happened that Mr. Dance, a member of the Royal Institution, took me to hear one of Sir Humphry Davy's lectures. My desire to escape from trade, which I thought vicious and selfish, and to enter into the service of science, which I imagined made its pursuers amiable and liberal, induced me at last to take the bold and simple step of writing to Sir Humphry Davy and asking him whether he could help me to carry out my ideas. When, at a personal interview, he agreed to comply with my wishes and take me to work at his laboratory, he thought it necessary to point out that science was a stern mistress, who brought little financial reward to those consecrating their lives to her."

Since Davy had recently married, and was proposing to take his wife with him on a great Continental tour, Faraday's offer came at an apt moment. Davy, the indefatigable experimenter, had no inclination to allow this journey to interrupt his researches and therefore intended to take with him a "portable chemical laboratory," that he might go on with his work wherever opportunity offered. He therefore suggested that the enthusiastic bookbinder should come with him as bottle-washer, valet and secretary. Faraday, whose one wish now was to work under Davy, gladly agreed. But this journey was destined to lead to an experience very disagreeable both to master and servant. When Davy unsuspectingly engaged a journeyman bookbinder as assistant, he had no idea that the new bottle-washer was anything more than a self-taught enthusiast fit only for hodman's work. But Faraday quickly outgrew the roles that had been assigned to him, so that ere long he had caught up with his master in knowledge and ranked with him as an experimental chemist.

Again and again this skillful servant was sufficiently clever and inventive to arrive at independent chemical discoveries. It became obvious to the perturbed Davy that in Faraday he was educating a formidable rival. At first he tried to suppress his not unnatural jealousy, but Lady Davy, who was annoyed by the transformation of the bottle-washer into a man of learning, urged her husband to put Faraday in what she regarded as his proper place.

When, at Geneva, de la Rive the physicist was interested in Davy's learned assistant, and asked him to dinner as well as Sir Humphry and Lady Davy, the latter induced her husband to refuse the invitation, with the reply that they could not possibly sit down to table with their servant.

Lady Davy, whose feminine dislike for the "upstart" continually grew, found day by day fresh ways of annoying Faraday, taking particular delight in interrupting his experiments by setting him menial tasks.

Faraday patiently swallowed these humiliations, having no wish but to continue his education, at any cost. "I am so delighted at the chance of enlarging my knowledge of chemistry and the sciences," he wrote to a friend. "That is why I continue this journey. But I have to make considerable sacrifices to secure the advantages, for Lady Davy's behaviour often makes it very difficult for me to get on with her and Sir Humphry."

Nor did Davy's attitude toward Faraday improve much when they returned to London after a year and a half. A special circumstance increased the difficulties of their mutual attitude. Davy had reached the climax of his successes at the age of forty-three when, in consequence of overwork, he had a nervous breakdown of a very serious character. Faraday, on the other hand, was young and strong; his powers were unimpaired; he was full of new ideas and at the opening of his career. With growing annoyance, Davy watched the rise of his sometime servant. His jealousy led him into all kinds of intrigues. Thus he declared that Faraday, in studies concerning the liquefaction of gases by cold and pressure, had stolen his, Davy's, thunder; and that the assistant's first important inventions in the field of the relations between electric currents and magnets had been filched from another investigator, Wollaston.

These charges were extremely distressing to Faraday, but did not impair his zeal for research. He went on studying and experimenting, and was soon rewarded for his pains. He was entrusted with the management of the laboratory, and was even proposed for the fellowship of the Royal Society. Davy, who was then president of the Society, threw all his influence into the scale against Faraday's nomination, but in vain. At the ballot, only one blackball was cast —Davy's.

Faraday did much of his most important work while assistant in Davy's laboratory. It was then that were laid the foundations of his electro-chemical researches. He discovered many compounds containing chlorine and carbon, liquefied various gases; and happened upon the exceedingly volatile series of hydrocarbons known as the butyls.

It was during his researches into these differences between the vapors given off by substances that are fluid at a normal temperature and the true gases, that he learned the soporific nature of ether vapor, a discovery which was to be of much importance to the development of anesthesia.

In 1730, the chemist Frobenius directed attention to ether, and the pneumatologists had tried it. Richard Pearson, Woolcombe and Beddoes administered ether vapor to asthmatics by inhalation, and Niessen went so far as to declare in his *Dictionary of Medicine* that ether was the most important known remedy for respiratory diseases.

But the pneumatologists, in their practice, became acquainted only with the temporary relief which ether can give to asthmatics, for they never learned the soporific and narcotic effects of ether— or if they did so, they paid no attention to them.

The discovery made by Paracelsus in the earlier decade of the sixteenth century had passed into oblivion. Not until now when Faraday, equipped with the latest knowledge and appliances for the study of the chemistry of gases, compared vapors and gases and examined their effects, did he discover that ether could put people to sleep. In the *Quarterly Journal of Science and the Arts* Faraday wrote in 1818: "When the vapour of ether is mixed with common air and inhaled, it produces effects very similar to those occasioned by nitrous oxide. By the incautious breathing of ether vapour, a man was thrown into a lethargic condition which, with a few interruptions, lasted for thirty hours."

This marked an important step in the discovery of anesthetics. Davy, in his experiments with laughing gas, had never got beyond the production of "numbing states of intoxication." But these experiments with ether showed that by the use of vapors and gases it is possible to push the state of intoxication into one of complete unconsciousness and profound sleep. Still, this knowledge which was of so much importance for the conquest of pain was not, for some time, to arouse medical interest.

Faraday, who had so many other irons in the fire, merely made a casual allusion to the fact in the *Quarterly Journal of Science and the Arts*. The doctors of his day ignored the pointer, so no attempts were made to use ether for the conquest of pain. Once more this important item of knowledge lapsed into oblivion.

CHAPTER SIX

Morphine

AT ABOUT the time when Davy and Faraday were laying the foundations upon which the production of anesthesia by inhalation were to be built, the "artificial second nature" created by chemistry provided mankind with a new and powerful instrument for the relief of pain. In the year 1803, Friedrich Wilhelm Sertürner discovered morphine.

Not unlike Davy, who made his first secret experiments with laughing gas when at Penzance as Borlase's assistant, young Sertürner was a chemist's assistant in the country when he made his first investigations with morphine. Sertürner's master was a pharmacist named Cramer who lived in the Westphalian episcopal town of Paderborn.

In other respects too, there was a similarity of circumstances between the two discoveries. Like Humphry, young Wilhelm had received no scientific education, and the technical appliances available at Paderborn were as primitive as those at Penzance, so that Sertürner had himself to make the requisite chemical apparatus.

In the daytime the assistant did his duty at the dispensing counter or in the laboratory, while by night, like Davy in Cornwall, he pored over chemical books or experimented in the profoundest secrecy. But in due time he was able, out of crude opium, to prepare in the pure state an alkaloid with remarkable analgesic and soporific effects.

How did this come about? In the pharmacy the assistant had learned that both doctor and chemist were practically powerless against the devastating effects of pain. Of course there were vari-

72

The heroic Sertürner risked his life experimenting with his discovery, morphine.

Charles Gabriel Pravaz, inventor of the hypodermic needle.

Pharmacy in Paderborn where Sertürner made his discovery.

The vice of Asia.   Picture by Henry Vollet.

OPIUM—CURSE AND BLESSING.

ous vegetable narcotics, the most important of which was the dried juice obtained from the seed capsules of the white poppy, *Papaver somniferum*. This solidifies to form a brown solid, the opium of commerce, which has an acrid and bitter taste, but was found in practice to be so untrustworthy and dangerous that doctors had grown more and more disinclined to administer it.

Cramer the chemist, and the doctors of Paderborn, had had to reconcile themselves to the fact that they unfortunately knew of no effective remedy for pain. Wilhelm Sertürner, however, was cut out of the same cloth as his British colleague Humphry Davy, and wanted to find out for himself whether his elders were right.

His first business was to discover why crude opium was so uncertain that on one patient it would have no effect at all, while another would be killed by what seemed to be the same dose. He solved the riddle, finding that the reason why opium was so uncertain was that its true active principle was still unknown. The doses, and consequently the effects, of the drug were therefore extremely variable.

Sertürner, a born investigator, was not content with this answer. He went on to say to himself that, in nature, the active principle of the plant was mixed with all sorts of other substances; but that if he could free the pain-allaying substance from these extraneous ingredients, if he could get hold of the pure "active principle," then the doctor would be able to regulate the dose with certainty and to produce whatever intensity of effect he desired.

What was the object of the science of pharmacy, if not to perfect nature by the isolation of such "active principles"?

To stand day after day in Cramer's shop, mixing and dispensing ointments and powders which were always of the same kind, was no sort of life to content an aspiring young man like Friedrich Wilhelm Sertürner. The times were so stimulating. At the turn of the century, science was celebrating one triumph after another, and discovery pressed on the heels of discovery. Friedrich Wilhelm was by no means inclined to hide his light under a bushel. He would devote all his energies to promoting the victory of science. He would find something important, something new, which would bring him honor and glory.

A young man's empty dreams? By no means. Sertürner had set himself a very definite task. He would unlock the mystery of opium's soporific effects, would isolate the "active principle" and add it to the pharmacopœia.

Unwittingly he was following the general trend of chemical research. In England, at this time, Davy and Faraday were using electrolysis to break up chemical compounds into their elements. For his part, Sertürner tried to find the active principle of plants by the use of solvents and crystallization, which were to disclose so many alkaloids.

For weeks and weeks he treated crude opium, first with distilled water, then with alcohol and then with various other solvents which he hoped would enable him to "extract" the principle of which he was in search. Then, one evening, after he had poured liquid ammonia over the opium, strange crystals appeared before his astonished eyes. He purified them by washing them with sulphuric acid and alcohol until at length a white crystalline residue lay before him. This was the main alkaloid of opium, in the isolated state, to be called at first the "somniferous principle of opium."

In Cramer's cellar there were mice, and Sertürner set traps to catch them. Pariah dogs ran at large in the outskirts of Paderborn. After dark, Sertürner lured them into the back yard by offering them bones. Inviting both dogs and mice to a banquet, he powdered their food with the crystalline powder, watched the effect, increased the doses and went on increasing them until his subjects paid for their appetites with their lives.

Soon he discovered, in the case both of mice and dogs, what dose could not be safely exceeded; but the main thing was to find out what quantity of the alkaloid the human organism could endure. Like Davy, he experimented first upon himself; then he found three lads, friends of his, who agreed to let him experiment upon them.

When they came silently, at the appointed hour, Sertürner admitted them to his laboratory. Every detail of the experiment had been carefully thought out. The four young fellows seated themselves at a round table and Friedrich Wilhelm allotted the doses, each receiving half a grain. Heroically each swallowed his share, and after a little while they all became aware that they felt extraordinarily cheerful. A sensation of warmth became diffused through the body and limbs; the cheeks were flushed; and a general sense of comfort pervaded their frames; they exchanged ideas. For half an hour they carried on a lively conversation, luxuriating in their remarkable sensations.

Then Friedrich Wilhelm arose and, walking round the table, gave each of his friends a second dose, another half-grain. As leader, and already experienced, he took more himself. "Now, fellows," he said, "watch out and tell me what happens, for this is of the utmost importance to my experiment."

The young fellows obediently tried to watch out, but their eyelids were heavy. It was hard to keep the eyes open. Their limbs were oppressed by a paralyzing fatigue. All the same, they continued to sit bolt upright. Their friend had impressed on them that the experiment did not concern him alone but had a vast importance for mankind at large. They were determined therefore to keep awake as long as possible. With hesitant tongues, they gave their reports: "Fatigue, weight in the limbs. . . ."

They were getting out of touch with reality. They wanted to tell their friend all about it, wanted to cling to the strange images that were coursing, though sluggishly, through their minds. But their tongues refused to articulate, and nothing but an incomprehensible murmur emerged. Their eyelids grew heavier and heavier and, though forced open with the fingers, closed again and again.

Wilhelm, having tried the powder several times before, was a little more able to resist its effect. Besides, the experiment was not ended yet. To learn the full effect, they must each take another half-grain. He watched how the heads of the three round the table were nodding, for they were drunken with sleep. There was no time to lose. He must give them the third dose while they could still swallow. They thrust away the powder, but he would not be denied, and as soon as he had persuaded them to take it, he took his own last dose, a little more than he gave to the others. Then he tried to take observations and make notes, but everything began to swim before his eyes. Visions mocked him, darkness enveloped him, his thoughts were hopelessly confused, until he too went to sleep.

After long hours, the young men awoke to vomit. They were suffering intensely from nausea and headache. The three friends staggered home. During this experiment the four bold fellows at the Paderborn pharmacy had taken, each of them, twice the amount of morphine today regarded as the maximum dose.

A second experiment had been planned for the next evening, but Sertürner could not persuade his friends to it. He alone was bold enough to stick to his guns. With scientific dispassionateness such as is proper to the born investigator he realized that they had had an overdose, that the third half-grain had been too much for them and that the miseries of the awakening had been a sign of poisoning.

The chief experimenter, therefore, tried again next evening, again on the third, again and again for weeks and months. His period of apprenticeship was over, and he became a full-blown assistant.

Years passed, and he was an independent pharmacist in the Hanoverian town of Einbeck—still engaged in his researches, determined to find out everything about the white alkaloid. He knew now what was the percentage of the "somniferous principle" in an average specimen of crude opium; he knew how long the influence of the drug lasted, and the intensity of the effects which followed a given dose. This was after he had studied the subject for fourteen years.

The remarkable parallelism between the work of Davy and Sertürner persisted down to the minutest detail. Like Davy, Sertürner obtained the most important items of knowledge during a violent attack of toothache. What better opportunity could there be for learning how effectively the narcotic could relieve pain? When the agony was most intense he took a dose, to find that the tension relaxed and that the intensely disagreeable feelings were replaced by a sense of well-being. A number of lively impressions and ideas, unrelated to space and time, chased one another through his mind; and when he had taken a second dose, after a few minutes he fell sound asleep.

Now he was convinced that the white alkaloid he had discovered possessed the power to allay pain. Because of the pleasant dreams which a suitable dose could bring, Sertürner called the drug "morphium" (subsequently shortened to "morphia" and "morphine") after Morpheus who, in Greek mythology, was the son of Somnus and was the god of dreams.

Thus Sertürner found a really effective remedy for pain, which could be quickly absorbed into the circulation, acted on the sleep centers and within a few minutes allayed pain. But his success held a more general significance. He had shown it was possible to obtain the "active principle" from a medicinal plant, recognizing that an ostensibly uniform substance was really a composite of substances having various degrees of solubility, so that by the use of different solvents, and crystallizing them out, they could be separated one from another. The method was simple. Moreover, each crystalline substance forms its own peculiar type of crystal, with which no other crystalline substance having a different type of crystallization can mingle. Sertürner thus opened a new field of chemistry by discovering the first alkaloid, and these substances were to be of profound importance for chemo-therapeutics.

At the very time when Davy in London was giving his successful lectures upon laughing gas, Sertürner made public the results of his discovery and study of morphine; and at the time when Faraday made known his observations concerning the effects of ether, Sertürner was publishing his second and definitive monograph, *Ueber das Morphium als Hauptbestandteil des Opiums*.

The scientific world gave Sertürner due credit for his achievements in the field of the new chemistry. In March, 1817, the German Mineralogical Society met at Jena. Johann Wolfgang von Goethe took the chair and, on his initiative, Sertürner was elected an honorary member. The same year the philosophical faculty of Jena conferred on him a doctoral degree. This example was followed by the Universities of Marburg, Berlin, St. Petersburg, Batavia, Paris and Lisbon.

In 1821, a wealthy philanthropist named Montyon left a large sum of money in trust in order that all those who had made discoveries or inventions of great importance to the commonweal were to be entitled "Benefactors of Humanity" and to be allotted the Montyon prize. In the year 1831, Sertürner received this distinction, the Institute of France nominating him for the Montyon prize and bestowing on him two thousand francs for his discovery of morphine.

More powerful, however, than the acclamations and recognitions were the disfavor and hostility which set in immediately after these successes and were to dog Sertürner to the last.

The envy of experts and the gossip of small towns—the two most outrageous forms of human malice—combined, with a resulting force with which Friedrich Wilhelm Sertürner was not able to cope. Of a sudden it seemed that this modest country apothecary had powerful foes at every large university in the country. His discovery was decried as "amateurish nonsense," unworthy of scientific notice, while he was personally reviled as a swindler and a quack.

This onslaught was due to scientific envy and was reinforced by evil tongues at Einbeck. Calumny was heaped upon calumny, until Sertürner found it necessary to seek a new home in Hamelin.

In fourteen years of unremitting labor, Sertürner had found a means of relieving many of mankind's worst pains; but mankind showed him no gratitude. Embittered by the world's unkindness, the misunderstood benefactor, like Davy, abandoned further attempts to advance the healing art.

He turned to a very different field, and studied guns and projectiles. Strangely enough, Davy, too, when his experiments upon laughing gas were less successful than he had hoped, tried for a time to invent a new kind of gunpowder.

But for Sir Humphry Davy, to whom many fields of work were open, this diversion to gunpowder proved a mere episode. Sertürner, however, devoted all his inventive faculty and his whole ambition to the new field. With the same zeal that he had previously displayed in the attempt to free his fellows from pain, he now addressed himself to the task of rendering the instruments of death more trustworthy, and he actually produced an alloy of lead and antimony which greatly increased the range of firearms. Later he invented a new and more perfect breechloader.

The Hanoverian government appreciated Sertürner's achievements, and honored him for his "patriotic deeds" as an armaments inventor. Not a voice was now raised against him, for mankind prizes those who produce deadly weapons more than it prizes its true benefactors.

But the fame which accrued could not make Sertürner forget his previous disappointment. His most heartfelt dream had been to find an analgesic remedy which would be universally accepted by medicine, and this dream had not been fulfilled.

Davy, when his experiments with laughing gas proved frustrate, instead of being disheartened turned with undiminished courage to other fields. Consequently, he pursued the path of fame to the end. Sertürner lacked this indomitable energy. The demon of disillusionment haunted him to the close of his days. He could never overcome his wrath at the stupidity of the world, which ultimately broke him down. Becoming a misanthrope, he shunned human intercourse, living as a solitary, until at last he became melancholic.

To fill his cup of bitterness, this man who had made it his first business to lessen the sufferings of mankind passed the evening of his days in torment.

During his last years, gout made his life a hell. In his intolerable pain, he naturally turned to the remedy which previously he had used only for experimental purposes, and which now offered him his last hope of relief. At first, indeed, the morphine made his sufferings more bearable, but when his stomach was weakened he could no longer retain it, so that he forfeited even this relief.

For week after week he lay in an agony nothing could assuage, until death claimed him in the year 1841.

CHAPTER SEVEN

Physician to the Poor and Needy

LAUGHING GAS, ether and morphine, the first modern analgesics, were the gifts of chemists to mankind. Scientific zeal and material interests had been the spurs to the experiments which led to these discoveries. Priestley wanted, as pioneer, to explore the world of gases, and one of the first fruits of his search was laughing gas. Davy's inquiring temperament led him to find out that this gas is an anesthetic. Faraday's examination of the likenesses and differences between vapors and gases made him acquainted with the soporific effect of ether. It was pharmaceutical fervor which induced Sertürner to apply the methods of extraction and crystallization to opium in order to obtain its active principle.

Not one of them was primarily instigated by a desire to achieve the conquest of pain. Thus the scope of their researches was restricted by their lack of universal sympathy.

True, they all found means by which pain could be relieved; but since their main object was to succeed in a scientific experiment, once having done so they turned aside, believing their task to be fulfilled.

To make a successful experiment, they considered no sacrifice excessive; death counted for nothing in the balance, and they staked their lives upon a cast: but not one of them was self-sacrificing enough to devote a lifetime to one discovery.

Their experiments provided them with instruments for the relief of pain. But as soon as difficulties arose, they ceased to put up a fight on behalf of their discoveries. When other paths of research allured them, they cared no more about analgesics or anesthetics, and became immersed in other experiments. The discovery of a new chemical compound, no matter for what it might be used, was their main object. That was why Davy and Sertürner, after one of them had played for a while with laughing gas and the other with morphine, devoted themselves, the Englishman to making an improved kind of gunpowder, and the German to the manufacture of more deadly firearms.

One spring afternoon in the early years of the nineteenth century a light-hearted youth was amusing himself at some games with his schoolfellows when they heard shrieks of agony come from the adjoining road. Young Henry Hill Hickman outpaced his companions to see what was the matter. A workman who had had an accident lay on the ground, writhing in pain. A doctor was sent for and speedily arrived.

"Send him to the hospital at once," said the medico. "He will have to be operated on as soon as possible."

"But I've no money, sir," groaned the man.

However, a cart was fetched; he was lifted into it and driven away.

Henry Hill Hickman had heard every word of the brief conversation. The boys ran back into the playground to continue their game. But Henry was moody, did not play and soon stole away.

When he got home his parents were pleased to see him, but the lad was unresponsive, and when they asked him what was the matter, he only said, "Nothing."

Next day he was still extremely thoughtful. It was a holiday and his schoolfellows came to fetch him. Matters went on much as usual, but for Henry everything was changed, since he had seen the poor man after the accident and had heard the plaintive remark: "I have no money to pay for an operation." Since then, games were no longer amusing to Henry; his parents' kind words meant nothing to him. What was the use of anything, if people had to suffer like that without help? He was filled with a burning desire to know what had happened to the poor workman.

The sight of suffering, poverty and illness has caused a change in many. It turned Buddha, the king's son, from a sinner to a saint, and has made others renounce the pleasures of life. Young Hickman did not become an ascetic. The effect on him was to produce a wish to give practical help.

That was why he made up his mind to become a doctor, a physician to the poor, a surgeon to operate without fees on those who needed it. With the fervor of one possessed, he devoted himself to the study of medicine.

When three-and-twenty, he attended an operation in Edinburgh. Operations in those days were no less horrible than they had been in the Middle Ages. "A humiliating spectacle of the futility of science," said John Hunter (1728-1793); and the same authority, the leading anatomist of his day, whose brother William Hunter (1718-1783) was a famous surgeon, said that a surgeon was "a savage armed with a knife."

Hickman had to watch the patient being forcibly held down, yelling and groaning, and he lacked the callousness which Celsus described as the first need of the good surgeon. Every cry tore at his heartstrings, and his inability to prevent this horrible pain made him utterly miserable when he left the operating theater.

"There is no help for it," said his colleagues.

"There must be a help for it," answered young Hickman. "We must find out something. It is barbarous that anyone should suffer like that. How silly to be a doctor and not discover a way of preventing pain."

Hickman saw another operation, and many more. Each time he heard the same cries of agony, and suffered the same despair. Herbal narcotics were so untrustworthy and dangerous that no one ventured to use them. Mesmerism had been dismissed as humbug. What on earth was to be done about this pain?

After qualification, Hickman began to practice at Ludlow in Shropshire. Now he was going to fulfill his boyhood's dream. Over the door of his surgery he hung a board saying: "At Home every Tuesday from ten o'clock until four; for the purpose of giving advice gratis to the poor and labouring classes!" There were plenty of poor persons to crowd the waiting room, but others came as well. His unceasing kindliness and his skill inspired confidence in the well-to-do, so that a great multitude of the maimed and the halt and the withered flocked to consult him or called him to their bedsides.

In his extensive country practice, Hickman was often called upon to perform amputation, to cut for the stone, to operate in cases of strangulated hernia or to do tracheotomy. He worked swiftly and confidently, as the surgeon had to work in those days, but he could not avoid inflicting the usual torments.

During his student days at Edinburgh, he had always been in revolt against the idea that the pain of surgical operations was absolutely inevitable. But here in Ludlow the agony of suffering humanity wrung his heart even more. In Edinburgh he had been an onlooker. The patients had been strangers. Now those who groaned under his knife were his friends and acquaintances: the poor, workmen and workwomen, agricultural laborers and their wives and children; fellow citizens with whose joys and sorrows he was intimately acquainted. He felt every pang that he inflicted as if it had been inflicted on himself.

As he said in a letter to his friend T. A. Knight, in those days every operation was approached with a shudder, and it was a perpetual distress to him that he could do nothing to avoid giving his patients so much pain.

Before long Hickman went to Shifnal for a time, to act as locum tenens for a doctor there. This visit was of great moment to him, for Shifnal was the birthplace of Dr. Beddoes, the founder of pneumatology. By this time, no doubt, pneumatology had fallen into discredit, almost into oblivion. Still, there were living in Shifnal persons who remembered Beddoes as a local notable. Some of them were firmly convinced that Beddoes had been on the right track, and they gave Hickman the idea of trying to discover whether, after all, something could not be done with gas therapeutics.

On getting home to Ludlow, Hickman devoted all his spare time to the study of gases. He looked up the records of the work of Priestley, Davy and Faraday, and went on to make fresh experiments of his own. Being a doctor with a keen sense of responsibility, he began by making trials upon mice, dogs and chickens rather than on human beings. His surgery was his laboratory. Directly the last patient had left, his laboratory work began. At first he tried oxygen, then carbonic oxide and then nitrous oxide.

On March 20, 1824, he recorded concerning these experiments:

"I took a puppy a month old and placed it on a piece of wood, surrounded by water, over which I put a glass cover so as to prevent the access of atmospheric air; in ten minutes he showed great marks of uneasiness, in twelve minutes respiration became difficult, and in seventeen minutes ceased altogether; at eighteen minutes I took off one of the ears, which was not followed by hemorrhage; respiration soon returned and the animal did not appear to be the least sensible of pain; in three days the ear was perfectly healed."

Of another experiment:

"A mouse was confined under a glass, surrounded by water; by means of a small tube a foot long, I passed carbonic acid gas very slowly prepared into the glass; respiration ceased in the minute. I cut all its legs off and plunged it into a basin of cold water. The animal immediately recovered . . . apparently without pain. . . . Later I took a fully grown dog and plunged him in an atmosphere of the same gas. Within twelve seconds he was completely insensible. He remained so for seventeen minutes. Meanwhile I amputated a leg without his giving any sign of pain. . . . Next day, I filled a glass globe with the gas exhaled from my own lungs, into it I put a kitten. In twenty seconds I took off its ears and tail, there was very little hemorrhage and no appearance of pain to the animal."

These experiments on animals were successful. Why? The experimenter had deprived the animals of fresh air, so that they were half-asphyxiated. It was plain to Hickman that the condition of stupor accounted for the absence of pain, and that the stupor was due to suffocation. Yet he felt that it would be premature to recommend death's assistant, suffocation, to his colleagues as a means for preventing pain during surgical operations.

But each new experiment advanced him a stage, and helped

him to reduce the dangers. After a while, having made an animal breathe stertorously by administering carbonic acid, he then gave pure laughing gas. In this way he induced unconsciousness which seemed free from any danger of suffocation.

The long-desired moment had come. The experiments were ripe for use in practical surgery. All that he needed was authorization to repeat them on human beings. In this matter his friend T. A. Knight could be of great help to him. Knight, horticulturist and botanist, was an F.R.S. and an intimate friend of both Davy and Faraday. Surely Knight would be able to draw these distinguished scientists' attention to the matter.

"Having made experiments on various animals," wrote Hickman to Knight, "I feel perfectly satisfied that any surgical operation might be performed with quite as much safety in an insensible state, for the performance of the most tedious operation. . . . I believe there are few if any Surgeons who could not operate more skilfully, when they were conscious they were not inflicting pain. . . . I certainly should not hesitate a moment to become the subject of such an experiment, if I were under the necessity of suffering any long or severe operation. . . . If by my labours," Hickman went on with characteristic modesty and unselfishness, "I could add a grain of knowledge to what has been ascertained about the means for dulling pain, I should be amply rewarded."

Knight responded to the appeal, calling without delay upon Davy and Faraday to show them the letter and to discuss the significance of Hickman's experiments. He urged them to have the matter brought before a committee of the Royal Society. But nothing was done.

Davy was immersed in work on behalf of the chemical industries, and was by no means eager to have these waters stirred. He had had enough of laughing gas. Faraday could not think of anything outside the domain of his electromagnetic problems. Neither of them took the smallest interest in the story of Hickman's experiments. No committee of the Royal Society would take up the cudgels on behalf of these experiments if they left Sir Humphry Davy and Michael Faraday cold. It was not even thought desirable to have a public reading of Hickman's report.

At Ludlow, meanwhile, the sick continued to flock to Hickman. They came with damaged organs to be excised, with painful limbs to be amputated. They groaned or screamed, as before, under the knife. Hickman would not allow himself to be discouraged. He continued to believe that the secret of the prevention of pain during operations was to be found in a gas.

After a while he had a chance of reading before the Medical Society of London a paper on his researches. With scientific precision he reported the reactions of mice, dogs and chickens to laughing gas. The audience of eminent doctors listened politely, but without interest, to the reading of the paper and, when he had finished, a profound silence ensued.

Silence? For him this silence was broken in his imagination by the cries of pain uttered by those on whom he had operated in Ludlow. Cold, dull, unmoved eyes stared at him. What he saw was the pain-distorted faces, the agonized eyes, of his patients in Ludlow. He resumed his address, not speaking now of the mice and dogs he had put to sleep, but of the suffering human beings in the town where he lived and practiced.

There was an uneasy stir in the audience. What was the fellow talking about? The sufferings of the people in Ludlow were of no importance to the learned doctors of London. "It seems to me that Dr. Hickman is a dreamer, not to say a fool," said one of them. The words went home, for the others nodded their gray heads approvingly. "Dreams of this sort are a danger to the faculty," declared another. "Yes, a danger to the faculty," echoed through the room. The comments, the nods and the glances grew threatening. "What this gentleman has been telling us is simply absurd," exclaimed another. They laughed. They all laughed at the country doctor from Ludlow.

Disappointed once more, Henry Hill Hickman returned home. His heartfelt aim to free his fellows from pain was laughed to scorn by his medical colleagues. Still, after all, this country doctor was not fighting mainly for recognition on the part of the Medical Society of London or any other scientific body. What he wanted was to free his fellows from the agonies of the surgeon's knife. A mere chemist, one who passed his life amid insensitive flasks and test tubes, might have given up the game; but Henry Hill Hickman, whose mission it was to relieve without fee the sufferings of workers and the poor, was not a man to relinquish the struggle.

His only inference from the scorn of his London colleagues was that the Londoners must be back numbers. He knew that patients who were operated on had to suffer horribly under the knife, and this knowledge inspired him with greatness, a greatness which was fortified by truth.

The medical faculty in England did not understand; the doctors of London were reactionary. Well, England was not the world. What London would not heed, for lack of understanding, might be heeded in Paris, the metropolis of the world. Charles X, son of Louis XV, brother of Louis XVI and Louis XVIII, now sat on the throne of France. Politically he was a reactionary, but had always shown unprejudiced interest in scientific advances. In April, 1828, Hickman, writing to King Charles, told the monarch about his researches and asked permission to give a demonstration before the medical faculty of Paris. Conveying his petition to Paris in person, he handed it in to the proper quarter.

"To His Most Christian Majesty, Charles Tenth, King of France.

"Sire—In addressing Your Majesty upon a scientific subject of great importance to mankind, I feel a properly humble, but a firm confidence in Your Majesty's universally known disposition to countenance valuable discoveries. . . . Permit me, Sire, to state that I am a British Physician, Member of the Royal College of Surgeons, London, who has visited Paris in part for the purpose of bringing to completion a discovery, to which I have been led by a course of observations and experiments on suspended animation. This object has engaged my practical attention during several years: It appears demonstrable that the hitherto most agonizing dangerous and delicate surgical operations, may now be performed, with perfect safety, and exemption from pain, on brute animals in a state of suspended animation. . . .

"Paris the great Metropolis of Continental Europe is the place, above all others, where the profound studies of humanity are, with the utmost facility, carried to their highest extent and perfection, and, Sire, I feel confident, that I do not say too much, with a due regard for the scientific distinction of my own Country, in avowing that these facilities have deservedly conferred on Your Majesty's Chief City the eminent title of the Centre of Science to the civilized world. . . . Should my labours meet with the approbation of Charles Tenth, I shall ever enjoy the grateful satisfaction of believing, that I have devoted myself to my profession to a distinguished and to a happy end. . . ."

Hickman went on to beg the King to bring his proposals before the Academy.

With a suitable recommendation, His Majesty passed on the petition to the Royal Academy of Medicine. The Academy called a meeting for December 28, 1828. It was attended by many of the most noted physicians in France. Monsieur Guérardin read a report upon the young English doctor's proposals. But the leading lights of French medicine were no less antagonistic than those of England had been. "Operate under laughing gas? What foolhardy, what dangerous nonsense."—"Nonsensical, criminal. Yes, it would be nothing but a crime to expose a human being to such needless perils."

Among all the physicians present, only one was interested: Baron Dominique Larrey, who had been an army surgeon under the great Napoleon, had accompanied the Emperor in a number of campaigns and had seen the miseries of the *Grand' Armée* on the frozen plains of Russia. He alone understood what Henry Hill Hickman was driving at. No other Paris practitioner had been so profoundly impressed as this army surgeon by the tragedy of human suffering. At least a trial should be made before rejecting what might prove of the utmost value to humanity. "I myself," he said, "would be willing for Mr. Hickman to administer laughing gas to me, and see what would happen." But the majority of the members of the Royal Academy of Medicine outvoted Larrey, and declined to have anything more to do with the "crazy scheme."

Hickman returned home. This was another terrible blow, but he would not be downhearted. The day would come when people would understand him. Notwithstanding his defeat, he continued

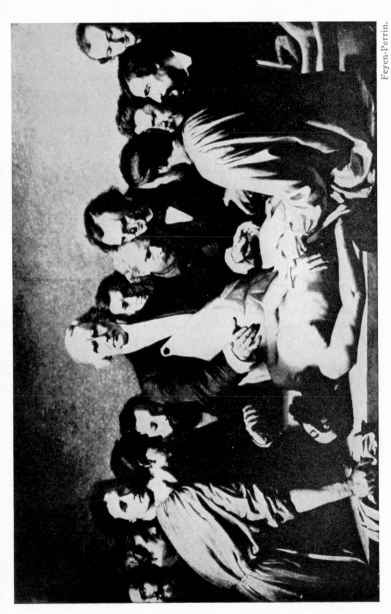

Feyen-Perrin.

Velpeau, who believed pain and the healing knife inseparable, at work at the Charité of Paris.

Hickman experimenting with animals in an attempt to alleviate the agony
of the operating table.

to believe that pain during surgical operations could be prevented, and he went on with the struggle.

But what the indolence of experts had not been able to do, death achieved, robbing the dreamer of his dreams, imposing silence on the enthusiast. He died prematurely, on April 5, 1830, when only twenty-nine.

Here is a patient's own account of what he felt in those pre-anesthetic days:

"I at once agreed to submit to the operation, but asked a week to prepare for it, simply because I wished to prepare for death and what lies beyond it whilst my faculties were clear and my emotions comparatively undisturbed. The morning of the operation arrived. The operation was a more tedious one than some which involve much greater mutilation. It involved cruel cutting through inflamed and morbidly sensitive parts, and could not be despatched by a few strokes of the knife. Of the agony it occasioned I will say nothing. Suffering as great as I underwent cannot be expressed in words, and thus, fortunately cannot be recalled. The particular pangs are now forgotten; but the black whirlwind of emotion, the horror of great darkness, and the sense of desertion by God and man, bordering close upon despair, which swept through my mind and overwhelmed my heart, I can never forget, however gladly I would do so. Only the wish to save others some of my sufferings makes me deliberately recall and confess the anguish and humiliation of such a personal experience. During the operation in spite of the pain, my senses were preternaturally acute. I watched all that the surgeon did with a fascinating intensity. I still recall with unwelcome vividness the spreading out of the instruments, the twisting of the tourniquet, the first incision, the fingering of the sawed bone, the sponge pressed on the flap, the tying of the blood-vessels, the stitching of the skin, and the bloody dismembered limb lying on the floor. These are not pleasant remembrances. For a long time they haunted me, and, though they cannot bring back the suffering, they can occasion a suffering of their own, and be the cause of a disquiet which favors neither mental nor bodily health."

Read the words written at about the same date by a young doctor to Professor Simpson, the obstetrician who had been his chief in Edinburgh:

"Before the days of anæsthetics a patient preparing for an operation was like a condemned criminal preparing for execution. He counted the days till the appointed day came. He counted the hours of that day till the appointed hour came. He listened for the echo in the street of the surgeon's carriage. He watched for his pull at the door-bell; for his foot on the stair; for his step in the room; for the production of his dreaded instruments; for his few grave words, and his last preparations before beginning. And then he surrendered his liberty and, revolting at the necessity, submitted to be held or bound, and helplessly gave himself up to the cruel knife."

In like manner Dupuytren, the famous French surgeon, reports the misery of his Parisian patients before an operation, many of them dying of dread: *"La douleur tue comme l'hémmoragie,"* he exclaims.

Letters from patients and doctors, clinical reports and other documents, tell of the pain of amputation, reduction of dislocations, childbirth, etc.; of the inconceivable torments of those who were made fast to the operating table.

Many operators dreaded what they would have to face hardly less than did their patients. The sensitive Cheselden never slept a wink the night before an operation, and he once said, "No sufferer can ever be more terrified than I am on these occasions." Robert Liston made a stirring plea for the restriction of the field of surgical operation.

The domain of such "minor surgery" as the pulling of teeth was ghastly enough, both by anticipation and in actuality. "What a terrible operation," wrote Heinrich Heine when he had to submit himself to the dentist. "I am sure no one would endure this operation, or rather execution, were it not that toothache becomes absolutely unendurable. Were I offered the choice between a bad tooth and a bad conscience, I should say, 'Give me the bad conscience.' "

The unrelieved torments of surgical operation were still being endured day after day long after Davy had discovered that laughing gas can prevent the pain of operations, after Faraday had drawn attention to the potency of ether and after Sertürner had discovered morphine and Hickman had implored the medical faculties of England and France to introduce the use of laughing gas into surgery. Concerning this period, John Bigelow of the Massachusetts General Hospital in Boston wrote later: "People's attitude towards methods of anæsthesia suggests that they must have inhaled ether vapour and have been drugged into sleep for decades."

Perhaps we can best judge how far the repudiation of analgesic measures had gone when we read the utterance of one of the greatest of French surgeons of the first half of the nineteenth century, Alfred Armand Louis Marie Velpeau: "To escape pain in surgical operations is a chimera which we are not permitted to look for in our days. A cutting instrument and pain in operative medicine are two ideas which never present themselves separately to the mind of the patient, and it is necessary for us surgeons to admit their association."

Similar were the words of Magendie, another medical luminary of the period. He declared it to be an "unworthy attempt" to try, by artificial sleep, to transform the body into an "insensitive cadaver" before beginning to use the knife. Copland, too, was averse to the idea. Speaking of attempts to make surgery painless, he bluntly remarks: "Even were the reports of persons who felt no pain during an operation credible, this would not be worth the consideration of a serious-minded doctor."

"I should not care to be a doctor without morphine at my disposal," said a famous clinician in our own days. But during the first half of the nineteenth century official medicine set itself against the use of morphine. It is true that the distinguished French physicist Gay-Lussac was strongly in favor of it, and asked Robiquet to repeat Sertürner's experiments. When Robiquet, having done so, reported it was undeniable that morphine could markedly assuage pain, and suggested that its analgesic effect might be greatly intensified if it was administered by intravenous injection, decades had still to elapse before the remedy came into general use.

Why did official medicine, medical societies and famous surgeons refuse to avail themselves of those methods of allaying pain which had actually been discovered? Why oppose their use? Why ignore them, and leave patients in torment?

It is one of the most insoluble puzzles why man, doomed to suffering, should always have neglected and scorned possibilities for alleviating his lot. Almost invariably a long time has had to elapse before the investigators who did invaluable work in this field were honored by their fellows, before garlands were laid upon their neglected tombs and monuments erected to those whose lives were devoted to the relief or prevention of suffering. Late, far too late, were the gates of the Pantheon opened.

Posterity, the posterity to which we ourselves belong, having accepted with enjoyment and taken as a matter of course what earlier generations despised and rejected, is apt to suppose that the narrow-mindedness and envy of experts must have led to the long-lasting disregard of so many valuable discoveries.

Yet when we look back after the lapse of a century upon the stupidity of those dead experts, it seems to us to have been in keeping with the blindness and deafness which afflicted them with regard to so many other innovations. At the very time when poor Hickman was vainly trying to induce the British medical faculty to heed his discoveries, George Stephenson, a hungry and neglected inventor, was finding it extremely difficult to persuade anyone to adopt his "traveling engine," first on a tram road, then on the Stockton and Darlington Railway and finally, twenty years after the tram road, on the Liverpool and Manchester Railway. The iron horse came into its own slowly and with difficulty, amid almost universal ridicule. It was regarded as dangerous as well as absurd. Who can tell how much longer people might have had to wait for the introduction of locomotives, had not the sporting instinct of the British aristocracy given the new invention a chance! The suggestion was made that a race between the iron horse and the old-style flesh-and-blood animals would be amusing, and people of rank and fashion assembled at Rainhill to see the show.

Picture by Fra Giacomo di Beaulieu.

Seventeenth-century foot operation.

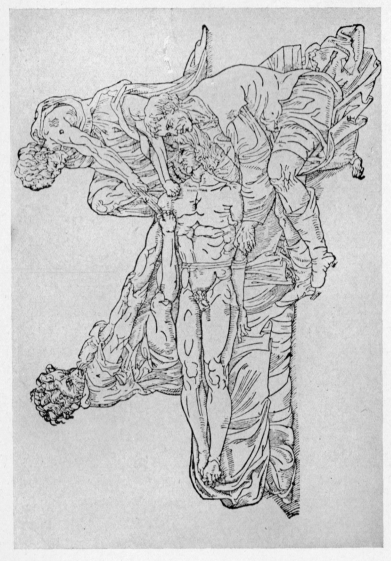

Medieval patient strapped to the operating table while surgeons pull his limbs.

When Stephenson's locomotive was an easy winner, the future of railways was assured, although for a long time Stephenson's innovation was regarded as an accursed disaster.

The narrow-mindedness of experts, the reactionary attitude of entire generations, would seem to be part of man's primal curse. It is a curse which smites us with blindness so that we do not see when someone offers us salvation, with deafness so that we do not hear his words, and hardens our hearts so that those who are eager to help us perish with their gifts in their hands unused.

CHAPTER EIGHT

Ether Parties in the United States

OFTEN DECADES, and sometimes even centuries, had to elapse before some newly discovered means for alleviating pain secured recognition. Who can tell how long laughing gas and ether would still have remained unutilized after the experiments of Davy, Faraday and Hickman, for what ages they might have lapsed once more into oblivion, had it not been for the clownish amusements of certain high-spirited young fellows?

Over and above their analgesic effects, ether and laughing gas have a quality which can be turned to account for various jokes of a "practical" kind. They can make people very drunk indeed, giving rise to wonderful visions and uncontrollable hilarity. As it happened, these subsidiary effects of intoxication with ether and laughing gas were to prove of the utmost importance to the future of pain-tortured mankind.

Since there have always been young people inclined toward a little harmless amusement and toward practical jokes of a diverting kind, the inhalation of ether vapor and nitrous oxide gas became a fashionable amusement among those who had nothing better to do.

The European youth of that period was less frolicsome. Men in their early twenties were enthusiastic admirers of Byron; in Germany young men with more money than brains regarded *The Sorrows of Werther* as Goethe's greatest work, had a liking for the "night side of life" and were devotees of the Romantic movement.

94

In France there was a passion for freedom; young men, like the circle of Enjolras, Grantaire and Marius in Victor Hugo's *Les Misérables,* liked to describe themselves as *"les amis de l'A. B. C."* Youth was slowly cutting its wisdom teeth, amid struggles. Between reason and romanticism, *Weltschmerz* and skepticism, liberalism and reaction, there was in progress a decisive contest as to the form which the new European society was to assume. Science was dragged into the fight, being itself one of the prizes for which people fought. Amid so much that was serious, laughter had gone astray.

But it was decreed by Providence that in a world which seemed lacking in the talent for laughter, heedless youth should keep the pain-allaying substances in the public eye until science was ready to attend to them. And precisely because the delight in laughter was lacking in Europe, Providence turned to the New World.

There in the United States, scientific instruction was free from the heavy European touch. Lectures were far less didactic, and the students were less "earnest," having, in great measure, the spirit of a child eager to satisfy youthful curiosity. Learning was a pastime. Especially in the domain of physics and chemistry, many experiments could be made no less amusing than they were instructive, so that astonishment would enlist the attention, and convert the acquirement of the exact sciences into a genuine amusement.

One of the most remarkable and popular among scientific demonstrations was that in which people were made tipsy by the inhalation of ether vapor and laughing gas. The students to whom the professor administered these substances became quaintly drunk. They lost control over their limbs, staggered or danced on the platform, talked nonsense, burst into fits of unmeaning laughter— laughter in which the rest of the class and the professor joined. When the intoxication passed off, the subject reported having been in a thoroughly agreeable and "elevated" state of mind, and having seen pleasant visions.

These experiments, with their cheering accompaniments, became so much the vogue that the young fellows got into a way of amusing themselves with them on their own, out of class. Laughing-gas parties and ether parties became as popular in American universities among carefree youth as wine parties were at the Oxford and Cambridge of those days.

It was not long before persons "on the make" found they could turn the remarkable effects of laughing gas and ether to profitable account. Since drinking, card-playing, the circus and even the theater were anathema among the New England children of the Puritan Reformation, there was a general yearning for distraction. Traveling showmen, therefore, moved on from town to town, from village to village, giving "highly instructive lectures," illustrated by the use of these substances—lectures at which not even a Puritan could complain.

The itinerants talked, not about "laughing gas," but about "nitrous oxide," leaving it to the audience to discover how much amusement was to be got out of these "chemical lectures." They gave demonstrations in the public squares or in booths or tents. The lecturer would make his way along the road wheeling his portable laboratory in a handcart. When he reached a suitable street corner in a town, he would borrow a table from the nearest tavern, set up his apparatus and summon the crowd with the ringing voice of a barker. As soon as loiterers had assembled, and persons willing to inhale the gas had been found, they were given a sufficiency of it and amused the onlookers with contortions and laughter, while the itinerant went round with the hat to collect the stipulated entrance fee of twenty-five cents. As the audience began to break up, the itinerant, using a megaphone, would bawl: "Will any gentlemen who would like to inhale the gas in private, oblige me with their names and addresses."

From North to South, from East to West, moved the showmen, and wherever they had set foot young people began to amuse themselves on their own account with ether and laughing gas.

It was thus that the fashion of having "ether frolics" made its way to Athens in Clarke County, Georgia, the seat of the University of Georgia. There college boys and factory girls assembled once a week in Mr. Ware's house outside the town, to intoxicate themselves with ether. The initiator of the frolics was a student named P. H. Wilhite.

One evening when the mood of the gathering was exceptionally festive, Wilhite caught sight of someone staring open-eyed through the glass door of the room. It was a Negro boy who had for some time been watching the strange antics. The intoxicated student dragged the youngster into the room and, amid vociferous applause, proposed to the company that ether should be administered to this uninvited guest. Seizing the ether flask, he held it under the black boy's nose, but the patient resisted and tried to escape. He was firmly held while Wilhite, amid riotous acclamations, pressed a handkerchief saturated with ether against mouth and nostrils. The boy, terror-stricken, struggled with all his might. Then his eyes suddenly closed and his muscles relaxed. He lay motionless. The tormentors ceased to hold him down. The lads and lasses stood round him in a circle, expecting him to begin the usual foolish tricks. When, after a while, he did not move, Wilhite pinched his arm, someone else gave him a kick, but nothing could awaken him. There he lay, as still as death, and, amid an anxious silence one of the girls screamed: "He is dead! We have killed him!" Whereupon all the girls fled in terror from the room.

Left to themselves, the young men stared at one another. The Negro lad lay motionless. "Fetch a doctor!" exclaimed someone, and Mr. Ware's servant was sent hotfoot to Athens, five miles away.

The anxiety of the practical jokers steadily increased. What on earth were they to do? They decided not to await the coming of the doctor, but to make themselves scarce before the authorities had been informed about the disastrous result of their prank.

Wilhite ordered horses to be saddled. Those who wished to escape being prosecuted for manslaughter were about to ride for the frontier of Georgia when Dr. Reese, fetched by the servingman, appeared on the scene. He had a bucket of cold water flung over the boy. No result, so he knelt and began to rub the region of the heart. Still no result, so he gave the obstinate sleeper two sound boxes on the ears. Whereupon the boy awakened, stared in wonder at the doctor and obviously did not know what had happened. The students recovered from their alarm, promised Dr. Reese that they would hold no more "ether frolics"—and hoped to forget this misadventure as soon as possible.

The upshot was that no one grasped the deep significance of this clownish trick. All those present had seen that in the Negro boy there had ensued, instead of a cheerful state of "elevation," a profound sleep, attended by complete loss of consciousness and absolute insensibility—but their understanding went no further.

Three years later, in the winter of 1841, at the village of Jefferson, likewise in Georgia—a hundred and forty miles from the nearest railway, a place surrounded by huge cotton plantations, in a district peopled chiefly by cotton planters and their darky slaves—a gas demonstration took place. The appearance of an itinerant lecturer was a remarkable incident in this remote spot. The planters of the whole neighborhood, and their wives and children, assembled in mass.

The only notable inhabitant of the village who missed this lively evening was the doctor, a young man of twenty. He had been called out early that afternoon to visit someone who had been taken seriously ill at a plantation many miles away. The younger members of the audience missed him very much, for Dr. Crawford Williamson Long was always the center of entertainment when there was anything lively on hand; and, the tall, slender, handsome young fellow with light blue eyes who dressed in the height of fashion was the darling of the ladies.

When the lecture and demonstration were over, Long's friends assembled outside his house to await his return. They were greatly excited by the strange things they had seen and heard. Perhaps Long, who was a graduate of the University of Pennsylvania, would be able to explain the remarkable happenings that had been the outcome of the inhalation of the vapor.

While thus awaited, Long was riding home over the frozen roads. The wind blew keen, but was not strong enough to dispel the mist which delayed his progress. Still, he was used to discomfort and late hours. The life of a country practitioner in a remote southern township inured him to hardship. He often had to ride long distances to see his patients. What did fatigue, what did loss of sleep, matter, so long as a man did his duty?

The night was far advanced when at length he reached Jefferson. His friends welcomed him uproariously, hardly giving him time to dismount and to take his medical paraphernalia out of the saddlebags before they urged him into the house and began—all speaking at once—to inform him and question him about their bewildering experiences that evening.

The young doctor listened to what they had to say as to the itinerant's proceedings, and replied that he must have time to consult his medical books before he could give them a full explanation. "A moment's patience, friends," he went on, departing for the surgery. Within a few minutes he was back, carrying a bottle and a handkerchief. Saturating this last with ether, he thrust it beneath the nose of one whom he chose at random, then did the same thing to a second and a third. Almost before they realized what was happening, Long's victims began to talk nonsense, to laugh, to dance, to sing and to quarrel.

Long, who during his student days had grown familiar with the effect of ether, looked on with a smile. When his friends' fugitive intoxication was over, he said, in bidding them all good night: "You see, your doctor here in Jefferson can give as good measure as any stranger."

The young folks admired Long all the more for the prank he had played on them. Next day, the next and the next, a number of them called on him and made him repeat the experiment.

Even before this, during the long winter evenings the doctor's house had become a meeting-place to which people came to learn the latest news of the world's progress, to discuss art and literature, to drink straight whisky, play chess or whist and have a good time. But now the previous amusements were replaced by "ether frolics."

In the cotton plantations round Jefferson there was so much talk about the ether parties that the young women became as eager as their brothers not to miss the fun. They determined to ask the doctor to let them join such a party. One day a number of them drove to Long's and proffered their request. A deputation of pretty damsels took his surgery by storm.

The leader of the deputation was Caroline Swain, a girl of sixteen, regarded as the local queen of beauty. Long, who had made her acquaintance when she was a chit of fourteen, had already determined to ask her hand in marriage as soon as she was a little older. When Caroline looked at him languishingly and told him what she and her comrades wanted, he found her irresistible, and promised to have a girls' ether party on Christmas Eve.

Long's stock of ether had run low, so he wrote at once to Robert H. Goodman, a friend of his who ran a drugstore in Athens, asking for a fresh supply:

"Dear Bob:
"I am under the necessity of troubling you a little. I am entirely out of ether and wish some by tomorrow night if it is possible to receive it by that time. We have some girls in Jefferson who are anxious to see it taken, and you know nothing would afford me more pleasure than to take it in their presence and to get a few sweet kisses (?)."[1]

When the great evening arrived, Long made his preparations carefully. Being, as aforesaid, a dandy, he devoted a long time to his toilet, and to making sure that his cravat was tied according to all the rules of art.

The party was a great success. As soon as his fair visitors had assembled in the surgery, he solemnly took the ether flask out of his pocket and explained that he had sent for a fresh supply, but, after due consideration, he had made up his mind not to inhale any of the stuff, for he would not be able to answer for what he might do under its influence. His words had the desired effect. The young women unanimously assured him that any extravagance he might commit would be ascribed by them solely to the ether. Caroline Swain was even more encouraging than the others, so at length Long allowed himself to be persuaded: "All right," he said, "I'll inhale some, if you all promise not to hold me responsible for anything I may do."

The doctor lodged with two elderly women, sisters. They were strict Quakers, who detested everything in the nature of amusement, so he was careful to lock the door communicating with their sitting room before he started inhaling. As soon as he had

[1] James Thomas Flexner, *Doctors on Horseback*, Viking Press, New York, 1937, p. 311.

taken a few breaths, he began to stagger about the room and kissed all the girls in turn.

They were greatly amused and, when the doctor's intoxication (real or assumed) had passed off, Caroline Swain begged him to give her a sniff of ether. So did the other girls, each of whom tried this delightful intoxicant. Next day, some of them came again; and the next day, and the next. In a word, "ether frolics" became the fashion in Jefferson.

What for the others was no more than an amusement, was for Dr. Long a reason for careful observation. "On numerous occasions I inhaled ether for its exhilarating properties," he reports, "and would frequently, at some short time subsequent to its inhalation, discover bruised or painful spots on my person which I had no recollection of causing and which I felt satisfied were received while under the influence of ether. I noticed my friends while etherized received falls and blows which I believed were sufficient to produce pain on a person not in a state of anæsthesia, and on questioning them they uniformly assured me that they did not feel the least pain from these accidents."

Long began to wonder whether this loss of sensibility to pain might not be of moment from the medical standpoint. After making a great many observations, he came to the conclusion that the effect of ether during a surgical operation would probably be the same as that which he observed at the ether parties. Perhaps, he thought, in the intoxicating effect of ether vapor might be found the weapon against pain for which the medical profession had so long been searching.

A practical proof was all that was needed to transform this supposition into certainty. Long had a young friend, a student named James M. Venable, who for some time had been troubled by two small tumors on the nape of the neck. The doctor advised him to inhale a large quantity of ether and, while he was under the ether intoxication, Long proposed to remove the tumors without causing any pain. At first Venable refused; but when Long reminded him that, during the ether parties, he had frequently sustained slight injuries without suffering any pain whatever, Venable finally agreed.

One afternoon he came to the surgery, where there were already assembled a number of the young fellows who were wont to attend the ether parties. He stretched himself upon the couch, and the others looked on curiously. Venable breathed in ether vapor from a saturated handkerchief and when he lay, to all seeming, in a quiet sleep, Long thrust a needle deep into the arm. The patient gave no twitch and uttered no cry. Obviously he was quite insensible to pain. Resolutely Long took up a surgical knife and enucleated one of the tumors. Having stitched up the incision and bandaged the wound, he removed the ether-drenched handkerchief; and after a time Venable recovered consciousness.

The country doctor's surgery in Jefferson was the first place in which a surgical operation on a human being was painlessly performed under ether. Yet, even now, Long found it hard to accept the evidence of his own eyes and to believe that the painlessness during the operation had been exclusively due to the ether. It seemed to him more probable that he must be gifted with mesmeric powers. Ether might, perhaps, have intensified a mesmeric sleep, but it would be going too far to ascribe the insensibility wholly to the ether.

The friends who had witnessed the operation took the same view. It seemed to them far more probable that Venable's profound slumber had been brought about by mesmerism.

But Long had enemies, persons to whom his popularity had always been a source of envy; and they hastened to spread the rumor that the young doctor possessed a means of making people unconscious, that this was an extremely dangerous poison which deprived people of their reason. It would be well for everyone to avoid falling into the hands of such a physician.

To guard himself against the unfortunate outcome of such rumors, Long determined to make further trials of his remedy. The question was, on whom? The story about the "dangerous poison" had aroused so much alarm that not even those who had cheerfully frequented the ether parties would now allow their friend to administer the drug.

One day, however, the long-desired opportunity came. As in Athens, so here, it was a Negro boy on whom the anesthetic effect of ether was to be demonstrated. The son of a slave, a child of eight, had burned two of his fingers so badly that they would have to be amputated. He gladly agreed to "take something" which the doctor proposed to give him so that he should feel no pain during the operation. Here was a splendid chance for trying what ether could do.

Long made his experiment with coolness, the callousness proper to a scientific investigator. He amputated one finger in the ether sleep. The boy lay quite still, and apparently felt nothing. The other finger was cut away when the effect of the ether had passed off. The poor youngster yelled at the top of his voice, and Long had to tie him down before finishing the operation.

Well, the experimenter had found the objective evidence of which he was in search, and could now be sure that ether and nothing but ether was the cause of the insensibility. He might have gone on to do more operations under ether, proud of his new method, which would have made of him the pioneer of an overwhelmingly important discovery, the introducer of anesthesia, of which even the name did not yet exist.

He had made trustworthy observations, and had drawn the right conclusions from them. His original supposition was shown to be correct. All that he lacked was the confidence of faith. Doubt is pusillanimous, questions the value of observation, undermines knowledge, discredits proof. Doubt is anxious, shrinks from avowal, rails against the dangers of innovation, and can be overcome only by unhesitating courage.

Although the experiment on the Negro boy had shown Long that ether was an effective analgesic, he still doubted whether the pain-relieving effects of this vapor would last long enough for major surgical operations. "In this operation," he writes, "the inhalation of ether ceased before the first incision was made. Since that time I have invariably desired patients, when practicable, to continue the inhalation during the time of the operation."

Books, reports, monographs discussing the nature and effects of ether, its dosage, all the data collected in the various Pneumatic

Institutes, should have sufficed to dispel Long's doubts. Discussions with well-informed colleagues, and the expert study of his experiments in hospitals, would have sufficed to confirm his belief. But Jefferson was a cotton-planting center far away in the wilds. There were few books, no hospitals, no well-instructed physicians there.

Dr. Crawford W. Long was left to himself in his uneasiness. The only person ready to inspire him with confidence and hope was Caroline Swain, who had now become Mrs. Long. Her love inspired her. She was convinced that her husband was the man to bestow this great boon upon humanity. The gossips of Jefferson counteracted her influence. If love made her take one view, envy and detraction made the rest of Jefferson take another. "Sooner or later this fellow Long will kill someone with his experiments, if we don't put a stop to them." Such was the general opinion throughout the district.

His practice was falling off, for people were afraid to consult him. He was cold-shouldered in the streets. The well-to-do planters refused any longer to bid him good morning.

One day some of the elders of the village called on him. Benevolently enough, they advised the young doctor to abandon his follies, for, they said, if he should have a mishap and kill someone with ether, there was not a doubt that he would be lynched.

The generality of the opposition was too much for him. From having been universally popular, he had come to be regarded as the bogey man of the neighborhood. All because of ether! Well, he would bow before the storm.

As soon as he announced his decision, confidence was restored. When he performed operations as his fathers had done before him, generation after generation, without trying to put people to sleep and to the usual accompaniment of agony, the village forgave him his "devilish experiments." Year followed year; Long rode on his rounds through the plantations, carrying on his practice like any other country doctor.

In all, before he yielded, he had performed eight minor operations under ether, but what he had observed when doing so was speedily forgotten. The news of his discovery did not spread be-

From *History of Modern Anesthesia.*

Horace Wells, luckless investigator of the anesthetic properties of laughing gas, and onetime partner of William Morton.

From *History of Medicine in the United States.*

Dr. Crawford W. Long, Georgia physician who administered ether during a minor operation in 1842, but abandoned his experiments.

yond the confines of Jefferson, and once again the possibilities of anesthesia remained frustrate.

One morning in December, 1844, a dentist named Horace Wells, a man of twenty-six who practiced in Hartford, Connecticut, sat in his office reading the paper. It contained the following news item:

"A grand exhibition of the effects produced by inhaling *NITROUS OXIDE, EXHILARATING OR LAUGHING GAS*! will be given at Union Hall this (Tuesday) evening, December 10, 1844.

"TWELVE YOUNG MEN have volunteered to inhale the gas to commence the entertainment.

"EIGHT STRONG MEN are engaged to occupy the front seats to protect those under the influence of the gas from injuring themselves or others.

"N.B. The gas will be administered only to gentlemen of the first respectability. The object is to make the entertainment in every respect a genteel affair."

On the evening of December 10th, Wells and his wife went to Union Hall, where all the "best people" were assembled to enjoy the "genteel affair." Gardner Colton, the itinerant lecturer, gave an amusing account of the remarkable effects of laughing gas, and then, to inspire the audience with confidence, he himself proceeded to inhale a considerable quantity.

The first of the spectators to mount the platform in order to try the gas was a young man named Samuel A. Cooley, a clerk at the largest drugstore in Hartford. Hardly had Colton handed him the gas-filled silk bag, and the inhalation been started, when Cooley began to behave like a lunatic. Jumping to his feet, he danced about the stage. Then he caught sight of a fancied enemy and began to thrash the air with his arms.

In the second row on the floor of the hall was a little fellow, an assistant at the rival drugstore. Seeing Cooley's absurd behavior, he burst out laughing. Now Cooley had found a real enemy. He jumped down from the platform and, evading the attempts of the "eight strong men" to interfere, flung himself upon the derider. The other pharmaceutical assistant fled in terror, while Cooley chased him from row to row. The alarm and excitement of the audience grew intense, as everyone made way. Cooley tumbled over a bench, but was on his feet again in a moment and kept up the pursuit. He had almost reached the quarry when he suddenly stopped dead, for the effects of the gas had passed off. As if awaking from a dream, Cooley looked round in bewilderment, while a fervor of applause followed; and, smiling somewhat ruefully, the involuntary hero of the evening sat down upon the nearest vacant chair. Next to him was Horace Wells.

While the attention of the spectators was concentrated upon a new candidate, Cooley became aware of a pain in one of his shins. Pulling up his trousers, he discovered, to his amazement and dismay, a gaping wound below the knee. Not until Wells reminded him that, while chasing the other drugstore clerk, he had stumbled over a bench, did Cooley realize that he must have struck his shin a violent blow without feeling it. Demonstrations continued. The general hilarity was intensified as each successive victim became elevated after inhaling the gas. Everyone rocked with laughter. Wells remained a solitary exception, for he was thinking over the way in which Cooley had sustained a considerable wound without feeling a trace of pain.

When the audience dispersed, Wells chummed up with Cooley, with whom he had no previous acquaintance, and accompanied the man with the broken shin to a room in the outskirts of the town. On the way, he besieged Cooley with questions as to whether there had really been no sense of pain during the accident. Mrs. Wells, who went along too, was puzzled why her husband should take so much interest in this insignificant clerk from a drugstore. She was shivering with the cold of a December night, would have much preferred to go straight to bed and was out of humor all the way to Cooley's habitation. Returning home, she vented her spleen on her husband, but he answered, with no less animus: "If you could only realize what this evening may mean for me, you would not snap my head off in that way. Now that I have seen the wounded shin and heard from Cooley that he did not feel any pain, I know that if anyone were to inhale enough gas I could extract a tooth without his feeling it."

Next morning, early, Wells called on Colton, who was staying in a hotel, and begged the itinerant lecturer to give him a supply of the gas. He intended, he said, to administer it before extracting a tooth and, should the method prove successful, he would be willing to give Colton a share in what obviously would be a profitable business.

Wells was both bold and cautious. He would try the effect of the gas upon himself before administering it to patients. He therefore approached a colleague, another Hartford dentist whose name was John M. Riggs, with the request that the latter would extract one of his (Wells's) own teeth under gas. The extraction took place in the afternoon of December 11th. Colton administered the gas and Riggs extracted the tooth without Wells's feeling any pain. As soon as the effect of the gas had passed off, Wells enthusiastically exclaimed: "A new era in tooth-pulling!" He went on to say that he had not felt a trace of pain, but that during the administration his sensations had been remarkably pleasurable.

An unparalleled perspective was opening for Wells. The "new era in tooth-pulling" offered him a prospect of relief from grave pecuniary embarrassments.

On qualifying as a dentist in 1842, Wells entered into partnership with another dental surgeon a little younger than himself, William Thomas Green Morton. Full of hope, the two young men opened an office in Boston.

The practice did not thrive, and a year afterward, in November, 1843, Wells wrote to Morton:

> "We can both of us see at a glance that it is madness for us to go ahead under present circumstances, for the reason that our receipts will barely pay the cost of materials used. I am satisfied in my own mind that our enterprise will be a total failure. . . . I . . . give you notice that I wish to get out of it as soon as our agreement will permit.—We have both exerted ourselves to the utmost, and I believe that our ill-success cannot be attributed to either of us so far as '*goaheaditiveness*' is concerned."

Having dissolved his partnership with Morton, Wells returned to Hartford. There, too, he made a poor job of it. To be successful, a dentist had to have specialized skill and knowledge which would give him an advantage over his competitors. Wells lacked these advantages, and therefore found it extremely difficult to make a livelihood in Hartford.

The Cooley incident, and the success of the painless extraction of one of his own teeth, must have seemed to him like a revelation from God. "Painless extraction" would make him a specialist able to get ahead, not only of his colleagues in Hartford, but also of the dentists in the far more important town of Boston. These latter, and his own sometime partner Morton, had all longed for something of the kind. They had failed to discover it, but now he, Wells, had done so. He saw a chance of realizing his dreams, of becoming a famous dentist. He would be able to resume practice in Boston. Since he had failed in his first attempt to establish himself there, a victorious return would be triumphal.

He devoted all his energies to developing the new method in such a way that he would be able to take Boston by storm. In his subsequent experiments with laughing gas he had fifty per cent of successes, and he ought to have gone on longer with the preliminary trials, assiduously, conscientiously, not desisting until he had increased his fifty per cent of successes to a hundred. But the call of Boston was too strong, the anticipated success seemed so near; in a word, he had not the patience to wait.

In the beginning of January he went back to Boston. His earliest call in that city was, naturally enough, upon his former associate Morton, who was to be the first to hear of this epoch-making discovery and whom he expected to help him. Morton's advice was that before rushing into publicity Wells should apply to a noted chemist named Jackson. The pair of them went to visit Jackson in his laboratory.

With the coolness of a man who had made his mark, Jackson listened to the representations of the two eager young men and, after brief consideration, advised Wells to go no further. The proposed method was too dangerous. Scientists had universally rejected the idea of inducing painlessness by the inhalation of gas,

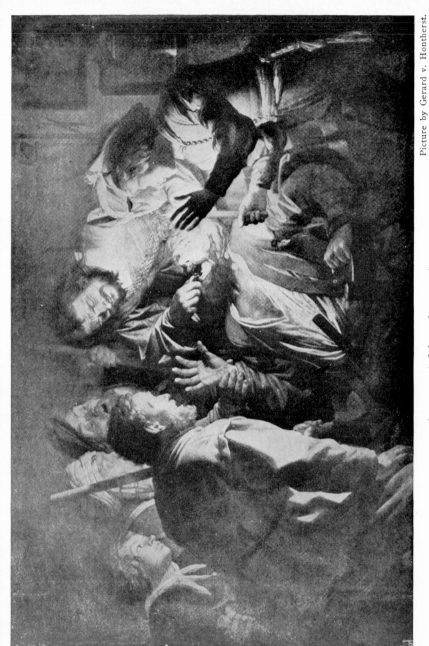

Picture by Gerard v. Hontherst.

A very painful tooth extraction.

Wells has a healthy tooth of his own extracted to demonstrate the anesthetic qualities of laughing gas.

and to tamper with the notion would almost certainly discredit Wells as a dentist.

But Wells's recent memory of the painless extraction of one of his own teeth under laughing gas was too vivid for his faith to be shaken. What had been successful in Hartford would also be successful in Boston. Success would be the acid test, and would secure him the approval of scientific circles.

He managed to secure permission to make an experiment before the students at Harvard and the medical faculty of the university. Morton, who as a dentist was himself greatly interested in the prospects of the innovation, was ready to help his ex-partner. Lending Wells the necessary forceps, he assisted him in the administration of gas.

But luck was against Wells. He had to pay for his impatience. Although he knew the effects of the inhalation of laughing gas, he had not yet acquired enough experience to regulate the dose.

One of the Harvard students had already volunteered to inhale the gas for the public demonstration of the method. Wells administered it, applied his forceps, and began to extract a tooth. The student yelled with pain. "Humbug! A swindle!" shouted the indignant onlookers. Some of them stormed the platform, mobbed Wells and ignominiously ejected him from the lecture-theater.

The defeated experimenter, greatly abashed, left Boston next morning and returned to Hartford.

Still he did not abandon hope. His failure in Boston must be due to the fact that, before the Harvard audience, he had withdrawn the gas bag too soon. In Hartford he gave another demonstration and administered a very much larger dose. But this time he produced a too profound insensibility, and the patient nearly died.

Now Wells lost confidence, and therewith the courage for further experiments. His hopes of becoming a specialist in painless extraction were abandoned, so, disappointed and embittered, he relinquished practice as a dentist.

To make a living, he now tried various occupations. The Hartford dentist who had dreamed of making a great discovery became a bird fancier, and traveled through Connecticut with a troupe of singing canaries. In one town after another he gave shows, and tried to sell his birds. The proceeds of the traffic were, however, so slender that he soon had to find something new. At that time in America great attention was being paid to hygiene. Wells turned this to account, attempting to sell shower baths and coal-sifters. This failed to drag him out of the pit of destitution. Another craze of the day was that every moneyed American considered it his duty to possess engravings or paintings by noted European masters. Wells went to Paris, in the hope of buying these cheap there and selling them dear in the United States.

While struggling for a pittance in these and other more or less ingenious ways, he completely forgot his first great ambition, the discovery of a method of painless extraction.

Although the administration of gases to human beings had been despised and rejected by scientists and had been degraded to a mere source of hilarity and entertainment, now and again, as we have seen, during the first half of the nineteenth century it was recognized to be a serious and promising field of inquiry. Two Americans, one in the southern states and the other in the eastern states, had drawn the right conclusion. Both Long and Wells became aware that the inhalation of ether vapor or that of nitrous oxide gas could prevent pain during operations. The rural practitioner in Jefferson was defeated by the resistance of an angry and suspicious village; while the Hartford dentist pusillanimously abandoned everything which was not immediately successful—his practice in Boston, his bird-fancying, his shower baths, his artistic wares and finally laughing gas. Wells had taken up Davy's great scheme of fifty years before, and had tried laughing gas to prevent pain during an operation, but he lacked the courage and persistence that were needed to carry the scheme to a successful conclusion.

CHAPTER NINE

The Boston
Dentist

"**M**ENTAL INERTIA" is handed down in our race from generation to generation, being as old as mankind. To make
novelty triumph over this inertia something more is
needed than the intuition of genius, than ambition and zeal. Those
who would win through must have staying power which will bring
them victoriously to the goal; courage which shrinks from no responsibility; resolution which pays no heed to obstacles. He only
who combined all these qualities could hope to bestow upon his
fellows the boon of anesthesia.

The man to achieve this wonder, the greatest hero of the struggle against pain, was the Boston dentist William Thomas Green
Morton, Wells's sometime partner. At the age of twenty-seven he
delivered us for all time from the pain of surgical operations, and
thereby earned the gratitude of the world.

Before this wonderful achievement, his life ran on ordinary
lines. He knew joys and sorrows, he loved, made a humdrum livelihood, experienced successes and disappointments, was sometimes
short of funds and at others fairly well off—the usual things that
happened to an American philistine of his day.

Morton was born at Charlton, Massachusetts, in the year 1819.
As a child he often, like so many others, played at "doctor." At
school he was not particularly distinguished for diligence; he was
sent down from college for some youthful peccadillo; and, studying elsewhere, he suffered too much from homesickness to stay out

his time. His ambition was to become a doctor of medicine, but his father could not afford to support him through the years of unremunerative training that would be needed, so he had to be content with a dental diploma which could be more quickly obtained.

At that time dentistry, hitherto in the hands of quacks and charlatans, had just been recognized as one of the ancillary sciences of medicine. In 1840 was founded the Society of Dental Surgery, and the first independent College of Dental Surgery in Baltimore came into being to mark a turning point in the history of American dentistry. Morton was one of the first students entered at Baltimore. He began to practice in Farmington and Cheshire, two small townships not far from Hartford, where his acquaintance Wells practiced, and the two young men aspired to open a dental office in Boston.

They did not lack enterprise, but they were short of money, so, going to an old lady who was a friend of theirs, they persuaded her to lend them one thousand dollars. With this in hand, they put up their plate at 19 Tremont Row, Boston. Wells, as we have seen, soon lost courage and returned to Hartford, but Morton, being more of a sticker, left no stone unturned in the endeavor to make his practice pay. At length success began, the practice increased and with it his income, so that within a year he was able to return the old lady's money.

In the spring of 1844 he paid a visit to Farmington, where he met Elizabeth Whitman, the niece of his former creditor. He fell in love with the girl at first sight. Her gait, her voice, her dress, aroused his keen admiration, and directly he got home he described every detail in his diary. Her words, her attire, her slender figure, her hat and the pretty poise of her head were all enthusiastically noted.

As soon as he was back in Boston, Morton began to grow a mustache, thinking this the one essential to success in his marital schemes. When the mustache was sufficiently grown to make him look somewhat older, he went back to Farmington and asked Edward Whitman for the lady's hand in marriage. He encountered unexpected resistance. "Dr. Morton," wrote his wife later, "had paid me attentions which were not well-received by my family, he being regarded as a poor young man with an undesirable profession. I thought him very handsome, however, and he was very much in love with me, coming regularly from Boston to visit me."

The father could not stand out against him for long. Elizabeth insisted that she would never marry anyone else. Morton promised to resume his medical studies; and if he should become a doctor of medicine he would have a higher standing than a dentist. While Mr. Whitman was still hanging in the wind, the aunt came to the rescue, and espoused the young people's cause. Why should this proposal be rejected? It was true the young man had no private property, but he was ambitious, assiduous and sure to make his way in the world. Besides, Elizabeth's brother, now working for a commercial firm in Boston, could find a job in Morton's dental office. In the end the father gave way, and the marriage took place on May 29, 1844.

Writing to her son in Boston, Elizabeth's mother gives an account of the wedding which conveys all the charm attendant upon such a middle-class festivity in the middle of the nineteenth century:

"It has been a very busy and interesting time with me and I suppose you have got the bridegroom and bride with you in Boston. The wedding passed off very pleasantly and I believe much to the satisfaction of all present. Most all of the young ladies and gentlemen of your acquaintance were here. It was truly delightful to see so much youth and beauty on such an occasion. W. and E. appeared very dignified and composed during the ceremony. They were both dressed very handsomely for the occasion. You never saw E. look more sweetly. She wore a pretty white muslin dress and long flowing white veil.

"The young ladies were all dressed very handsomely. Many of them had new dresses for the occasion. There was much excitement and preparation with them for a few days previous and *all* seemed to take an interest. Charlie Norton and many of the little girls brought a profusion of beautiful flowers on the morning of the day and our friends cheerfully supplied us with silver cake baskets, china plates, glasses and shades, and coloured lamps.

"We had an abundance of cake and a large tub of lemonade. We had two coloured men dressed in white coats and long white aprons to serve and three women to superintend other matters.

"The happy pair were pronounced by some to make decidedly the best appearance of any in the party. The young gents prepared a few tunes for the occasion, and after the lights were out for the night gave the married pair a pleasant serenade."

His marriage to Elizabeth Whitman gave a fresh spur to Morton's ambition. Now he had to earn enough for two. Soon, indeed, there were three in the family, for in 1845 Elizabeth gave birth to her first son.

Morton was resolved to do everything he could to establish a big practice. The most important thing would be to find a specialty which would give him a lead. With a sound business instinct, he was quick to recognize the great possibilities of a new branch of dentistry. He had read about Dr. Mouton, the French dentist who, a century before, had made a gold crown to replace the natural crown of a decayed tooth in the mouth of the king's mistress. Hitherto the replacement of lost teeth had been mainly an affair for handicraftsmen, goldsmiths, ivory workers, etc.; now, in the United States, properly qualified dentists began to turn their attention to these technical matters. What in the eighteenth century had been the peculiar privilege of the mistresses of the kings of France, the up-to-date American dentistry of the nineteenth was to put at the disposal of every citizen's wife who could pay the requisite fees.

In all the dental parlors of Boston, experts were busily at work devising the best and most durable way of "crowning" teeth with gold. The methods hitherto employed had shown themselves to be unduly primitive. The galvanic process for affixing gold crowns always left an ugly black border. Some means had to be devised for avoiding this defect.

In those days a dentist who made a discovery would, in defiance of the spirit of modern science, treat it as his own property and conceal it as far as he could from his colleagues. No friendship, no corporate ties, could overcome this commercialism. Morton's technical knowledge was still inadequate. Being unable to learn what he wanted from scientific discussions or by simply asking those who knew, he decided to try what money would do, paying Dr. N. C. Keer, vice-president of the Dental Society, five hundred dollars, for which sum Keer opened the doors of his laboratory. This enabled Morton to turn the experience of older dentists to account.

Morton discovered a lute with the aid of which crowns could be attached to the vestiges of old teeth. This greatly simplified the problem of furbishing up a mouth which had suffered from the ravages of decay.

At this time Morton's yearly income was about ten thousand dollars. He could easily triple this were he to make free use of his new discovery, and would then become the leading dentist in Boston. But there was one obstacle which he had not taken into account. His method of crowning teeth, which involved other procedures besides the use of his lute, was painful. After the first sitting, a patient would say he would rather put up with the gaps in his mouth than endure such intolerable tortures.

Other dentists before Morton had vainly sought for means of rendering dental operations painless, but for him this had become absolutely indispensable if he was to turn his new discovery to practical account. He tried to apply Mesmer's methods, but without success, for directly he got to work upon a supposedly mesmerized patient, heart-rending cries showed that he had not succeeded in preventing pain. Brandy and champagne, laudanum and other preparations of opium, were essayed one after another, but all proved unsatisfactory.

At his wits' end, Morton now wrote to the medical faculty of Harvard proposing to resume his medical studies. Perhaps if he gained familiarity with general therapeutics he would get upon the right trail.

At Boston in the middle of the nineteenth century there lived a very remarkable scientist, Dr. Charles Thomas Jackson. He was a qualified medical man, had a chemical laboratory, was famous for geological researches, master of the state mint, conspicuous in many fields—what used to be called a polyhistor. *Inter alia*, he lectured at Harvard University, and Morton attended a special course under this professor. Since he was nothing if not thorough, Morton also secured bed and board from Dr. Jackson. Thus the enthusiastic student had the advantage of conversation with his host at meal times and during the evening in the family circle. The pair discussed a number of interesting medical problems. In the course of these private talks, Morton learned from Jackson a good deal about sulphuric ether, the legitimate medical use of which was then mainly confined to the treatment of asthma. In passing, however, Jackson mentioned that ether sprinkled on the skin could relieve pain.

"Do you think that I could use ether with advantage in my dental practice?" asked Morton.

"Why not?" answered Jackson. "I will give you a drop-bottle of it to try."

A few days later a lady from Gloucester, Massachusetts, came to consult Morton. She wished to have a tooth stopped, but shuddered at the thought of the inevitable pain. Was there nothing that Morton could do to lessen this? Oh, yes, Morton had something here in a small bottle. Let Miss Parott keep quite still, while the dentist poured a few drops into her hollow tooth. This was done. The remedy, after causing a preliminary smart, certainly made the tooth less sensitive, and Morton tried it again at subsequent sittings. Once, when he had used rather more than usual, Morton noticed that all the surrounding dentine had become insensitive. Still, the method proved untrustworthy, for the ether was so volatile that the insensibility was of very brief duration.

This was at the time when Wells was making a poor job of his demonstrations of laughing gas at Harvard. But while his Hartford colleague, discouraged by the failure, discontinued his search for an effective "pain-killer," Wells's demonstration gave a new turn to Morton's thoughts. Was there not something to be done in the way of inhalation of gas or vapor? Even though laughing gas was a failure, this only signified that he, Morton, must go on trying until he discovered something better.

By day and by night, Morton turned the thought over in his mind, until at length he had a brain wave. In Miss Parott's tooth the ether had worked locally. What if he were to try for a general effect? What if the influence of this volatile ether could be made lasting by applying it to the whole body? Then he would have found what he wanted. He had learned from Wells that laughing gas, though still more volatile than ether, could, when inhaled, dull pain throughout the organism. That was the line to take. Why not give his patients ether to inhale?

Morton knew very little about ether or the possibilities of administering it by inhalation. Jackson would have been the man to consult, but unfortunately he had had a breeze with Jackson. Sunday after Sunday there had been trouble because Morton (who, to his many other avocations, added that of occasional preacher) used to turn up late for midday dinner on Sundays. Once when Jackson, who was a stickler for punctuality, took the boarder roughly to task, Morton answered back and, taking his young wife with him, cleared out of Jackson's house bag and baggage. Although the two men remained on speaking terms, and Morton even sent his mentor a farewell present, the memory of the dispute rankled, so that Morton felt it impossible to apply to Jackson.

No, it would be better to rummage the shelves of libraries, and see what was to be found there about medical chemistry. At length, in Pereira's *Materia Medica*, under the heading "Ether," he found the following observation: "The vapour of ether is inhaled in spasmodic asthma, chronic catarrh, whooping cough, and dyspepsia, and to relieve the effects caused by the accidental inhalation of chlorine gas." For Morton this was the first indication that ether could be given by inhalation. But the item from Pereira was decisively confirmed when Morton read Faraday's monograph of the year 1818. Here the anesthetic effects of ether were compared with those of laughing gas. Now, at length, Morton's feet were in the right road.

That same day he said enthusiastically to his friend Dr. Gould: "I will have some way yet by which I will perform my operations without pain."

Gould smiled and told him, "If you could effect that, you would do more than human wisdom has yet done, or than I expect it will ever do."

Mr. Wightman, a surgical instrument-maker and later mayor of Boston, to whom Morton also spoke of his schemes, was less skeptical, saying to his wife: "You will see, Mary, this young dentist will be able to pull out our teeth without hurting us."

But Wells's fiasco at Harvard was to be a lesson for Morton. It showed that scientific discoveries should not be made public too soon. Besides, in Faraday's monograph Morton had read: "By the imprudent inspiration of ether a gentleman was thrown into a lethargic state." Here was an additional warning. It behooved Morton to discover how the dangers of ether might be obviated. He asked fellow students and pharmacists of his acquaintance whether they knew anything about the effects of ether vapor. The information he received was contradictory. A student named Spear, who worked as Morton's assistant, told the chief about the students' ether parties at Lexington. They had inhaled great quantities of ether, and no one had sustained any harm. On the other hand, one of the pharmacists told Morton about a man who had lain insensible for thirty hours after inhaling ether. Then Mr. Metcalf, a thoroughly cautious and responsible person, reported other cases in which the inhalation of ether had turned out ill.

After his conversation with Metcalf, Morton sat up all night staring at the ether bottle, wondering what on earth to do. It would be of no use to go on reading up a topic about which so little was known. Nothing but experiment could help him out of this blind alley. Next morning he called on a colleague named Grenville G. Hayden, and said:

"Grenville, I want you to be good enough to take charge of my practice for a time. I have some important business which will take me out of town for a few days."

When his practice began to make headway, Morton had bought a piece of land at West Needham (now Wellesley), about fifteen miles southwest of Boston, and built a country house there. That was where he was now going. Having secured a large supply of ether from Burnett, who ran a drugstore in Boston, Morton drove off to West Needham accompanied by his wife and children.

This country retreat was hung with ivy and surrounded by old lime trees, a retired spot where Morton could make his experiments secure from interruption. He began upon a family pet, a spaniel named Nig, and was more than a little uneasy, for he knew that he would never hear the last of it from his wife should any mischance befall this beast. Saturating a piece of cotton wool with ether, he put this in a tin saucer and placed the saucer on the ground. Then he called Nig, and the creature bounded up joyfully. Grasping the spaniel's head, he held the muzzle over the saucer. The unsuspecting beast inhaled the vapor freely. "In a short time," reports Morton, "the dog wilted completely away in my hands, and remained insensible to all my efforts to arouse him."

In alarm, Morton thrust the saucer aside with his foot, and continued attempts at resuscitation until Nig was fully recovered. But for some hours Nig cringed in alarm whenever his master came near, and the animal's gait was unsteady. From Elizabeth, his wife, the dentist thought it better to keep the matter a profound secret.

Next morning the goldfish had vanished out of a glass globe. No one knew what had become of them. Elizabeth hastened to her husband's study to tell him what had happened, and there, to her horror, she saw the goldfish lying on the table, to all appearance dead. She burst out sobbing. Morton soothed her and, with a smile, picked up the goldfish which he threw back into the globe, still full of water. Elizabeth could scarcely believe her eyes, for now the fish, which she had believed to be dead, were swimming round and round the globe as usual. To his wife's questions, Morton now replied that he had been making an experiment, trying a new remedy. Elizabeth thereupon made him promise that he would never again experiment on any of her pets, above all not on Nig. The thought was unendurable.

Next morning, when Elizabeth went into the garden, she was surprised to see her husband with his trousers rolled up above the knees. He was wading in the brook, and trying to catch fish with his hands. She watched him for a long time, while he was wholly absorbed in this occupation, and saw him catch several fish. Then he clambered out of the water and went off to the study with his prey. There he put the fish to sleep one after another. Next day he was off to the woods for hours, returning with a number of beetles and other insects, caterpillars, and worms. On these, too, he tried the ether.

Elizabeth, who was only eighteen, though used by this time to Morton's eccentricities, was puzzled by his latest craze. On their wedding journey he had taken along a skeleton. When she awoke at night and found he was no longer in bed with her, she knew he was studying this gruesome relic of mortality. She asked him why he behaved in so strange a fashion, and he merely replied: "It's part of my work." When she said she was afraid of the skeleton, and that, though several of her girl friends had married, not one of them had had a husband who brought a skeleton upon the wedding journey, he was content to answer that he had a purpose in life which he could not forget even during a honeymoon.

Yes, William was a queer fellow. Here they were alone together at Needham, and yet he scarcely had a word to fling at her. Instead, he spent all the days and a great part of the nights alone in his study. As for the summer house, whose building she had lovingly supervised, and which she had kept so sedulously clean, it was now filled with various winged or crawling creatures, sometimes apparently killed by Morton's mysterious fluid, and then flying or wriggling as briskly as before.

A strange, uncanny man. He would rise and go to his work at four in the morning, long before the maids got up. Often he locked himself in the study for the livelong day.

He loved her. She could not doubt that for a moment, for he was always tender and affectionate; but he seemed to take no interest in her girlish prattle. Even at mealtimes he was often absent-minded. She simply could not understand what was the matter with him, or what these ridiculous experiments on animals could have to do with his dental practice. She felt that at Needham she might just as well be living in an enchanter's castle.

One day Morton surprised Elizabeth by telling her that he had written to Dr. Hayden begging the latter to take charge of the practice in Boston for some time longer, since he himself had more work to do at West Needham. Elizabeth was alarmed lest her husband should lose his good practice in Boston through neglect, and timidly said as much, to which he answered: "Have patience, darling; it will all come right."

But now something happened which made the young wife really angry. William had solemnly promised to leave her pets in peace; but Nig could not be found. Of course Nig must be in the study. Elizabeth, her patience at an end, went there, and knocked angrily.

"Go away," answered Morton from within. "I'm busy."

A minute or two later, hearing no more, Elizabeth opened the door, and a terrible sight met her eyes. Nig was all right, but Morton was lying on the floor motionless, with a handkerchief pressed to his nose. At first she thought he must have had an accident, or have been suddenly taken ill, so she burst out crying and screamed for help. But soon Morton came to himself.

"You do such horrible things!" she angrily exclaimed. "I am afraid of you, and will not put up with it any longer."

He looked vacantly at her for a little while, as he pulled himself together, and then tried to appease her saying:

"I have work to do in this world, Lizzie. The time will come, my dear, when I will banish pain from the world."

It was true that Morton had intended, breaking his pledge, to try the ether on Nig once more. But as soon as the dog recognized the smell he broke away from his master's grip and, in the struggle, kicked over the ether flask which was on the floor. The contents of the bottle escaped. Seized by a sudden determination, Morton, before the pool of ether could vanish, had drenched his handkerchief in it and put it to his own nose. As he inhaled the volatile substance, he became aware of a numbness of the senses and then completely lost consciousness.

When he awoke to see his wife in tears before him, his first

thought was: "It is plain that the inhalation of ether can cause unconsciousness, and that this unconsciousness lasts long enough for
the painless extraction of a tooth."

But to make sure, he must try the effects of the vapor upon
someone besides himself.

Several weeks had elapsed since the Mortons left Boston for
West Needham. All that time Elizabeth had been extremely
anxious, and the long hours which Morton spent in his study were
a torment. But one morning when he awoke he said without circumlocution: "Pack up our traps, Elizabeth. We are going back
to Boston today. I must continue my experiments there, on human
beings this time."

Elizabeth could hardly believe her ears. Continue his experiments, on human beings? She recalled Nig's whining; thought
of the seemingly dead goldfish upon the table. Then there was
the still more terrible remembrance of how she had found her husband lying insensible on the floor. Life had been horrible here,
but the proposed return to Boston offered still greater terrors. What
new abominations would William perform there?

Dr. Hayden had been greatly puzzled by his colleague's prolonged absence. He knew Morton to be industrious, keen on his
job, hitherto wholly devoted to the dental practice. Now the man
had been away for months, engaged upon incomprehensible researches. But Dr. Hayden's amazement reached its climax when
Morton, on returning, begged his friend to go on with the practice
for a while, since he himself had some more experiments to make,
in Boston this time, and while performing them he must be free
from business cares.

Morton had two dental students as assistants, Thomas Spear
and William Leavitt. He intended to experiment on these young
fellows. Spear had already participated in the ether parties at
Lexington; and Spear had persuaded Leavitt to agree that Morton
should administer ether to him.

When the appointed day came, Spear, acting on Morton's instructions, procured from Messrs. Brewer, Stevens and Cushing,
wholesale druggists in Washington Street, half a gallon of ether.

The experiments began as soon as Dr. Hayden and the rest of the staff had gone home. Morton intended to begin by watching the reactions of the two students to ether; and then, when Spear was completely under the influence of the vapor, to extract a tooth. To the experimenter's astonishment, at the very first breath both the students passed into a condition of indescribable excitement. They yelled, made thrashing movements with the arms, upset tables and chairs, and behaved as if they had taken leave of their senses. Only by the utmost exertion of his strength was Morton able to prevent them doing him or themselves a mischief. He was greatly puzzled by this unexpected excitement, which was a complete contrast with his personal experience of the inhalation.

The unforeseen result of these experiments left Morton in the lurch. Both the young fellows refused to inhale any more ether. What was to be done? Controlled experimentation was needed at any cost. The offer of money to Leavitt and Spear was unavailing. The former bluntly refused, while the latter said he would think things over. He asked his parents, but they were outraged, threatened Morton with prosecution and strictly forbade young Spear to play any further part in the investigations.

Since Morton could not persuade them to revise their decision, he decided to try what he could do in the dock quarter of South Boston. He called at various taverns frequented by laborers and sailors, and struck up acquaintances with some of them. At length, standing treat in one of these saloons, he tried to persuade a sturdy Irish seaman. The man was already half-drunk when Morton made his definitive proposal:

"I will give you five dollars if you will let me pull out one of your teeth. There will be no pain, I guarantee that. Do you agree? Look, here are the five dollars!"

The Irishman stared at Morton open-mouthed. Despite the fumes of alcohol, he was suspicious, and his suspicion grew. At length the sturdy fellow rose, spat on the floor in front of this sinister dentist and departed without another word.

Nor did Morton fare much better when he made the same proposal to a stevedore. The man laughed incredulously, shrugged his shoulders and turned his back. Nothing doing!

Since none of these lower-grade workers would earn an easy five dollars by becoming the subject of experiment, Morton had no resource but to try the ether on himself once more. He went home, and took deep breaths of the vapor. Immediately he was seized by the same excitement as that from which his two assistants had suffered on the occasion of the last unsuccessful experiment.

Morton was faced with a puzzle. He hastened to Wightman, the instrument-maker, a trustworthy friend to whom he could speak frankly. Did Wightman think that the failure of these last experiments was due to some flaw in the method of inhalation? Should not some sort of apparatus be devised, and then matters might go better? Or perhaps the unfavorable issue of these last experiments was due to something wrong with the quality of the ether? Wightman did not feel competent to decide these questions.

"I think," he said, "you had better consult Dr. Jackson, who is certainly the leading chemical authority in this city."

Morton hesitated for days. There was no doubt that Jackson was the leading expert. No one was better able than Jackson to advise in this delicate matter.

Still, Morton found it hard to take Wightman's advice. Although he had not completely broken with Jackson, the two men had seen little of each other since the aforesaid tiff. A more serious matter was that Morton did not trust Jackson, but rather feared him as a possible rival.

Not long before there had been a fierce dispute for priority between Jackson and Morse, the famous inventor of the electric telegraph and the Morse code. It was a good many years since Samuel Finley Breese Morse, then a portrait painter, returned to America from France. On the same ship traveled Charles Thomas Jackson, a young doctor who had been studying in Europe and intended to settle in Boston.

The voyage lasted forty days. Morse spent the time in working at his telegraphic apparatus, one of the first inventions to turn electricity to practical account. Jackson had, from curiosity, bought a new electromagnet in France, and showed it to his fellow passengers, one of them being Morse. Subsequently he had a number of talks with Morse about the future possibilities of electricity.

In America Morse perfected his invention. Congress took it up, rewarded Morse for his services; and he became a wealthy man. Then, to his astonishment, he came across a paragraph in a Boston newspaper which ran as follows: "We learn that the discovery of the electro-magnetic telegraph, which S. F. B. Morse of New York claims to have made, was really made by our fellow-citizen Charles T. Jackson, who first conceived the idea of such an instrument during his return from Europe on board the packet-ship 'Sully' in October, 1832."

Jackson insisted that on the boat Morse had not even an inkling of the telegraph; and that when he (Jackson) had spoken to Morse about electromagnetism, Morse had said: "Electromagnetism, what is that? How does it differ from other magnetism?"

Morse angrily protested against what he stigmatized as monstrous falsehood, speaking of Jackson as a "lunatic" and an "intolerable nuisance." Jackson, however, stuck to his guns so obstinately that it took Morse seven years before he could persuade the world that Jackson's claim was false, and had been made by a "dangerous monomaniac."

Jackson's previous history in the Morse matter made Morton feel that it might be extremely hazardous to let him know what was now afoot. The dentist would have done everything he could to avoid informing Jackson, and yet he could not get on without the man's advice. It was with a heavy heart, therefore, that, on September 30, 1846, he called on Jackson at the latter's office in Somerset Street, believing himself competent to procure the information he wanted without giving Jackson any clue as to his own purposes.

"Can you let me have an airtight gas-bag, my dear doctor?" said Morton, after the men had exchanged greetings. "I have a lady patient who has to have a tooth extracted. She dreads the pain, and wants me to give her a pain-allaying gas out of a gas-bag."

"The gas-bag is in my rooms," answered Jackson. "You seem to be all equipped minus the gas. But if you'll take my advice, you'd better not try any trick like that, or you'll be set down as a greater humbug than poor Wells was with his nitrous oxide. Why don't you let your patient inhale ether vapor? Then she will go to sleep and you can do whatever you please."

The use of the word "ether" gave Morton a great shock, for he was afraid that Jackson must be on the track of his discovery and would steal his thunder. Still, he kept his composure, and said, in an indifferent tone: "Ah, yes, those ether drops about which you advised me once before. But they did not do much good. I have given up trying them."

"I was not talking about ether drops," answered Jackson. "That was chloric ether [ethyl chloride], which has only a local effect. For inhalation you must use sulphuric ether, highly recti-fied, and you can get it only from Burnett. Impure ether will produce most uncertain effects."

"Sulphuric ether!" exclaimed Morton, with well-simulated as-tonishment. He was terribly afraid lest Jackson should pluck the heart out of his mystery, so he continued to play the innocent. "What is that? Is it gas? Show it to me!" It was clear to him that he was on the verge of finding out what he wanted to know. Jackson's two assistants were at work in the laboratory, and could overhear what was being said, and so he decided to lead them astray. "I have never heard of sulphuric ether." Then, to find out whether Jackson had himself experimented with sulphuric ether, he went on: "Have you ever watched the effect of that kind of ether on human beings?"

"Watched it?" said Jackson lustily. "That would not do much good, but I have inhaled it myself." Jackson, who was by nature garrulous, was led by his vanity, which made him want to show off before this renegade disciple, to be more loquacious than ever. He reeled off one anecdote after another about his numerous ex-periences with ether.

"One evening," he said, "my friend Burnett, the pharmacist whom I have just recommended to you, was coming to tea with me. I wanted to light the lamp under the teakettle, but noticed that there was no oil in it. Burnett ran off to his drugstore to fetch some. When he brought it, I poured some out of the bottle into the lamp, and the smell instantly told me that Burnett had made a mistake, and had brought ether instead of lamp oil. So we didn't bother about tea, and sat down to while away the time with a game of cards. As we began to play, I noticed a sense of extreme fatigue, so that my arms and legs felt like lead.

"I don't know what happened after that. Anyhow, I must have gone to sleep, and did not awake until my assistant shook me up next day. Coming early in the morning as usual, since no one answered his knock, he forced the door open. To his astonishment he found Burnett and me seated at the table sound asleep with cards in our hands. When I had collected myself a little, I glanced at the flask which, the previous evening, I had half-emptied into the lamp beneath the teakettle. Now the rest of the contents had evaporated. I came to the conclusion that the profound sleep which had taken possession of us while playing cards must have been due to the inhalation of the ether vapor." But Jackson had not finished: "Another time, in the winter of 1841, I was experimenting with chlorine in my laboratory, when I broke the container. As I attempted to save it, I leaned forward, and got a deep breath of chlorine. Almost choked, I reached out for the ammonia, and then, changing my mind, for the ether bottle, for I knew that ether was an antidote for chlorine poisoning. So it proved in this case. I felt easier at once."

Morton had got the information of which he was in search, and rocked nervously from one foot to the other, impatiently waiting till the talkative Jackson had finished, so that he could escape. But Jackson, still eager to show off, went on prattling for several minutes. Then, when Morton was actually leaving, Jackson said that there was something better than a gas-bag for the administration of the ether. From a shelf on the wall he took down a flask with a glass tube thrust through the cork, and pressed it into Morton's hands, saying, "Here: pure, highly rectified sulphuric ether is the stuff, my young friend, and be sure to get it from Burnett." Such were his parting words.

"Pure, highly rectified sulphuric ether, and be sure to get it from Burnett"—the words rang in Morton's ears as he hurried down the stairs, out into the street and round to Burnett's in Tremont Street. "Burnett—how strange!" he thought. Burnett and he were old acquaintances. Burnett's drugstore was only a few doors from his own office. Burnett was the leading pharmacist in Boston, the man from whom he purchased his own supplies. It was from Burnett he had got the ether he used for the experiments at West Needham; but later he had gone elsewhere, lest the pharmacist should be put on the alert by too-frequent purchases.

The mystery was solved. Burnett's ether was pure ether, and that was why the experiments on the animals in Needham, and his own inhalation there, had been successful. But the ether from Washington Street, which had had so different an effect upon his assistants, must have been impure ether; that was why Spear and Leavitt had behaved like lunatics.

There was not a moment to lose. Entering Burnett's drugstore, and controlling himself with difficulty, he ordered various medicaments, and casually (as if it was a matter of trifling importance) asked his friend to add to the other chemicals a small flask of rectified ether.

Having given orders that he was on no account to be disturbed, he locked himself into his office, sat in his dental chair and, watch in hand, pressed a handkerchief drenched with the ether beneath his mouth and nose. Here is his own report of the experiment, sent later to the Paris Academy of the Arts and Sciences:

"I looked at my watch and soon lost consciousness. As I recovered, I felt a numbness in my limbs, with a sensation like nightmare. I thought for a moment I should die in that state, and the world would only pity or ridicule my folly. At length I felt a slight tingling of the blood in the end of my third finger, and made an effort to touch it with my thumb, but without success. At a second effort I touched it, but there seemed to be no sensation. I gradually raised my arm and pinched my thigh, but I could see that sensation was imperfect. I attempted to rise from my chair but fell back. Gradually I regained power over my limbs and full consciousness. I immediately looked at my watch, and found that I had been insensible between seven and eight minutes.—I am firmly convinced that at that time a tooth could have been drawn without feeling of pain or consciousness."

Dr. William T. G. Morton, whom the French Academy of Science called "Benefactor of Mankind" for his heroic achievement to free the world from pain.

Elizabeth W. Morton, wife of Dr. Morton.

McClure's Magazine, 1896.

Dr. Morton's birthplace in Charlton, Massachusetts.

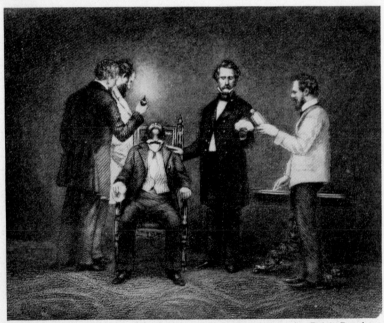

From *Trials of a Public Benefactor.*

Morton extracts the tooth of the musician Eben Frost without any pain
by administering ether.

Morton had discovered something which would be a boon to suffering humanity. His body was still inert from the ether, but his mind rejoiced as he thought of the far-reaching consequences of his experiment.

As soon as he had completely recovered, he unlocked the door, went into the workshop, and shouted, "Eureka! Eureka!" He danced about the room, laughed boisterously and clapped his assistants on the back. His problems had been solved, his doubts had been dispelled, the discovery was completed.

When he told Dr. Hayden of all that had taken place, the latter at length understood why Morton had neglected his practice. His colleague shared Morton's delight when Morton made the significance of the discovery clear. For hours the two talked matters over, discussing its enormous importance. Then they went through the list of names booked for the following day, to decide upon which of the patients they would try the ether. Only then did Morton realize that he would have to wait another day before turning his discovery to practical account. But this his impatience would not suffer, and he promptly begged Dr. Hayden to pull out one of his (Morton's) healthy teeth. It was absolutely essential that the efficacy of the ether should be proved without a moment's delay.

But let Morton report.

"Toward evening, a man residing in Boston came in, suffering great pain, and wishing to have a tooth extracted. He was afraid of the operation, and asked if he could be mesmerized. I told him I had something better, and saturating my handkerchief, gave it to him to inhale. He became unconscious almost immediately. It was dark, and Dr. Hayden held the lamp while I extracted a firmly-rooted bicuspid tooth. There was not much alteration in the pulse and no relaxing of the muscles. He recovered in a minute and knew nothing of what had been done for him. He remained for some time talking about the experiment. This was on the 30th of September, 1846."

Here is Eben Frost's own story, countersigned by Hayden:

"This is to certify, that I applied to Dr. Morton at six o'clock this evening [Sept. 30, 1846], suffering under the most violent toothache; that Dr. Morton took out his pocket-hand-kerchief, saturated it with a preparation of his, from which I breathed for about half a minute, and then was lost in sleep. In an instant more I awoke, and saw my tooth lying on the floor. I did not experience the slightest pain whatever. I remained twenty minutes in his office afterward, and felt no unpleasant effects from the operation."

About ten years earlier, a New York pharmacist who claimed to have discovered a panacea called upon James Gordon Bennett, then an almost unknown journalist. Bennett's office was in a dark cellar, where he himself wrote, set up and printed the newspaper. The pharmacist wanted to advertise this panacea in the newspaper. Bennett drafted and set up the advertisement, which was so adroitly worded that it became a source of wealth both for the newspaper and for the advertiser. James Gordon Bennett's newspaper became famous as the New York *Herald;* and advertising is now a world power.

Within ten years, advertising speedily took its place as a notable part of business life. Morton was quick to use it on behalf of his discovery. On the evening of September 30th, the very day of the extraction, Morton brought Frost and Dr. Hayden as witnesses to the editorial office of the Boston *Daily Journal,* and Dr. Hayden thrillingly described what he had so recently seen. In the morning edition of October 1st appeared the following notice:

"Last evening, as we were informed by a gentleman who witnessed the operation, an ulcerated tooth was extracted from the mouth of an individual without giving him the slightest pain. He was put into a kind of sleep, by inhaling a preparation, the effects of which lasted for about three-quarters of a minute, just long enough to extract the tooth."

"A new era in tooth-pulling," Wells exclaimed when making his experiment with laughing gas. But when, subsequently, a public demonstration failed, he abandoned both laughing gas and extraction. That is why the new era in tooth extraction did not begin with the Hartford dentist, who was a quitter, but with William Thomas Morton, Wells's former associate.

The founder of this "new era in tooth-pulling" was a true son of his day, both in respect of thought and action.

New England was then in the throes of fulfilment. Industrialization was beginning, and therewith a new life had come for merchants, manufacturers and working people. The nation had been seized by a frenzy of progress. Work was regarded as a moral duty, and work was the source of wealth. Money-making therefore became the keynote. But the puritan spirit was so dominant in New England that uncontrolled devotion to material interests had to be justified in terms of faith and elevated to the rank of a virtue. With this end in view, the puritan conscience had entered into an alliance with economic advance, and piety sanctified money-making. Business success and wealth were henceforward regarded as tangible evidence of God's approval, and of man's "justification" before his Creator. Since the offspring of the puritan immigrants regarded themselves as the chosen of God, they were convinced that in all they did, including their business affairs, they were testifying to the glory of God. Thus was money-making declared a virtue.

Morton was devoted to this virtue. He planned the spread of his discovery according to all the rules of a money-making enterprise which should be highly pleasing to the Almighty.

When, on the morning of October 1st, Richard H. Eddy came to open the Boston Patent Office, Dr. Morton was awaiting him at the door. The dentist had come to apply for a patent without loss of time. This would equip him with the monopolistic use of his discovery, and thus insure that he would be the only person to make money out of it.

Boston, in those days, was the fourth town of the United States as far as population was concerned, its 78,000 inhabitants giving it the rank of a great city. Still, it was small enough for news to spread rapidly. What the lawyer knew was known the same day to the chemist, the doctor, and the merchant—to Mr. Wightman, Dr. Gould, Dr. Dana, Burnett the pharmacist, Tremont Street, Washington Street, Somerville Street—and naturally to Dr. Jackson as well.

Dr. Jackson was the last person in the world to hide his light under a bushel. To everyone who came to him with the news, he made it plain, in many words, that Morton would never have made the discovery had it not been for his (Jackson's) advice. But when his friends inquired whether he intended to leave all the glory to Morton, and advised him to seek publicity for his own contribution, he refused, saying: "No, no, I will have nothing to do with the matter. Ether is not so harmless as you imagine. It should be used with the greatest care. It would be very likely to injure the brain if repeated, and there would be great danger in giving it for a long time on any one occasion, as, if it were, asphyxia, coma, or even death might ensue. Morton is a reckless, dare-devil fellow, and will kill somebody yet. He is sure to have a mishap of some sort. Well, let him go on with it. I don't care what he does with it, if he don't bring my name in with it." Such was Dr. Jackson's opinion on the afternoon of October 1st.

He spent the evening with Eddy. Of course they talked about Morton, and the prospects of his patent. Eddy said: "I wonder you don't take part in it. As your friend, I am much more interested in you than in the dentist. If I were you, I would settle matters with Morton." But Jackson was still afraid to become involved.

Nevertheless when, in Jackson's hearing, Dr. Gould and Mr. Burnett began to talk of the vast sums of money Morton was likely to earn, Dr. Jackson began to sing a different tune, and decided to approach Morton:

"I hear from Eddy that you are doing well with the ether, and are applying for a patent. You will make a good deal out of the patent and, since my advice has been useful to you, you ought to give me some compensation. I was thinking of $500. For that sum I should be willing to renounce all my rights or any claim to priority in the invention."

These words came as a great surprise to Morton, but since he did not wish to quarrel with Dr. Jackson, and more especially since he needed peace of mind in order to make the best use of his discovery, he agreed that next day in Dr. Eddy's presence he would sign a document to that effect.

Jackson was the first to keep the appointment at Eddy's, and told the latter what had been arranged. Eddy expostulated, saying: "It is absolutely absurd that you should renounce all claims to priority for a single payment of $500. You should join in the application for the patent and insist on Morton's paying you at least ten per cent."

This was a ticklish position. Certainly Jackson did not want to renounce participation in Morton's patent if it was likely to bring in such large sums of money as Eddy expected. But, as an ethical physician of high standing, Jackson knew himself forbidden to make a secret of any remedy he discovered. This affair of the patent might lead to Dr. Jackson's expulsion from the Massachusetts Medical Society. Would it not be better to content himself with a moderate sum in cash, and to leave the patent, with all the responsibilities it would entail, to Morton alone?

But even while stating these arguments, Jackson began to wobble. Perhaps Eddy was right, and it would be better to think things over before coming to a decision.

Now Morton turned up at Eddy's with the witnesses Dana and Gould, ready to sign the document. Jackson raised various objections, and the matter was postponed till next day. On the way home, Jackson asked Gould what would be the best course. Gould said that Jackson's fears of expulsion from the Medical Society were groundless, for the rules of the Society were extremely flexible, and Jackson's sharing in the application for the patent could not lead to such a result as was feared. Thereupon Jackson turned about, went back to Eddy's office and instructed the lawyer to inform Morton of his demand for ten per cent.

On hearing of Jackson's claim, Morton strongly protested against the view that Jackson had had any share in the discovery and was therefore entitled to ten per cent or any other percentage of the earning. He said, which was perfectly true, that he had only consulted Dr. Jackson as an expert chemist. Eddy rejoined that, all the same, Morton would do well to avoid disagreeables by allowing Jackson to participate in the application for the patent, even if Jackson had no legal right to do so. "I have ample experience of patent cases," said Eddy; "and I have known many in which the application for a patent was dismissed because of personal disputes of this kind as to priority. For instance," he went on, "if you don't work with Jackson, he might put in a demurrer which could lead the issue of the patent to be long postponed, or even wreck the whole affair." Nor should Morton underestimate the high value of Dr. Jackson's reputation in the scientific world, in consequence of which, with Jackson's participation, the importance of the discovery was likely to be recognized far sooner. Dr. Gould, whom Morton now consulted, said that he agreed with the lawyer. In the end, therefore, Morton decided to take the advice of two men with so much experience as Eddy and Gould.

Directly it became bruited abroad in Boston that Morton the dentist had discovered a new method which made extraction painless, patients from the town and neighborhood flocked to his office. His appointment-book was crowded with names. He worked with his two assistants from early in the morning till late in the evening, day after day, without being able to clear off the waiting list. Soon it became plain to him that he must have a larger office.

Dr. Keer, to whom Morton had once paid $500 for information regarding the secrets of dental practice, was now glad to enter into a partnership with Morton and learn the methods of painless extraction. Keer and Morton published in the Boston *Evening Traveller* an advertisement which ran as follows:

"The subscribers, having associated themselves in the business of dental surgery, would respectfully invite their friends to call on them at their rooms, No. 19, Tremont Row; they confidently believe that the increased facilities which their united experience will afford them of performing operations with elegance and dispatch, and the additional advantage of having them performed without pain, by the use of the fluid recently invented by Dr. Morton, will not only meet the wishes of their former patients, but secure them additional patronage."

The rival dentists of the city were not prepared to sit with folded hands in face of competition of this sort. Under the chairmanship of Dr. J. F. Flagg, of Winter Street, they organized a committee to fight against the "sinister new discovery." Morton's adversaries were able to produce "witnesses"—mostly young girls—who declared that, as the result of the inhalation of ether administered at Morton's and Keer's office, they had suffered from blood-spitting, melancholia and other evils. The parents of a little boy testified that their son, having had a tooth "painlessly" extracted by Morton, had been so exceedingly ill that they had had to call in a doctor.

Dr. Keer, alarmed by this well directed onslaught, thought it advisable to withdraw from the lucrative partnership with Morton, but the public continued to besiege Morton's office. To the great annoyance of his enemies, Morton's income steadily increased. Before long, it had doubled.

This rapid financial advance made Dr. Jackson raise his claim. Taking advantage of the fact that Morton was being fiercely attacked by the aforesaid committee, he made it plain to Morton that his (Jackson's) collaboration would be of the utmost value, and demanded a share of no less than twenty-five per cent.

Morton was unperturbed by the hostility of his colleagues, and ignored Jackson's veiled threats.

CHAPTER TEN

===

Triumph over Pain

===

UNTIL RECENTLY, Morton had had but one aim. His ambition was to find a painless way of crowning teeth with gold, and thus increase his income. Well, he had succeeded beyond expectations. He had found the painless method, and his practice had enormously increased. Yet now it seemed as if he did not care a rap.

His office was crowded with patients from morning till night. But Dr. Morton would not see them himself, leaving all the work to his assistant Dr. Hayden. The victory he had won, the success he had gained, the money he was earning, did not seem to interest him. Days would elapse without his coming to the office, or even troubling to inquire how many patients there had been and how the money was coming in.

Where was he? How did he spend his time? A very strange thing had happened to him. Setting out to find something which would relieve the pangs of dentistry and therefore make his practice more remunerative, he had discovered that which was destined to do something more, a great deal more, than satisfy the ambitions of a Boston dentist. What he had discovered would deliver mankind once for all from the agonies of the surgeon's knife.

Already, on the evening of September 30th, Morton had envisaged these possibilities.

He was overwhelmed with rapture during the hours after he had extracted a tooth from Eben Frost without giving the patient any pain. Yet he reacted, first of all, as the money-grubbing dentist who hurried off to a newspaper office to insert an advertisement in the paper.

But that night, as he lay sleepless from excitement, and began to collect his thoughts, what thrilled him far more than the hope of an extending practice was the possibility that his discovery might be applied to surgical practice in general, so that mankind might be freed from the pain of all operations.

This was a far-reaching idea, almost too comprehensive for the mind of a Boston dentist. Next morning, therefore, he applied for a patent, lest any colleague should overreach him and win the advantages of his discovery. Then he had to see his patients, stipulate for fees, see to the increase of his practice. Ambition and avarice gave him a thousand things to think of. Again and again, however, the ideas that had raced through his mind during the first sleepless night took possession of him once more. Could not his discovery be used for the general conquest of pain? If so, his previous successes, the goal he had reached, were but beginnings of something still to be attained, still to be fought for. Of little moment, now, seemed what he had been fighting for. A great dental practice, an increased income—what did these matter? It was a pitiful ambition to become a successful dentist when he might be the man to free his fellows from surgical pain.

Thus, though he went on negotiating with Eddy, pressed for the granting of a patent, reacted against envious colleagues—at bottom he had been translated into another world, a newer and more beautiful world still in the making, to a world in which there would no longer be any pain—a world which it was his mission to create. He behaved, henceforward, like a man possessed, like one whose *id* has taken charge.

The members of his immediate circle—his assistants, his friends and his wife—were puzzled and rendered anxious by his inexplicable change. What did it all mean? He no longer bothered about his practice, shut himself up once more in his study, passing all his time in ever-renewed experiments. Why? Why? What was he driving at? What was going on in the dentist's unresting mind? Had he inhaled too much ether, and thus besotted his understanding? That seemed the most plausible explanation of his strange behavior.

Dr. Morton, the Boston dentist, had undergone a transformation which was beyond the comprehension of those of his own household—the transformation to greatness.

Destiny works in accordance with laws of her own when she picks a man out from among the crowd to make of him something very different from the others. Morton, the dentist, was a little man with a little mind whom petty motives had led to make a discovery. But his discovery was overwhelmingly important. Thereupon the miracle was worked. The great discovery took charge of the little man. Its greatness snatched him out of the sphere of little things, imposed greatness upon him, so that, by the caprice of fate, the petty dentist of Boston became one of the supreme benefactors of mankind.

Disregarding practice, money, health and family life, Morton lived henceforward for his idea. The pain-allaying remedy had been found. The next task was to discover how a physician could regulate artificial sleep at will, could strengthen and extend it as he pleased. Only if the duration of the ether sleep could be sufficiently prolonged would it be possible to perform major surgical operations under its influence.

He must be the subject of his own experiments. Day after day he took larger and more dangerous doses of ether. "I only knew that his clothes seemed always saturated with the smell of ether, and I did not like it," writes his wife when reporting these days.

During the early phases of his experiments, he became aware that he would never reach his end by the open inhalation of ether from a drenched handkerchief, and that some kind of apparatus would be needed to produce the sort of sleep of which he was in search.

Soon he was on the track of what he wanted. He sketched the design for an inhaler, a small two-necked glass globe. Into one of the necks was inserted a wooden tube controlled by taps, while the other permitted the free ingress of air. Putting the wooden tube in his mouth, the patient inhaled air across the surface of ether in the bottle, and thus the air became charged with ether vapor.

Armed with this sketch he went to Chamberlain, an instrument-maker, whom he asked to produce the actual apparatus. He spent hours with Chamberlain, explaining the details. Before he approached the Boston surgeons, Morton wanted to be sure of his ground. Where major operations were being performed, life was always at stake, failure would lead to death, and the accidental death of a patient during the inhalation of ether might wreck Morton's schemes for the conquest of pain—and even lead the inventor to the gallows.

Having got thus far, and having tried the inhalation on himself again and again, he visited some of the most noted Boston doctors and demonstrated the new procedure. Not one of them would undertake the responsibility of using Morton's apparatus during the performance of a major operation. But this indefatigable propagandist ran from one to another prepared to demonstrate the effects of his discovery upon his own person, and thus afford conviction of the trustworthiness and safety of his method. Whithersoever he went, he took along with him the musician, Eben Frost.

The situation had really taken a comical turn. The discovery of a painless method of tooth-extraction had completely altered the life, not only of the man who had made the discovery, but of the first patient to have a tooth painlessly extracted.

Eben Frost was a music teacher and nothing else down to the evening of September 30th, when he entered Morton's office; a man to whom life meant nothing but the giving of music lessons—music lessons from morning till night—until one of his molar teeth began to ache badly.

But from the moment when his tooth was extracted under ether, his life belonged to the great discovery. He was the first person to whom the blessings of ether narcosis were vouchsafed; was the first and principal witness to show that Morton's discovery was free from risk and genuinely effective.

His name was often in the newspapers; everyone wished to see him, hear his story, learn what he thought of Morton. Thus he became important, nay indispensable, to the discoverer; a living "exhibit," so to say. It was scarcely possible to speak of Morton without mentioning Frost, so that he shone by reflected glory. As early as the evening of September 30th, he had grasped his own importance, signing a report, accompanying Hayden and Morton to the newspaper office and appearing next day at Eddy's patent office to support Morton's application. In a word, he followed Morton like a shadow. When he talked about the discovery, he spoke of it as "ours"; the words "Morton and I" were perpetually in his mouth.

Even when Morton passed beyond the idea of painless tooth-extraction, and was working at the construction of his apparatus for the inhalation of ether during major surgical operations, Eben Frost remained closely associated with Morton's work. "We are engaged on a yet more important task," he would say. "Our discovery will soon relieve mankind from all pain."

Devoted though he was to Morton, and keen as he was upon the victorious diffusion of "his" and Morton's great discovery, he was at times distressed to think that when ether came to be used in general operative surgery more pains would be relieved than those attendant upon the mere extraction of a tooth; that some other than himself would then lie upon the operation table, would snatch from him the supreme part he had played in Morton's discovery and enjoy the fame which now attached to himself.

While Morton was still lobbying the doctors, to try to convince them of the value of his apparatus, Eben Frost was an indispensable aid with his testimony. "Come along, Frost," the dentist would say as they left the house. Frost was always ready to "come along." He sat in the waiting room, expecting this demand. He no longer gave music lessons; he was Morton's "accompanist" solely. His whole life was devoted to the new task of shadowing Morton and perpetually retelling the story of the painless extraction.

He had to relate it many, many times in Boston, for Morton was on the go day after day. Morton was indefatigable in his assault upon doctors, chemists and others, making propaganda for his discovery.

The energy with which Morton advocated his ideas was no longer inspired by the unadulterated business acumen of an avaricious dentist; it was the sacred fire of one who had made a great discovery and wanted to use it for the advantage of mankind.

But, though an idealist, Morton had, as a practical American, clearly understood that you must trumpet the good and the useful again and again before you find someone willing to listen and courageous enough to try a new thing.

There were all kinds of obstacles to the use of ether during surgical operations, as now recommended by Morton. For centuries medical experience in the use of narcotics had been most unfavorable; Wells's experiments with laughing gas had resulted in a fiasco; the dangers attendant upon putting a patient into an artificial sleep for a major operation were considered to be too great for any further attempts to be justifiable. Who would face such a responsibility? Not one, at any rate, of the surgeons whom Morton first wearied with his appeals. After all, they were justified in their incredulity by the fact that Morton was only a dentist and not a properly qualified medical man, and that he was in ill repute as a fee-snatcher. Why should one suppose that such a man could have discovered what the greatest doctors in history had failed to discover?

There could be no doubt that a recommendation from Dr. Jackson, who, besides being a physician, was a scientist of great repute, would have been of much value to Morton at this juncture, and would have inspired the medical world with confidence. But Jackson had nothing to say about Morton; Jackson held aloof; Jackson seemed to care for none of these things, and to have no interest in publicity. In any case, he was guaranteed ten per cent of the profits from the patent. For the rest, Dr. Jackson had no concern. Morton would push the discovery, and if his methods were really good he would insure their acceptance. Jackson felt it would be unwise for him to come to the front and imperil his scientific reputation on behalf of a discovery still unconfirmed.

Naturally, then, during this crowded fortnight, Morton found it difficult to interest any Boston physician or surgeon of outstanding reputation. Who would place confidence in this dentist and his comic accompanist Frost? Major surgical operations were far more important than the mere extraction of a molar, for life was at stake. Death during an operation when a new and untried remedy was being used to allay pain might ruin a rising surgeon's career and even cost him his liberty. No doubt a patient's sufferings under the knife were terrible; but it was assuredly better to let the patient suffer than to run the risk of a failure to awaken from artificial sleep.

"Your discovery is one of extraordinary interest. I do not doubt for a moment when you tell me that your method is free from risk; but I do not care to try it myself. Perhaps one of my colleagues may be more enterprising." Such was the answer Morton received on all hands.

On all hands? No, there was one who believed, not from politeness, but from conviction, or perhaps from an instinct which told him that the young dentist was right; anyhow one who knew that the patient's suffering in an operation was so intolerable that Morton's remedy was worth trying.

The man willing to run this formidable risk, the man who did not care a straw that Morton was only a dentist and not a qualified medical man, was Dr. John Collins Warren, senior surgeon of the Massachusetts General Hospital. He was one of the founders of this hospital, and had been its chief for thirty years. What Warren supported, could be sure of scientific recognition.

When Morton, after many refusals, told his friends he intended to apply to Dr. Warren, they advised him against it. They were sure that Warren would never agree.

During years of experiment, the Massachusetts General Hospital had grown weary of persons who approached it claiming to have discovered the means for achieving the conquest of pain. Hardly a month passed without some mesmerist, somnambulist or other sanguine inventor approaching the chief with the declaration that a trustworthy method of preventing pain had been found.

In Europe during the eighteen-twenties and eighteen-thirties there were few surgeons as sensitive as Hickman or Larrey. Most of them were men with strong nerves, like Velpeau and Magendie. Of late, however, there had been not a few surgeons to revolt against Celsus' callous injunction that the surgeon must "ignore cries and pleadings and do his work regardless of complaints." Such men eagerly advocated the "humanization" of operative procedures.

John C. Warren was one of these, and the compassionateness of his disposition was reinforced by the fact that at the Massachusetts General Hospital several patients had committed suicide from terror at the pain they would have to endure during an amputation or a gallstone operation. Consequently the senior surgeon was always ready to try anything recommended for the prevention of pain during operations. One attempt after another had led only to disappointment. Not long before, he had been present at Wells's demonstration of laughing gas at Harvard, and had grieved to watch the pitiful failure. As time went on he grew skeptical, and it was no longer easy for an inventor to gain a hearing.

"Can you give Professor Warren any guarantee that what you propose is effective and harmless?" said Morton's friends. "He has had so many unfortunate experiences that of late he has been loath to embark upon the use of untried innovations."

But Morton would not be dissuaded, and applied to John C. Warren.

It was not easy to gain admission to the hospital. The porter said that Morton could only see Professor Warren's assistant. That gentleman was busy, and Morton had to wait. Then the assistant came in, in a great hurry, and said a brisk "Good morning, sir. What do you want?"

"I'm sorry, but I can explain that only to Professor Warren in person."

"I can't disturb Dr. Warren at this moment, for he is performing an operation."

"All right," said Morton. "I can wait."

Morton had to wait a long time, for Warren, having finished the operation, went on his rounds.

At length the assistant came in again, saying: "I'm sorry, but you can't possibly see Dr. Warren today after all. Tomorrow, perhaps. But you'd better let me know what it is you want to see Dr. Warren about. Quickly, please; I'm pressed for time."

Morton began a long explanation, that was cut short with the words: "Oh, well, you'd better write to Professor Warren about it."

Nevertheless Morton stationed himself in the anteroom of the operation theater, and waited. The porter told him to clear out, since no one could wait there without special permission. Morton went into the passage, and continued to wait. The hour grew late. At length Professor Warren appeared in the corridor wearing hat and overcoat, and about to leave.

"Dr. Warren, I want to talk to you about an extremely important matter." Giving Warren no time to tell him to come tomorrow, Morton went on, without pausing for breath, to explain that he had discovered a way of making surgical operations painless. Let the professor give him a chance of showing the apparatus and the method proposed. With the means he (Morton) had discovered, pain during operations could be averted for all time.

Professor Warren was a tall, lean man, with a rather stiff manner. Having sharply cut features and a formidable nose, he looked somewhat forbidding as he stared at the intruder from beneath bushy gray eyebrows. His mouth had a skeptical twist, and his voice was authoritative. As Morton continued his importunate harangue, Warren grew stiffer and more reserved, his expression more truculent; the skeptical twist of the mouth became almost mocking, and the voice with which he at length asked Morton to be good enough to step into the study was one of icy displeasure. When the two men were in the study, Warren was still utterly aloof, and his first words showed distrust and incredulity.

Morton was scarcely aware of this forbidding attitude, and began to tell the professor all about his discovery, not noting his auditor's manner until Warren relaxed, began to listen with interest, leaned forward appreciatively, looked at the visitor warmly and heard what Morton had to say to the end. Then the surgeon said, encouragingly:

"Very well, I will give your method a trial. What you have said sounds convincing."

When the pair said good-by to each other that evening they were already friends and allies, the famous professor and the comparatively unknown dentist.

"Ever since I performed my first operation," said Warren, "I have been longing for some such means as you describe. I will let you know as soon as I have a suitable case."

"If the operation goes off successfully without the patient feeling any pain, the game will be won," thought Morton, as he left the General Hospital.

"If the operation goes off successfully, without the patient feeling any pain, then everything will have been won," thought the professor on the way home. That afternoon, before Morton insisted on speaking to him in the passage, he had amputated a young man's leg, and the patient's agonizing shrieks were still ringing in his ears.

The dentist's proposal was certainly an audacious one. Failure would compromise, not Warren alone, but—and this meant much more to the surgeon—would discredit the hospital which had been his creation, was his pride, his all.

Warren turned these matters over and over in his mind as he walked home. Nor did he forget that the man who had made this proposal was only a dentist, coming without any letter of introduction. Morton, being no more than a dentist, could not have a medical practitioner's keen sense of responsibility, could not realize what it meant to risk a human life for experimental purposes.

Still, he had faith, so strong a faith that he had inspired Warren with it. A great many persons before this dentist had come into Warren's study and assured him that they had discovered the one and only means of preventing pain during surgical operations—but not one of them had been inspired with Morton's contagious enthusiasm.

Once only in a lifetime was a man likely to have so much faith in a cause, so Warren was ready to trust the dentist and try his method. The screams of the patient on whom he had so recently operated had been heart-rending. He would try what Morton recommended.

There would be no mishap. Morton's faith had convinced Warren, inducing him to say with an easy conscience: "I will try your plan in my next operation."

There would be no misadventure. Even if Morton, not being a medical man, could not have a medical man's high sense of responsibility, at any rate he had the sense of responsibility that an inventor feels for the honor of his invention.

In truth no one could have worked more untiringly on behalf

of any cause than Morton had worked on behalf of his discovery, renouncing sleep, renouncing family life. Now, since he had received Warren's assurance, Morton could think of nothing beyond making sure of the success he must secure by preventing pain under the knife. The inhaler was ready, but there were various little ways in which he could perfect it, and he devoted himself to this task. Again and again he administered ether to himself. What did it matter that he might be injuring his health and that, apart from the transient insensibility produced by the drug, this use of ether made it impossible for him to sleep? All that he wanted was that every possibility should have been explored, that everything should be ready when Dr. Warren summoned him to administer ether at the first operation. Success was the only thing that mattered.

On October 13th a tall, thin young fellow, about twenty years of age, a compositor by trade, called Gilbert Abbott, was admitted to the Massachusetts General Hospital. Both his parents suffered from tubercular disease, and the malady had probably been transmitted to Gilbert. But the immediate trouble was a vascular tumor on the right side of the neck, which had existed since birth but had recently grown to an alarming extent.

Directly Warren saw the patient, he said to himself: "A case for operation. This is the man on whom I shall try Morton's method." To Abbott: "A young dentist of this city has discovered a way of preventing pain during operations. I should like to try this new method in your case. Do you consent?"

"Yes," answered Abbott.

Thereupon the operation was fixed for Friday, October 16, 1846.

By the first post on the 14th, Morton received a letter from C. F. Heywood, the house-surgeon at the General Hospital:

"Dear Sir: I write at the request of Dr. J. C. Warren, to invite you to be present on Friday morning at 10 o'clock at the hospital, to administer to a patient who is then to be operated upon, the preparation which you have invented to diminish the sensibility to pain.

"Yours respectfully,

C. F. HEYWOOD."

It was little more than a fortnight since Morton had made the first dental extraction under ether. Now, only sixteen days later, he was to be given a chance of demonstrating the value of his methods in a surgical operation at the largest hospital in the city of Boston. Only sixteen days, and a new era was about to begin.

"The night before the operation, my husband worked until one or two o'clock in the morning upon his inhaler," reports Mrs. Morton. "I was nearly beside myself with anxiety, for I had been told that one of two things was sure to happen: either the test would fail, and then he would be ruined by the world's ridicule; or he would kill the patient and be tried for manslaughter. Thus I was drawn in two ways; for while I had unbounded confidence in my husband it did not seem possible that so young a man (he was only twenty-seven) could be wiser than the learned and scientific men before whom he proposed to make his demonstration.

"After resting a few hours, Dr. Morton was off early in the morning to see the instrument-maker, for there were still changes necessary in the inhaler."

Chamberlain expected to be ready by eight; but nine struck and he had not finished.

"Hurry up, for God's sake!" shouted Morton, tramping impatiently up and down the workshop. At ten Morton snatched the inhaler from the instrument-maker's hand and rushed off to the hospital, followed by his shadow Eben Frost.

The clock on the wall of the operating theater at the General Hospital struck eight. Silent in the corners of the room stood Egyptian mummies. To right and to left were human skeletons, and glass cases containing surgical instruments of polished steel. Ropes and pulleys hung from the ceiling. The operating table stood upon a low dais. Facing it, tier upon tier, were rails behind which the spectators would sit.

At half-past eight the hospital porters came in, carrying mops and buckets, to clean the floor and put clean sheets over the operating table.

At nine, in the anteroom, the assistants began their preparations. The theater was filling up. The leading surgeons of the town, W. J. Bigelow, S. D. Townsend, Samuel Parkman, and Drs. J. G. Pearson, Gould and Wellington, arrived, ready to watch the operation. They were in the front row, the other tiers being filled with students.

It was nearly ten o'clock. Gilbert Abbott, in shirt and drawers, was lying on the table, his neck bared for the operation. George Hayward, Warren's chief assistant, finished his preparations. Professor Warren turned to the audience and, articulating clearly, said: "Gentlemen, colleagues, and students, before beginning this operation, which seems likely to be of the greatest importance to the art of surgery, I wish to say a few words. I have been forty years a surgeon in Boston. On every instance when the knife was applied to live tissue, there was pain. I doubt not that every one of my colleagues among operating surgeons has had the same distressing experience. And now we have a gentleman here who tells us that he has a liquid preparation by the inhalation of which the pain will be entirely done away with in the operation. Dr. Morton, a dentist of this city, wished for an opportunity to test its power in a surgical operation. I have asked him to be present this morning to administer the agent to this patient and he agreed to do so."

Amid a tense silence, Dr. Warren looked at his watch. It was a quarter past ten. He nervously smoothed his trousers, adjusted his coat tails, glanced at the door, looked at his watch again, and resolutely picked up the surgical knife, saying: "Since Dr. Morton has not appeared"—his tone was one of mingled sarcasm and disappointment—"I presume he is otherwise engaged." There was a ripple of laughter from the spectators, one saying, "What else was to be expected?" Another, "A miracle-worker whose miracle will not come off."

Warren was just about to make the first incision, when the door burst open. Morton came in, gasping for breath, followed by the no less breathless Frost. For a moment or two he was embarrassed, pulling at his mustache and clearing his throat. Then, collecting himself, he tranquilly made his apologies. The instrument-maker had been behind time in getting the apparatus ready. Now he had brought it, all complete.

During the entry of the pair, and while Morton was making his excuses, laughter continued—laughter and expressions of doubt.

Professor Warren did not interrupt Morton, but when the dentist had finished he said:

"Well, sir, your patient is ready."

Now there was silence in the theater.

Morton bent over Abbott, saying: "Are you afraid?" Pushing forward his accompanist, he went on: "There is a man who has breathed it and can testify to its success." Frost nodded affirmatively. His great opportunity had come, and he would be able to tell his story before the leading doctors of Boston.

He was about to begin an oration when his rival on the operating table forestalled him, saying: "No. I feel confidence, Doctor, and I will do exactly what you tell me."

Morton now took his place behind Abbott's head, and applied the inhaler. In the glass globe with its tube-like mouthpiece was a colorless fluid the name of which no one present knew. Morton put the tube into the patient's mouth and told him to inhale deeply and regularly. Within a few minutes the onlookers became aware of a strong, aromatic odor. They watched attentively what Morton was doing.

The patient's face was now flushed. He moved restlessly from side to side, breathing quickly and irregularly. Then he began to mutter unintelligible words. Warren turned to Morton and asked: "Is he ready yet?" Then he pricked the compositor's arm with a needle, watching the reactions closely. Abbott's face did not twitch, and there was no other sign of pain.

"Did that hurt you?" asked Warren in a loud tone.

Abbott answered, "No," but the word was barely audible.

Soon all signs of sensibility and intelligence had vanished. The patient answered no questions; his eyes did not react to light; and the few stammering words which issued from his mouth were but the last babblings of a narcotic dream. His voice grew weaker and weaker, and finally ceased. Now he lay plunged in profound sleep. The spectators were absolutely silent.

Morton stepped back a little from the table, and, bowing to the professor, said: "Dr. Warren, your patient is ready."

Warren began the operation. The assembled doctors and students watched him cut through the skin, incise the underlying tissues and cautiously enucleate the tumor. The patient lay motionless, breathing deeply, and smiling as if he were enjoying a pleasant dream.

Dr. Warren finished the operation, the assistants stitching up and dressing the wound. Gradually Abbott came to. His lips began to move; he uttered incomprehensible words which sounded almost like repressed groans. Were these signs of pain? Within a few seconds more he was fully awakened, and looked round in astonishment. Warren, who had been a little disconcerted by the groans, asked Abbott whether he felt any pain.

"No, sir," said the patient. He did his best to tell Warren what his feelings had been like when he was going to sleep. For a moment he had felt as if someone was moving a blunt instrument roughly across his neck, but that had been his last sensation. Dreams, wonderful dreams. This was all he could remember.

In the silence of the theater, his words could be plainly heard on the uppermost tier.

The spectators, too, were like men slowly awaking from an enchanted dream. The doctors looked at their watches. It was little more than five minutes since Morton had taken up his position at the head of the table to apply the inhaler. Now everything had passed off without a cry, without a moan. Something wonderful had happened.

Dr. Warren could not restrain his enthusiasm. Turning to the spectators, he called, with great excitement: "Gentlemen, this is no humbug!"

Thereupon Bigelow, one of the most highly respected and original professors at Harvard, chimed in: "No, gentlemen, we have not been deceived by a trick of the imagination. Did you notice how, throughout the operation, the patient's eyelids were closed, his head heavy with sleep, his mouth relaxed? These are infallible signs of profound sleep, of complete insensibility. We have today witnessed something of the utmost importance to the art of surgery. Our craft has, once for all, been robbed of its terrors."

The others shared in the general enthusiasm. Those who, at first, had been skeptical and scornful were carried away in the stream. Surrounding the young dentist, they congratulated him and overwhelmed him with questions. Trembling with excitement, Morton stood among them, answering to the best of his ability, relating his numerous experiments, explaining how he had happened upon the discovery. This was the happiest moment in his life.

Elizabeth Morton sat at home, waiting. "I saw nothing of him for twelve hours. How they dragged along as I sat at the window, expecting every moment some messenger to tell me that the patient had died under the ether, and that the doctor would be held responsible. It was not until nearly four that Dr. Morton walked in, with his usually genial face so sad that I felt failure must have come. He took me in his arms, almost fainting as I was, and said tenderly: 'Well, dear, I succeeded.' "

The doubts of the medical faculty had been dispelled. Confidence was restored. Beyond question a new era had opened for surgery with the introduction of this method of preventing the pain of the "healing knife." Nay more, it meant a new era for medicine at large.

Warren had arranged to perform next day two operations with Morton's assistance. Hayward, one of Warren's juniors, had a tumor to remove from a woman's right shoulder, and the artificial sleep was successful, the patient being completely oblivious of the knife. Then Dr. Dix, Professor Warren's second assistant, did an operation upon an old woman's face. This involved the use of the actual cautery.

For a moment it seemed as if Morton's method was going to fail. The patient showed signs of pain when the red-hot iron was applied. At Dix's suggestion, Morton administered a larger dose of the ether. Thereupon the patient's face became extremely pale, and she ceased breathing. Dr. Bigelow, who was present at the operation, felt her pulse. The beats were feeble and irregular. He signed to Morton to remove the inhaler forthwith. Morton obeyed instructions. Bigelow felt the pulse once more. It was all right now.

Although the patient's condition seemed threatening for a moment, what happened on this occasion was to prove of the utmost importance for the future of anesthesia. Dr. Bigelow had learned a lesson from the danger. The pulse of a patient under ether must be continually watched, as a guide to the condition under the artificial sleep.

Now all passed off well. Having found, by pricking the skin with a needle, that the patient was completely insensible, Dr. Dix took up the cautery once more. While the spectators were inhaling the disagreeable odor of burned flesh, the patient lay sound asleep on the operating table, and there could no longer be the smallest doubt as to the efficacy of Morton's method.

The discovery of a method for making surgical operations painless was Morton's. The method was Morton's property. Yet its nature was such that it belonged to the whole of mankind. A conflict between individual interest and general interest was inevitable. It began immediately after the initial success.

Dr. Warren proved justified in his faith. Morton's discovery would unquestionably be of the utmost advantage to mankind. Warren wanted to spare all his future patients the agony of the knife. Operations were to be performed almost every day. The Massachusetts General Hospital must immediately procure its own inhaler, for use whenever needed.

He asked one of his assistants to call on Chamberlain, the instrument-maker, and order an inhaler to be made at once for the General Hospital.

"I am sorry, sir," said Chamberlain, "but I cannot supply you with one. This apparatus was invented by Dr. Morton, who has applied for a patent. If the hospital wants to use it, it must secure an authorization from the inventor."

Dr. Warren did not think there would be any difficulty. When the assistant reported what Chamberlain had said, Warren answered: "Well, then, we must pay Morton for the regular use of his apparatus. It will be of the utmost value to our poor patients, and I see no reason why the inventor should not make something out of his discovery."

Dr. Henry Jacob Bigelow after having witnessed the first painless operation exclaimed: "I have seen something that will make its way around the world!"

Prof. John Collins Warren, chief surgeon of the Massachusetts General Hospital in Boston, performed the first painless operation.

The original Morton inhaler, with which was performed the operations at Massachusetts General Hospital.

He sent a message begging Morton to call next day and discuss terms.

But the Massachusetts Medical Society protested. Some doctors who were not on the staff of the General Hospital got wind of the matter, and declared that any such arrangement on Morton's part would be unethical, and could not be approved by the medical faculty.

So long as the dentist stuck to his dentistry, well and good. Since, however, it appeared that Dr. Morton wished to push his way into medical ranks, he could not use his invention as a means for private profit-making, but must comply with the ethical demands imposed on the medical profession. It would be fundamentally improper, and quite out of keeping with the high ideals of the medical profession, that such a discovery as Morton's should be reserved as a means for private profit. The discoveries of science must be made freely available for the whole of mankind.

"Something must be done forthwith to put an end to such proceedings, which would be a scandal to our traditions," said the members of the Medical Society. "We cannot allow Professor Warren, in his credulity and out of the kindness of his heart, to become a tool of this avaricious little dentist!"

"We cannot discuss this further today," it was decided. "Let us hold a special meeting tomorrow."

At the special meeting of the Medical Society, held next afternoon, it was agreed that as long as Morton insisted on the use of his invention as a means for earning private profit, Boston medical practitioners were to have nothing to do with the matter. The resolution was carried unanimously and the staff of the Massachusetts General Hospital was officially notified of the decision.

This came as a great blow to Dr. Warren. He had a very special case in view for the next painless operation. A woman of one-and-twenty, Alice Mohan by name, had recently been admitted to the Massachusetts General Hospital and needed the amputation of a leg. This would be a far more formidable operation than those in which Morton's method had hitherto been used. More formidable—and more painful. It was a case in which Morton's method was eminently applicable. Now came this tiresome affair about the patent.

Professor Warren was animated by lofty professional ideals. The high position attained by the medical profession in the United States, and the general adhesion to ethical standards of practice, were largely his work. But he felt that it would never do to allow medical etiquette to stand in the way of the progress of a discovery which should have been a matter for universal rejoicing. Morton had found out how to prevent pain during operations. There was no lack of patients for whose relief the method could be used. Alice Mohan was about to have a leg amputated, and could have it amputated without pain, thanks to Morton. Surely this matter of medical etiquette could not be allowed to stand in the way?

All the same, Warren felt it impossible to disregard the unanimous decision of the Medical Society. He therefore wrote to Morton canceling the appointment at which the hour of Alice Mohan's operation was to be discussed. He informed Morton about the decision of the Medical Society, and said that the General Hospital would conform to it.

While Morton was still only a dentist, and had merely hoped to use his discovery for painlessly crowning defective teeth with gold, he had been responsible only to his own puritan conscience. When he took out a patent, thought of granting licenses for the use of his discovery in return for a pecuniary consideration in each case, his business instincts were in perfect harmony with the puritan ethics of New England. But such proceedings were incompatible with the behavior proper to one who wished to be a benefactor of the human race. As he thought things over, he found that the professional honor of the doctors weighed more with him than the ethics of those puritans who held that opportunities for gathering wealth were a sign of God's approval.

After all, for some time now, Morton had been much more concerned with the idea of the conquest of pain than with the notion of making money out of crowning teeth with gold.

When Professor Warren's letter came to hand, he replied, on the same day:

"Dear Sir, As it may sometimes be desirable that surgical operations should be performed at the Massachusetts General Hospital under the influence of the preparation employed by me for producing temporary insensibility to pain, you will allow me, through you, to offer to the hospital the free use of it for all the hospital operations."

But Morton went further than this in his unselfish generosity. The next time he met Warren after the exchange of letters, he asked the professor to supply him with as complete a list as possible of the hospitals and charitable institutions in the country, that he might give them all a free license to use his discovery.

The difficulties having thus been removed, Dr. Warren fixed the date of the operation on Alice Mohan for November 7th. It was announced in the Boston newspapers, and the physicians and surgeons of the city awaited the event with the greatest interest.

Dr. G. M. Angell of Atlanta, who was then on a visit to Boston and had come to the General Hospital to witness an operation under such novel conditions, has given a very lively report of what now happened:

"On the morning of the day set for the operation, I went as usual to the hospital, but much earlier, as I anticipated from the great reputation of Dr. Warren and the importance attached to the experiment that there would be a large attendance at the clinic. When I arrived, a very large crowd had already assembled in front of the hospital, reaching out to the sidewalk and street, but the door was kept closed until the usual hour of opening arrived. I passed in by a private door with a student: we went directly to the operating-room and chose our seats close to the railing and directly opposite to the operating theatre and impatiently awaited events. When the hour arrived and the doors were opened, the great hall was filled to overflowing with the rushing host, which filled the seats and aisles to their utmost capacity."

Dr. Angell had to wait a long time before the operation began. At least an hour passed, and the door leading into the anteroom from which the patient was wheeled into the theater had not been opened. Those who were thus kept waiting grew impatient, drummed on the floor with their feet, and began to exchange acrimonious remarks. No one could explain the delay.

Meanwhile, extremely dramatic incidents were taking place in the room behind the operating theater. Preparations had been made; Alice Mohan lay on a couch, ready to be taken into the theater. But at this juncture the vice-president of the Massachusetts Medical Society appeared, and addressed Dr. Warren as follows.

"Are you acquainted with the composition of the remedy with the aid of which you intend to perform this operation?"

"No, sir," answered Warren; "but before I undertook the responsibility of adopting Morton's method, I need hardly say that I convinced myself it would be free from risk. This seemed to me sufficient. I knew that Morton was keeping his remedy secret, and it seemed to me that there was no reason for asking him."

"I am very sorry, Dr. Warren," rejoined the vice-president, "but in these circumstances the Medical Society finds it necessary to protest against your performing the operation with the aid of Dr. Morton's remedy. Most of our members hold the view that Morton's willingness to supply his remedy and his apparatus gratuitously to the General Hospital does not suffice to meet the requirements of our faculty. Medical men have the right to know and must know the composition of a remedy which they propose to introduce into general practice. Prohibition of the use of any secret remedy is a worthy professional tradition, and we are all of us, Dr. Warren, resolved to abide by it. The use of secret remedies is a device of quacks, with which responsible medical practitioners can have nothing to do. The doctors of Boston are convinced that you and your collaborators will share our view."

Being themselves members of the Medical Society, Dr. Warren and his assistants could not disregard their colleague's protest. The only course was, it appeared, to proceed with the amputation in the customary painful fashion, and not to give Alice Mohan the advantage of the use of Morton's remedy.

Dr. Bigelow was present during this conversation. He had come to witness the operation, and hoped that Dr. Warren would defy the Medical Society. Here was an unfortunate young woman who could be saved intolerable pain, and was she to be deprived of this advantage by considerations of medical etiquette? Surely that was intolerable. Bigelow leaped to his feet and angrily intervened:

"No, no, and again no! This must not be. Are you all out of your minds? Don't you understand? This is not a matter for professional etiquette. We have a fellow human being whose leg is to be cut off. A poor young woman who will be mutilated for the rest of her life. But at least we have means of sparing her the horrible pain attendant on the act of mutilation. Are you going to tie her to the torture-table in the old way, and to proceed while she is fully conscious? The operating theater is crowded with spectators who came to see a painless operation. Are you determined to show them, instead, how a victim can shriek under the knife, that none of them can doubt the horrible nature of our handicraft?"

"Be good enough to remember, Dr. Bigelow, that we are not quacks, but reputable practitioners," came the tranquil voice of the vice-president in answer to the surgeon's fierce outburst. "Being this, we cannot permit the use of a secret remedy. Our sense of responsibility and the dignity of our profession forbid."

"The dignity of our profession!" rejoined Bigelow scornfully. "You would do better to say the arrogance of our profession; pride of the basest sort. It is professional arrogance, and nothing else, which has led you to intervene and to speak as you did. To talk of medical responsibility! Our sense of responsibility is to forbid the use of a secret remedy able to save a fellow creature from torment; but our sense of responsibility will allow us to subject a young woman to needless martyrdom. If professional etiquette means inhumanity, then I am ashamed to belong to such a profession."

Bigelow turned to Warren: "Dr. Warren, you to whose courage we owe it that we are at length able to turn this discovery to practical account, surely you are not going to take your hand from the plow? I implore you not to be misled by high-sounding words. Alice Mohan is waiting for the operation. Can you conscientiously decide to expose her to unnecessary pain? With all your experience, are you willing to make her face what awaits her in the operating theater if Morton's remedy is not used? Are you prepared to endure the sight of her writhing countenance, to listen to her screams, when you know that a remedy is at hand which could spare her all this agony?"

Bigelow was choking with agitation, and had lost command of himself.

Dr. Warren was shaken by these passionate words. Silently he turned to face the vice-president. What would happen?

Alice Mohan was ready for the operation, and had been kept waiting a long time. What was to be done?

"Would it not be well for you to have a word with Mr. Morton?" said the vice-president to Dr. Bigelow. "He need merely tell us the composition of his remedy, and then Dr. Warren can proceed with the operation. But it seems to me that the tone in which you speak of professional etiquette is unwarrantable, and that you are not entitled to hold us accountable for the pain the patient will suffer. What you have to remember is that Mr. Morton, simply from avarice, is keeping his remedy secret, and thus withholding it from general use. If anyone is responsible for the patient's suffering needless pain, surely it is he?"

"I have always thought that humanity is a doctor's first duty. Never mind, I will have a talk with Dr. Morton," answered Dr. Bigelow.

"This poor woman has been ready and waiting an hour for the operation," interjected Dr. Hayward impatiently.

"Well, I fear she will have to wait a little longer," answered Bigelow, "while I discuss matters with Mr. Morton."

Dr. Warren agreed to wait until Dr. Bigelow returned with Morton's answer.

The moment had come in which Morton would have to make a great decision. Would he prove equal to the test? Was the discoverer worthy of his discovery?

Unquestionably the man with whom Dr. Bigelow was now to talk things over was very different from the Morton who, the day after the painless extraction of Eben Frost's tooth, had hurried off to Eddy and applied for a patent in the hope of making money out of the new method. Yet less than six weeks had passed.

That had been October 1st; it was now November 7th. Thirty-seven days seem a brief period in which to transform a money-making dentist into an unselfish benefactor of the human race. Morton had not completely put off the old Adam.

"I would gladly agree to disclose the nature of my remedy, Dr. Bigelow," he said, "if the patent had already been definitely granted. But the matter still hangs in the wind. If I disclose my secret now, the patent will be invalidated. The matter may be settled any day now. Cannot we wait till then?"

"Wait, my friend? The patient is waiting for the operation. If I go back without being able to say to my colleagues, 'Morton is ready to announce the composition of his remedy,' then Alice Mohan will be operated on in the old way. I know my colleagues will not give way. The decision, therefore, rests with you alone. Consider carefully, Morton, whether the preservation of your secret and all the advantages you may hope to derive from it can justify you in allowing a fellow creature to suffer needlessly. Your discovery is far too important to remain any man's private property, even if that man be the discoverer himself."

Morton knew well enough that to keep his secret would be the best means of making the remedy profitable. He had, indeed, hoped for a large financial return. That hope flickered for another moment. Then he understood that one who had a mission in life must make sacrifices in its behalf. His mission was to free mankind from the pain of surgical operations. Very well; he would sacrifice the secret, would for the general advantage renounce the hope of private profit.

Bigelow found it easier to overcome the avarice of this hitherto inconspicuous Boston dentist than it had been to overcome the professional pride of his own medical colleagues.

The two men paced up and down the passage in silence, both of them fully realizing that Alice Mohan was awaiting the decision, which for her was the decision of fate.

William Thomas Green Morton had witnessed in his practice no more than the pain of toothache and extraction—distressing enough, but hardly in the same street with the agony inflicted by the surgeon's knife. Still, he possessed imagination.

"If the only question which remains at issue is that I should sacrifice my secret, then you can rest assured that Alice Mohan will be spared needless pain. I agree to divulge what your colleagues want to know, Dr. Bigelow. Let us go to them."

Morton and Bigelow entered the room, and Morton immediately said: "Gentlemen, to remove any objection to the use of my remedy, I have the honor to inform you that it is nothing more or less than pure rectified sulphuric ether."

There was an astonished silence.

Then Dr. Warren issued orders for the patient to be taken into the theater.

Impatience and excitement had reached a climax when the door leading from the anteroom opened and the porters wheeled in the operating table on which the patient was lying. The doctors followed. All eyes were turned on Dr. Hayward, who now solemnly declared:

"The medicament with which the patient is to be put to sleep is henceforward the property of science at large. With the approval of the medical faculty of Boston, the patient Alice Mohan will inhale a vapor competent to allay the pain of the operation. The fluid whose vapor will be used is sulphuric ether."

Let me proceed with Dr. Angell's report (paraphrased at first):

"After Hayward had spoken, Dr. Warren gave a brief account of the patient's clinical history, explaining why the operation was necessary, and that anesthesia was being induced with Alice Mohan's full approval. A profound silence fell upon his audience. From the bottom row to the top, not a whisper of comment, not the scratch of a pencil taking notes, was to be heard.

" 'Mr. Morton,' said Dr. Warren, 'will you come forward and administer your agent to this patient?'

"Morton came up to the table and put the mouthpiece of the inhaler to the mouth of the patient. He gave her a few whispered directions, and took the cork from the hole in the top of the globe. The patient's eyes were closed, like those of one in sleep and soon the chest rose and fell as in deep natural sleep.

"The intense silence was broken by Morton. He took the mouthpiece from the patient's mouth and said in a loud voice to Dr. Warren, 'She is ready for the operation, Sir.' Dr. Warren searched for a pin in the lapel of his coat. 'You think she will not feel any pain now, do you?' he asked. He took up the arm of the patient and forced the pin into her skin, at the same time looking at her face. The muscles of her face did not indicate that she felt any sensation. Dr. Warren turned quickly, picked up a catling, and rapidly performed the amputation.

"Not a muscle in her face twitched. His assistants completed the operation. Just as it was finished, she turned her head a little to one side and gave a groan. Dr. Warren took hold of her sleeve and called her name. She looked up at him in a dazed manner and said: 'Sir?'—'I guess you've been asleep, Alice,' he said.—'I think I have, Sir,' she replied. 'Well, we brought you here for an amputation; are you ready?'—'Yes, Sir,' she said, 'I am ready.' He reached out, picked up the amputated leg, showed it to her, and said: 'It is all done.'

"The scene which followed was one of pandemonium. Men were beside themselves with joy. They clapped their hands, stamped, and yelled. During this demonstration, the patient was carried into the ward and put to bed. Dr. Warren continued to walk to and fro on the stage. Finally, turning to the audience, he said in a voice shaking with emotion, 'Gentlemen, this is no humbug.'"

With these words closes Dr. Angell's description of the first amputation ever performed painlessly on a human being under ether.

Thenceforward the use of ether inhalation during surgical operations became a regular practice at the Massachusetts General Hospital, the method being officially endorsed by the American medical profession. John Collins Warren gave scientific consecration to Morton's discovery in the following enthusiastic phrases:

"A new era has opened to the operating surgeon. His visitations on the most delicate parts are performed, not only without the agonizing screams he has been accustomed to hear, but sometimes with a state of perfect insensibility, and, occasionally, even with an expression of pleasure on the part of the patient. That is the most amazing miracle of all. Who could have imagined that drawing a knife over the delicate skin of the face might produce a sensation of unmixed delight? That the turning and twisting of instruments in the most sensitive parts might be accompanied by a delightful dream? If Ambroise Paré and Louis, and Dessault and Cheselden, Cooper and Hunter could see what our eyes daily witness, how would they long to come among us and perform their exploits once more. It is the most valuable discovery ever made, because it frees suffering humanity from pain. Unrestrained and free as God's own sunshine it has gone forth to cheer and gladden the earth; it will awaken the gratitude of the present, and of all coming generations. The student who from distant lands or in distant ages, may visit this spot will view it with increased interest, as he remembers that here was first demonstrated one of the most glorious truths of science."

Boston was, indeed, proud to have been the starting point of the new method. Day after day appeared articles in the local press, scientists describing the importance of what had been achieved. When, at this date, Oliver Wendell Holmes, poet, novelist and physician, was delivering one of his much-frequented lectures, this man usually so skeptical exclaimed:

"Nature herself is working out the primal curse which doomed the tenderest of her creatures to the sharpest of her trials, but the fierce extremity of suffering has been steeped in the waters of forgetfulness, and the deepest furrow in the knotted brow of agony has been smoothed forever."

Morton's fluid still needed an appropriate name. The first expressions used to denote it were unsatisfactory, despite the universal enthusiasm—such names as mixture, preparation, gas, new discovery and sleeping gas. Enthusiasts were still in search of a suitable appellation.

Dr. Gould's house was in those days a place of assembly for all who had stood round the cradle of the new discovery. Evening after evening Morton and his friends discussed what it was to be called. Time pressed for a decision. One night Dr. Gould read a long list containing all the names hitherto suggested. There was one which Morton had not yet heard. When Gould said "Letheon," the discoverer jumped up, crying: "That's it! We've got it at last. There could not be a better name. *Letheon*, from the river Lethe of Greek mythology, a draught of whose waters could expunge all painful memories."

The men of science present on the occasion agreed with Morton that this poetical name was most apt. But Oliver Wendell Holmes, himself a poet, was unsatisfied, for he thought it would be better, since this was a scientific discovery, to find a name in the vocabulary of science. He promised to see what he could devise. The very next day he hit upon a name. Writing to Morton under date November 21, 1846, he said:

> "Dear Sir, Everybody wants to have a hand in a great discovery. All I do is to give you a hint or two, as to names, or the name, to be applied to the state produced and the agent. The state should I think be called 'Anæsthesia'. . . . The adjective will be 'Anæsthetic.' Thus we might say the state of anæsthesia, or the anæsthetic state. . . . I would have a name pretty soon, and consult some accomplished scholar, such as President Everett or Dr. Bigelow senior, before fixing upon the terms which will be repeated by the tongue of every civilised race of mankind. . . .
>
> "Respectfully yours
> "OLIVER WENDELL HOLMES."

Even when some stupendous success like this has been achieved, and when its value has been conclusively demonstrated, there will be found newspapers, societies and scientists to doubt, carp, revile and condemn. Discordant notes were uttered amid the general chorus of enthusiasm, unfavorable comments were made. Rarely indeed can anything be called "great" or "a miracle" without others describing it as "humbug" and "lunacy."

At all times there are "little men of little minds," the envious and the unduly skeptical, whose dissentient voices are raised amid the acclamations.

Thus when in Boston the medical miracle of anesthesia was performed, the *Medical Examiner* of Philadelphia took a strong line against the new discovery, calling anesthesia "a swindle" and "quackery," writing: "we should not consider it entitled to the least notice, but that we perceive, by the Boston *Medical and Surgical Journal*, that prominent members of the profession in that city have been caught in its meshes."

Most of the Philadelphia doctors took the same view, and in 1847 the staff of the Pennsylvania Hospital boasted of having never performed any operation under anesthesia.

A New York daily paper announced with malicious delight that "The last special wonder has already arrived at the natural term of its existence"; while from Baltimore a dentist wrote with strong disfavor about anesthesia, saying, "I protest against the whole business, because I verily believe the great discovery to be utterly useless. If we are to induce insensibility, I very much prefer whiskey punch to ether, because it is more certain and more permanent in its effects. It is less dangerous: and lastly, it will be easier to persuade patients to take it."

The most active hostility was shown in the South. "Why, mesmerism, which is repudiated by the *SAVANS* of Boston, has done a thousand times greater wonders and without any of the dangers here threatened," wrote the New Orleans *Medical Journal*. The writer went on: "That the leading surgeons of Boston could be captivated by such an invention as this excites our amazement."

It need hardly be said that objections were voiced from the religious side, the divines insisting that pain was the work of Providence, and that the attempt to subdue it was impious.

None of the objectors, however, were able to stop the victorious march of the great discovery. Within a few days after the first painless amputation, a New York journal wrote: "God bless the inventor of this last gift to man. It is the most glorious, nay the most God-like discovery of this or any other age."

New York was speedily followed by Chicago, Buffalo and St. Louis, all uttering praises. The newspapers and the medical faculties of those cities welcomed the new discovery with the same enthusiasm as Boston. The whole of America, the whole world, was soon to join in the chorus.

"I have seen something today that will go around the world!" exclaimed Dr. Bigelow after watching the first painless amputation, and his enthusiasm was to be justified.

In the middle of December, 1846, Dr. Bott of Gower Street, London, received a letter from Bigelow in which the latter drew his attention to the new discovery. On December 17th, Bott read this letter to a meeting of some of his colleagues. Matters moved quickly. On December 19th, a London dentist named Robinson extracted a tooth for Bott's niece, Miss Lonsdale, the operation being performed painlessly in Bott's house under ether narcosis.

As had been the case in Boston, so in London an extremely noted surgeon was to be the first to try ether in a major operation. This was Robert Liston of University College Hospital who, on December 21st, performed in England the first major operation under ether. Many of the leading members of the London medical and surgical faculties had been invited, and a good many of those who came to look on were surprised that a man of Liston's standing should take up this American innovation.

One of the most noted of them expressed his doubts before the operation, saying: "What the new discovery promises is too good to be true." But the success of the painless operation was speedily to convince all beholders.

The patient, a middle-aged man, lay down on the operating table, and Liston gave him ether to inhale. Almost immediately he lost consciousness, and Liston amputated the right leg. The patient quickly recovered consciousness, and was unaware what had happened. When the sheet covering his lower extremities was withdrawn, and he caught sight of the stump, he fell back sobbing on the pillows. All those present were greatly moved—too much moved to speak. But as soon as the patient had been carried away, Liston enthusiastically exclaimed: "Hurrah! Rejoice! An American dentist has used the inhalation of ether to destroy sensation in his operations. In six months no operation will be performed without this previous preparation." Another noted surgeon chimed in: "Beyond question, this is the most wonderful discovery ever made, for it enables us to conquer pain." Two centuries before, one of the greatest of English philosophers, Francis Bacon, had written: "So long as a thing has not been achieved, people are surprised when they are told it is possible; but as soon as it has taken place, they wonder why no one ever thought of it before." So was it now with the discovery of anesthesia.

After the success of Liston's operation, London was in a ferment. "Hail, happy hour," writes the *People's London Journal* on January 9, 1847, "that brings the glad tidings of another glorious victory. Oh, what a delight for every feeling heart to find the new year ushered in with the announcement of this noble discovery of the power to still the sense of pain and veil the eye and memory from all the horrors of an operation. This is, indeed, a glorious victory . . . the victory of knowledge over ignorance, of good over evil. Benevolence has its triumph. It is a victory not for to-day, nor for our own time, but for another age, and all time; not for one nation, but for all nations, from generation to generation, as long as the world shall last." Again, in the *Lancet*, we read: "The discovery of Dr. Morton—more striking to the general than to the scientific mind—will undoubtedly be placed high among the blessings of human knowledge and discovery. That its discoverer should be an American, is a high honor to our transatlantic brethren; next to the discovery of Franklin, it is the second and greatest contribution of the New World to science, and it is the first great addition to the medical art. Dr. Morton deserves, if his discovery stands the test of time, the gratitude and reward of every civilised people and government upon the face of the earth."

In the English medical periodicals, the American discoverer of anesthesia was repeatedly compared with the discoverer of vaccination. If Jenner had broken the power of the pestilence of smallpox, Morton's discovery had achieved the conquest of pain. Jenner and Morton had between them freed suffering mankind from two of the greatest of evils.

Anesthesia was quickly to win its place in Paris. To his friend Willis Fisher, an American who lived in the French capital, Morton sent an inhaler with commendations from Dr. Warren and Dr. Bigelow. Since Fisher was a Bostonian, Morton's letter aroused in him an access of local patriotism. So his native city had been the focus of this immortal discovery! It had been made by a Boston dentist with whom he was personally acquainted; and one of his former professors, Dr. Warren, had performed the first painless major operation.

Within a day after receiving the inhaler, Fisher made two experiments on himself. Then, taking it round to the St. Louis Hospital, he gave a demonstration to two famous surgeons there, Jobert de Lamballe and Malgaigne, and persuaded them to try the anesthesia on some of their patients. Fisher would not let the moss grow upon this splendid discovery which had been made by another Bostonian.

There still lived in Paris the two greatest adversaries of the method; Dr. Roux, and Louis Velpeau, who not very long before had declared the search for painless surgery to be the search for a chimera. As long as these two magnates were in the field, the conquest of Paris would be difficult to effect.

But the Bostonian, who was ready to fight for the reputation of his native city with all the vigor proper to an American, was not one to be daunted by great names. In this respect Fisher was of the same fiber as Morton. He would not let any hospital porter keep him out, would not be fobbed off by any underling's "to-morrow," was by no means daunted because a professor had put on hat and overcoat and was about to depart. He talked so long and so enthusiastically to Professor Roux and Professor Velpeau that in the end he persuaded them to perform an operation under ether anesthesia. The success was overwhelming.

"A glorious victory for mankind," said Roux. Only a few years before, Velpeau had declared pain and the surgeon's knife to be inseparable. Now he acknowledged that doubt was no longer possible. "Even the most incredulous must bow before the power of facts. We have seen them with our own eyes and must believe what we have seen. It was left for the New World and for the city of Boston to demonstrate something which had been believed forever impossible—to confront us with an accomplished fact."

By the middle of January, only two months after the operation in the Massachusetts General Hospital, all Paris was aware that a new miracle had come from Boston.

In Germany, too, there were skeptics at first. A noted Breslau surgeon declared that, although he was an atheist, when he had to perform an operation he would rely on prayer rather than on a narcotic.

But when, in Erlangen, on January 24, 1847, Heyfelder performed the first painless major operation to be made in Germany, the discovery was enthusiastically acclaimed.

"The splendid dream of conquering pain has become a reality," wrote Dieppenbach, the famous German surgeon, in a monograph *Der Aether gegen den Schmerz*. "Pain, our intensest consciousness, our keenest assurance of the imperfection of the human body, has had to retreat before the power of man's mind, before the advance of ether vapor. This discovery has gone far to rob death of its terrors, for we dread the pain of death more than we dread death itself. Does not our imagination lead us to fear the agony of a major surgical operation more than we fear death, so that we would do our utmost to avoid it? Now we can avoid this agony, to our wonder and admiration."

In Vienna, Josef Weiger, having watched Schuh perform the first operation under ether, declared: "This is the most important and greatest discovery of our century. I say the greatest discovery for, even though slowly, we could fulfil our other wishes though steamships and the electric telegraph had never been invented, what will be gained by the prevention of pain in surgical operations can only be understood by those who have had to watch operations performed without anesthetics."

From western Europe, the good news soon spread to Russia. In distant Crimea, the famous surgeon Pirogoff became the champion of anesthesia. Shortly afterward, a Russian journal described it as "the greatest blessing, a gift from heaven, one for which we owe the utmost gratitude to the discoverer."

The glad tidings spread to the farthest limit of civilization, and beyond. Missionaries and traders brought, not only the news, but the actual method, across lands and seas to the savages of remote islands.

Liston's declaration—"In six months no operation will be performed without this previous preparation"—had become a reality. Etherization was the common property of the medical world, had become a thoroughly reliable weapon against pain.

Everywhere gratitude was loudly expressed, by doctors, learned societies, hospitals, newspapers and the huge army of those who were now saved the pain of operations. All united in showering blessings on the man who had given humanity such a boon.

CHAPTER ELEVEN

The First Shadow

"**D**OCTOR MORTON's gloom of manner and evident depression made it impossible for me to believe the good news," writes Elizabeth [1] about her husband's return from the memorable operation. "It seemed to me as if he should have been so highly elated at having accomplished one of the most splendid achievements of the century, and yet there he was, sick at heart, crushed down, one would have said, by a load of discouragement. This was due, not only to bodily fatigue and the reaction after his great efforts, but to an intuitive perception of the troubles in store for him. It is literally true that he was never the same man after that day; his whole after life was embittered through this priceless boon he had conferred upon the human race."

On October 17, 1846, immediately after the operation on Gilbert Abbott, Morton wrote to his sometime partner Horace Wells about the triumph. Yes, he had succeeded in discovering a reliable means for allaying pain. His intention was to take out a patent, and he had immediately thought about his old friend. Perhaps the two of them might work together once more. Could not Wells push the patent affair in New York?

When Wells received Morton's letter he was staying at the City Hotel in Hartford, Connecticut, busy preparing a "Scientific Panorama Exhibition," and had also planned what he hoped would be a big business in French engravings and paintings. Still, Mor-

[1] In *McClure's Magazine*, September, 1896.

170

ton's proposal was certainly interesting. Food for thought. Perhaps it would give him a chance of earning a lot of money, and Wells couldn't afford to lose any chances.

In answer he wrote:

"I have received your letter and should not like you to throw away your rights for nothing. Before you make any arrangements whatever, I wish to see you. I think I will be in Boston the first of next week—probably on Monday night. If the operation of administrating the gas is not attended with too much trouble, and will produce the effect you state, it will, undoubtedly, be a fortune to you, provided, it is rightly managed.

"Yours in haste,

"H. WELLS."

Early next Tuesday, Wells called at Morton's office, where the pair talked over the possibilities. Then they visited Eddy at the Patent Office. This affair of the patent seemed to be still in an early stage, and, on closer study, Wells did not think it was so alluring as he had hoped. The trade in engravings and paintings looked likely to be far more profitable. "Good-by, Morton, and good luck. I shall go back to Hartford."

The Scientific Panorama at Hartford was a failure. Wells decided to leave for Paris, where he would buy a lot of engravings and paintings at rock-bottom prices. But a few days before he was to sail, came news of the wonderful success of the painless operation on Alice Mohan. In the Hartford papers, Morton was described as a great discoverer. What unexpected success! Wells hurried off to see Samuel Cooley, the man who had sat next to him at the Union Hall. "Look there," said Wells, pointing to the newspapers in his hand. "If I had only gone on with my experiments and pushed them to a successful conclusion, what a lot of money and fame I should have earned by this time!"

The thought rankled: "I could have done it." Then the thought took on a new complexion: "I ought to have done it." Then: "The discovery was really mine, and Morton merely filched it from me. It was I, I, who discovered that pain could be allayed by the inhalation of gas. All that Morton did was to use ether instead of laughing gas, and he has won fame by my discovery. When he proposed that I should help him to take out a patent, he was only trying to swindle me, thinking I should never notice he was a thief."

Wells knew that the best plan would be to go at once to Boston and insist upon his rights. But he could not postpone the journey to Paris. This would embroil him with certain friends who were financing the affair. Still, he would not let this fellow Morton snatch all the glory without putting up a fight.

On December 7, 1846, the day before the ship sailed, Wells had a letter published in the Hartford *Courant*:

> "As Dr. Charles T. Jackson and W. T. G. Morton claim to be the originators of this invaluable discovery, I will give a short history of its introduction, that the public may decide to whom belongs the honour. . . . When I was deciding what exhilarating agent to use, it immediately occurred to me that it would be best to use nitrous oxide gas, or sulphuric ether. I advised with Dr. Marcy, of this city, and by his advice I continued to use the former. . . . If Drs. Jackson and Morton claim that they use something else, I reply that it is the same in principle, if not in name. . . . After making the above statement of facts, I leave it for the public to decide to whom belongs the honour of the discovery."

Throughout the voyage across the Atlantic he was tormented by the idea that a wrong had been done him, that he had made the discovery and had been robbed of its fruits. When he reached Paris, it was only to have his bitterness intensified. Indeed, before he reached Paris, since his friend Brewster, the dentist, came to meet the boat. As soon as they had exchanged greetings, Brewster began to discuss the great discovery. All Paris was talking about the wonderful gift which had come from Boston. Jobert de Lamballe had tried it at the St. Louis Hospital; the Academy of the Sciences was looking into the matter; Roux and Velpeau, two leading medical authorities, had approved it.

Paris was the world. The whole world was buzzing with

news of the discovery. Everyone considered it to be the greatest gift ever made by America to mankind.

Wells was seething with indignation as he listened to what Brewster told him. At length his rage burst forth: "Do you know who really discovered anesthesia?" he exclaimed. "I, I was the discoverer!" Mortified pride, all that had been seething in his mind throughout the long weeks of the voyage, compelled this splenetic outburst. Brewster was amazed, and found it hard to grasp that the discoverer of this great boon was actually talking to him, and was no one else than his old friend the dentist Wells from Hartford.

Bubbling over with excitement, Wells explained how it had all come about, how he had gone to Morton and Jackson with his new discovery, how they had dissuaded him from going any further, and then stolen his thunder and publicly claimed the credit of the discovery.

"But have you any convincing proof of what you tell me? Did you bring the evidence over with you?"

Wells mentioned the names of various persons in Hartford and Boston. Dr. Marcy, Riggs the dentist, Colton the itinerant lecturer, Samuel A. Cooley—all of them could testify that he had made the first experiment in allaying pain by the inhalation of gas. Of course, he had not brought any evidence along. He had come to Paris to buy pictures. When he left the United States, he had had no idea that news of the discovery had gone farther than Hartford and Boston, and that when he reached Europe he would find the whole world talking about it.

It seemed to Brewster that only from inexperience, from innocence and simplicity, had Wells failed to bring incontrovertible evidence. His friend had been cheated, and Brewster was ready to do anything that could help. He would see that the truth was made known. Wells should be introduced to some of the notables of Paris. Certainly it would be most unjust, when the French metropolis was celebrating the boon of anesthesia, that the originator should have to spend his time peddling pictures for a livelihood. The world must be made to do justice to Wells.

Wells was carried away by Brewster's enthusiasm. His friend's uncontesting belief in his claims had removed the last traces of doubt from his own mind. He was now honestly convinced of his own priority, and the more often he told the story, the firmer became his conviction. Brewster was right. It was a scandal that such a man as himself should wear out shoe leather on the prowl for pictures. He would not bother about that pettifogging trade any longer. There was more important work to do. He must establish his claim to priority.

Everything to which Wells had turned his hand since abandoning his dental practice in Hartford had been a failure. Bird-fancying, the Scientific Panorama, and what not—all, all had come to nothing. Nor was this picture-peddling likely to be any better. These had been mere deviations from the true path. Now there opened to him prospects of escaping from that sort of thing to find wealth, honor and glory, a world-wide reputation. The hopeful mood of those weeks that followed the evening spent at Colton's laughing-gas demonstration was fully restored. In February, 1847, he sent in his claim to the Paris Academy of Medicine.

Brewster advised him to return forthwith to America, collect his evidence and then come back to Paris. Wells agreed, but before sailing he published in *Galignani's Messenger* an article in which he publicly claimed priority in the great discovery.

Wells was cold-shouldered when he got back to America. The newspapers were unqualified supporters of Morton. Many of the professional notables of Boston had seen the indubitable success of Morton's use of ether in the first operation ever performed under anesthesia, and if anyone remembered Wells at all it was only as the man who had made an unsuccessful demonstration of the use of laughing gas at Harvard.

When Wells called at the General Hospital to see Dr. Hayward, it was to face an enemy contemptuous of his claims. The very reception deprived Wells of the self-confidence he had had in Paris.

"Did you ever try to inhale sulphuric ether yourself?" asked Dr. Hayward.

"No, not ether, but . . ."

"Did you ever try to perform an operation under ether? Did you every try to make a patient insensitive to pain by the use of ether?" These were the questions of an inquisitor, and Wells did not know what to say. Hayward wanted an answer, but if Wells had answered, the reply would have been "No." Wells, therefore, was silent.

Hayward resumed, "The essence of the great discovery lies in the use of sulphuric ether. We are able to anesthetise patients because we give them sulphuric ether to inhale. Since this is so, do you still claim to have been the discoverer?"

With hanging head, Wells left the General Hospital, and went to try his luck with Morton. This interview, which lasted no more than a few minutes, was likewise a failure. Wells reminded Morton of the experiments with laughing gas, made in Boston, which involved the principle of inducing artificial sleep for the performance of operations. Instead of trying to convince his visitor by the use of words, Morton turned to his desk and extracted from one of the drawers the letter which Wells had written from Hartford in reply to his own. Would Wells have written such a letter, had he really believed himself to be the discoverer? Surely the answer to Morton's proposals ought to have been a claim to priority which would have invalidated Morton's right to take out a patent? But here in the letter it was plain that Wells did not expect any pecuniary advantage to result from taking out a patent. Now, when Morton's struggles had at length been crowned with success, Wells wanted to snatch the laurels.

The sometime partners were henceforward irredeemable foes.

To Wells, Boston was a city of ill omen. No one would believe him, wherever he tried to press his claims. By this time news had arrived of the article in *Galignani's Messenger*. A sentence in it was to prove most unfavorable to Wells's insistence on priority. It ran as follows: "The less atmospheric air admitted into the lungs with the gas or vapour, the better—the more satisfactory will be the result of the operation." By the lights of that day, Wells was considered to have shown himself an ignoramus. Had his advice been followed, considered the Bostonian doctors, the result would have been merely to produce asphyxia, and very likely the death of the patient. Boston held that Wells had had nothing to do with Morton's discovery. The errors in the *Galignani* article were enough to prove that.

Once more Wells left Boston a defeated man.

The proofs Brewster had advised him to collect were not forthcoming. There would have been nothing to gain from a second journey to Paris. But he could not make up his mind to resume the career of a picture dealer in Hartford. During his stay in Paris, he had greatly enjoyed being made much of by the members of Brewster's circle, had had a foretaste of fame, and the prospects at Hartford were most uninviting.

Morton had got ahead of him with ether, and Morton's ether had driven his own laughing gas out of the field. But there was another anesthetic, proved efficacious by a Scottish gynecologist named Simpson and recently introduced by him into midwifery and surgery—chloroform. In England doctors were beginning to regard chloroform as preferable to ether. In America, it was still almost unknown. Here was a great chance. He, Horace Wells, would introduce chloroform into America. Thus he could take revenge on Morton, the thief. If chloroform were to replace ether for surgical anesthesia, Morton's success would have been a mere episode, and Wells's name would become associated with the spread of anesthesia in America. Thus the game would be won after all.

Wells procured a large quantity of chloroform, and went with it to New York. There he tried to persuade the hospitals, leading dentists and doctors, to use the new anesthetic from Europe which, said Wells, was a far more effective anesthetic than ether. But most of those whom Wells approached had had excellent results with ether, their patients were satisfied with it and their practices were expanding. Why should they experiment with another anesthetic, little known and perhaps dangerous? Everywhere Wells encountered rebuffs.

There was only one way of overcoming hostility to the innovation. As he had done with laughing gas, so now he must try chloroform on himself. This time, however, he would proceed more cautiously, would go on experimenting until he had learned

Old Boston at the time of the discovery of anesthesia.

Dr. Charles T. Jackson, well-known scientist of the early nineteenth century, who disputed with Morton the title of "Benefactor of Mankind" for the introduction of ether anesthesia.

all about chloroform, how long its effect lasted, what doses were needed to produce a narcotic sleep, and the limit of safe dosage. He was resolved to show the world that not the ether of William Thomas Green Morton, but the chloroform which Horace Wells resolved to introduce into America, would be the true blessing for mankind.

Here, once more, Wells failed to secure the expected triumph. When he made his experiments with laughing gas in Hartford, impatience led to defeat, for he had tried to push his discovery before he had ripened it by persevering scientific work. Now another demon was to snatch success from his grasp.

Wells inhaled chloroform day after day, in order to ascertain the dosage; but in a little while he became a chloroform addict. The drug temporarily relieved him of the bitterness which the prospect of Morton's success caused. While under the influence of chloroform he forgot his disappointments, and a rosy light was imaginatively diffused over the grayness of his wrecked career. Hope still whispered in his ears.

For a time he continued to deceive himself, fancying that it was only for experimental purposes he continued to inhale day after day. Soon, however, it was plain that his experiments had lost their original purpose, that all he wanted was the pleasure of chloroform intoxication. As soon as the fumes of the drug had been dissipated, and Wells began once more to envisage the gloomy situation, his prospects of success seemed incredibly remote, his disappointments returned, his cares thickened. He could get relief only by renewed inhalation.

Wells had become an addict. Life was unbearable without chloroform. His health was undermined, his powers of resistance were diminished, by the unceasing use of the drug. Lucid intervals became shorter and more infrequent. He was unceasingly intoxicated. Meanwhile his wife and child were waiting vainly in Hartford, hoping for the return of the husband and father who had gone to build them a glorious future in New York.

Thus detached from everything which might have given him an anchorage in life, without occupation or means of livelihood, far from his family, uprooted, Wells aimlessly tramped the streets

of New York, and spent the long evenings in aimless peregrina-
tions. His life grew more and more futile and purposeless, and
such acquaintances as he had made in New York were no longer
interested in him. His only possible associates were waifs of his
own kidney, and streetwalkers. Haunted as he was by gloomy
thoughts, the streets were his sole refuge, for whenever he was
alone he was hunted by the raging torment of his ideas. He paced
up and down Broadway, accosting every prostitute he met, talking
without pause, if only to silence his own thoughts.

But the ladies who had to earn their livelihood by being picked
up on Broadway were quick to realize that they wasted their time
when they listened to this penniless and shabby dentist. They
turned away, now, when he made a sign to them. Wells realized
that he was being shunned, even by these outcasts, and this only
intensified his bitterness. His excitement and despair continually
increased.

Here was a man wandering aimlessly up and down the streets,
scarcely knowing whither he was going or what he was doing.
Only a trifle, a chance word, was now needed to push him over
the edge into actual insanity.

One night a derelict like himself struck up acquaintance with
him. Here, at length, was someone willing to hold converse with
him, and relieve his intolerable loneliness. The stranger began to
talk about one of the streetwalkers who, from pure malice, had
spoiled his only decent suit, so that he could no longer go about
among respectable people. "These whores," he said, "ought to be
exterminated like vermin. My father," he went on, "was a decent,
honest workman, a puritan of the old school. Often he used to
warn me against having anything to do with these bitches. Children of the devil, Dad used to say. If only I had listened to his
advice, then I shouldn't have had my suit spoiled like this. When
I come across the wretch again, I shall know how to revenge
myself."

Vengeance! The stranger's spoiled clothing, the anger of this
unknown, anger directed toward another unknown—these gave
the chloroform addict's delusions something to hang themselves on.
Vengeance! The spotted suit, stolen fame, the streetwalker's mis-

deed and Morton's success—all these things were jumbled together in a clouded mind, as a parable and as a means of paying out his enemies. Vengeance!

"I know how to give you satisfaction," he said to his chance companion. "Show me the girl, and leave the rest to me. Your father was a wise man, and knew what he was about."

They walked for hours up and down Broadway, until at length the stranger pointed to a girl standing in a doorway. "That's the one," he said. Wells looked at her carefully. He would know her again all right.

Next morning he bought a flask of vitriol, and waited impatiently till evening came, when he would be able to take vengeance for his chance acquaintance's spotted suit; to take vengeance, too, for all the wrongs that had been done him, the wrongs inflicted by Morton the thief, by Boston, by this inhospitable city of New York, by the painted girls who shunned him, by the whole ungrateful, inhospitable, callous world.

With the craftiness of a lunatic he made his preparations before going out. Luck favored him. As he was passing the Astor House, he caught sight of the girl with another prostitute. Yes, she was the one; he recognized her face, her walk, her hat and her dress. He had the flask of vitriol in his coat pocket. Taking it out, he removed the stopper and flung the contents at the two girls.

Now he had done it. He had taken vengeance. Was it because of the stranger's spoiled suit, or because of Morton's theft of his invention? He did not know which. He heard the girls screaming, was surrounded by an angry crowd ready to lynch him for throwing vitriol. Broadway had risen against him, and he was rescued from a worse fate by the hand of a policeman on his shoulder.

What subsequently happened seemed like a nightmare. He was taken to the station, and then brought before a magistrate. Name? Age? Residence? Why did you do this? He told the story of his acquaintance's spoiled suit. Then he was confronted with one of the girls. "Do you know her?" asked the judge. Wells said he could not remember her. "He is lying!" screamed the prostitute. "The man has accosted me often and often, and made himself an infernal nuisance. But I wouldn't have anything to do with a fellow like that." Another girl said that Wells had frequently pestered her with his advances, and had bored her by pouring out a long tale of his woes. A third confirmed the story. As to the vitriol-throwing, passers-by gave evidence of having seen him take the bottle out of his pocket, remove the stopper and fling the contents at the unsuspecting girls. All the witnesses were agreed. Turning to the accused, the judge said: "Tell me why you did this atrocious thing." Wells had almost forgotten the story of the stranger's spoiled suit. He broke into a long account of his grievances against Morton. Morton had filched his discovery. He, Wells, not Morton, had been the discoverer of anesthesia. The judge said that all this had nothing to do with the case. Why had the accused flung vitriol at the girls? Wells really could not say. The case was clear, the evidence incontrovertible. Judge Osborn had only to pass sentence. It was beyond his power to find out why the deed had been done. Osborn would have needed to be more than an ordinary man, to be a magician, if he was to unravel this tangled skein. There was enough to warrant a sentence of imprisonment.

Wells was conveyed to the Tombs for isolation in a cell. This was on Friday evening. On Sunday the prisoners attended service in the chapel. Except for the warders, all the members of the congregation were prisoners like himself. The chaplain mounted the pulpit and talked about the Saviour who had come to deliver us from sin. During the sermon, Wells thought about the wife and child who were awaiting his return to Hartford. The senseless, horrible nature of his crime became apparent to him. The sermon was over, and Wells went back to his cell. There he was left alone with his remorse. What had the chaplain said about the Saviour? The prisoner could not remember. A prey to remorse, he could think only of his crime, which was unpardonable. Imprisonment was too slight a punishment. Remorse was a harsher judge than Osborn. Wells passed a capital sentence on himself. He would kill himself at midnight.

He would grant himself only one alleviation. He would be able to use chloroform and thus mitigate the pangs of death. Anyhow this would make him more than even with the detested Morton. By using chloroform, he would convince the world that this, not ether, was the best means of evading the death-agony.

Although Wells had presumably been searched on admission in accordance with routine, he had managed to secrete a bottle of chloroform. He asked the warder for writing materials. Then he hid the flask of what had now become his favorite intoxicant.

On his Sunday evening round, between six and seven, the warder glanced through the judas in the door of Wells's cell. He saw the prisoner seated at the table, writing.

The next round was made at six o'clock in the morning of January 24th. Through the spy-hole the warder saw Wells seated on the edge of the bed, in a strange position. The prisoner was wearing his hat, and had a handkerchief over mouth and nostrils. The right leg was pendant, the left extended over the bench in front of the bed. On the bench were an empty bottle and an open razor. On the floor was a pool of blood. The warder hastily opened the door and went in. On the prisoner's left thigh was a big incision, severing the femoral artery. The man had bled to death. On the table lay two letters.

The governor was summoned. One of the letters was addressed to the public, while the other bore the superscription "To my Wife." The former, which the governor immediately read, contained the following passage: "I had during the week been in the constant practice of inhaling chloroform and on Friday evening last I lost all consciousness before I removed the inhaler from my mouth. On coming out of the stupor I was exhilarated beyond measure, exceeding anything which I had ever before experienced, and seeing the vial of acid standing on the mantel, in my delirium I seized it and rushed into the street and threw it at two females. My character, which I have ever prized above everything else, is gone. My dear—dear wife and child, how they will suffer. I cannot proceed. My brain is on fire." The letter to his wife ran: "Before 12 o'clock this night I am to pay the debt of Nature. Yes, if I were to go free tomorrow, I could not live and be called a villain. Oh, my dear mother, brother, and sister, what can I say to you? believing that God, who knoweth all hearts will forgive the dreadful act. Oh, my dear wife and child, whom I leave destitute of means of support—I would still live and work for you, but I cannot, for were I to live on, I should become a maniac. I feel that I am but little better than one already, and now while I am scarcely able to hold my pen I must bid all farewell. May God forgive me."

Having examined the empty bottle, the prison surgeon reported: "Suicide while laboring under an aberration of mind."

Next morning, January 25, 1848, the New York *Herald* reported:

"Quite an excitement was created yesterday morning in the Tombs, in consequence of the self-destruction of Dr. Horace Wells, dentist, who was detected in the act of throwing vitriol upon the dress of a young woman in Broadway. His body was conveyed on board the Hartford Steamboat, for that city where the deceased has a wife and child awaiting the dreadful news."

At the graveside the widow said: "My husband's great gift, which he devoted to the service of mankind, proved a curse to himself and to his family."

A few days after the interment, a letter bearing a French postage stamp and addressed to Horace Wells reached Hartford. His widow opened it, and read:

"My dear Wells,

"I have just returned from a meeting of the Paris Medical Society, where they have voted that to Horace Wells, of Hartford, Connecticut, United States of America, is due all the honour of having first discovered and successfully applied the use of vapours or gases whereby surgical operations could be performed without pain. They have done even more, for they have elected you an honorary member of their Society. This was the third meeting that the Society had deliberated upon the subject. On the two previous occasions Mr. Warren, the agent of Dr. Morton, was present and endeavoured to show that to his client was due the honour, but completely failed. Your diploma and the vote of the Paris Medical Society shall be forwarded to you. In the interim, you may use this letter as you please.

"Believe me ever truly yours,

"BREWSTER."

The letter came too late to save the unfortunate Wells from chloroform addiction, insanity and suicide. But it was of some comfort to the widow, and became the foundation of a terrible charge against Morton. Passed from hand to hand it was taken as evidence that Wells had been a great man tragically misunderstood, and as proof that William Thomas Green Morton had cheated his former partner.

The Hartford view of the matter was to the effect that "Morton, the Boston dentist, stole the idea of one of the greatest of our citizens, and thus drove his victim to madness and self-destruction." Nor was it long before the same ill-natured view gained currency in Boston, for Morton's adversaries made skillful use of the letter from Paris. In the French metropolis, Brewster saw to it that the charge against Morton should be pushed home, and managed to secure the insertion of the following remarks in a French newspaper: "While a young, unlucky man who had done so much to free mankind from the curse of pain perished by his own hand with a clouded intellect in some corner of the New World, another, undeserving of the fame he had snatched, was enjoying the credit which properly accrued to the prematurely deceased Wells."

Morton might easily have held his ground against the claims and allegations of a living Wells, for he could have produced facts to the contrary. Now he had to face the shade of a dead man, one to whom the affection of survivors had given a martyr's rank. This martyr needed no proofs, since Death spoke for him. It need hardly be said that those who were intimately acquainted with the circumstances insisted upon Morton's priority in the discovery of anesthesia, so that in the end truth came into its own. But false charges are apt to stick, and for the rest of his life Morton was by many held responsible for Wells's suicide. A shadow had fallen on the discovery.

CHAPTER TWELVE

Ships for Europe

A<small>N ADDITIONAL</small> curse was to be visited upon Morton's discovery. His victory brought misfortune after misfortune.

"Ether is not so harmless as you imagine. I will have nothing to do with the matter." Such had been Jackson's words on first hearing of Morton's discovery. For a while he hesitated to make joint application for the patent, considering it expedient—from caution and regard for his professional standing—to hold aloof from the publicity which ether was winning.

But when the operation on Gilbert Abbott proved successful, it appeared that Morton's discovery was watertight, and this led to a change in Jackson's attitude. The doctors of Boston were beginning to declare that beyond question the new method would make good, and the discoverer would secure an imperishable reputation.

This news troubled Jackson. After all, it was he who had advised Morton to use pure, rectified sulphuric ether. Surely it was not fair that the disciple should have all the glory, and most of the pecuniary reward, while he, but for whose expert knowledge the discovery could not have taken place, should be fobbed off with a shabby ten per cent of the profits from the patent. He had been diddled once before, in the affair with Morse. He, Jackson, had been first in the field with an idea, while the other, a painter who knew nothing of science, had got ahead of him, with the result that the whole world now acclaimed the crafty Morse as the inventor of the electric telegraph. This unscrupulous and pushing young dentist, a mere ignoramus in scientific matters, should not get away with such another trick.

Envy and anger gnawed at Jackson's vitals and kept him awake at night, for he could not bear the thought that another was to reap where he had sown.

On October 29, 1846, putting on a frock coat, he went to call on Professor Warren at the Massachusetts General Hospital. With becoming dignity, he spoke as expert to expert, as colleague to colleague: "Sir, I have the honor to inform you that the use of ether in surgical operations was my idea. William Thomas Green Morton was no more than a pupil of mine, acting on my instructions."

Professor Warren bethought himself how Morton had waited for him in the hospital corridor; of the words in which the dentist had explained his plans; of how Morton's hand had trembled at the time of the first painless operation, when applying the inhaler to the patient. This was not a man acting on instructions, but truly the discoverer in person. Such was Warren's conviction, not to be shaken by the tranquil assurance of even so highly respected a scientist as Dr. Jackson. Of course it would not do for him bluntly to deny what Jackson said, but still Warren would not accept it without demur. He made a proposal: "In a few days I have another operation to perform. Perhaps, Dr. Jackson, on this occasion you will administer the ether in place of Mr. Morton?"

This was an ingenious challenge, though not openly made as such, and was more disagreeable to Jackson than a flat repudiation of his claim would have been. He remembered how, overpowered by ether vapor, he had once gone to sleep during a game of cards, and how, another time, he had used ether to relieve the effects of inhaling chlorine. Of course, as a skilled chemist, he knew all that was to be known about ether. Still, he had never tried to use ether in the way it was used by Morton, and had never had Morton's inhaler in his hand. Too shrewd to expose himself by a blunt refusal, Jackson evaded the issue, saying: "I am very sorry, Professor Warren, but that will be impossible, since I am about to go into the hills upon a geological investigation."

But this painful incident did not induce Jackson to abandon his claims to priority. Of course it was true he knew nothing about the technique of administering ether as an anesthetic, but that was a minor point. In a little while, every tyro would learn how to put patients to sleep with ether vapor. The idea was his, and therefore the discovery was his.

After all, it could matter very little whom Professor Warren looked on as the discoverer. Boston was not the world. Boston was not competent to decide who had the prior claim to a discovery which would be used everywhere. Paris was the world, from this outlook. Only a body like the Academy of the Sciences in Paris was entitled to decide questions of such wide import. There they would know who should be believed, Dr. Jackson or Mr. Morton. Jackson had spent a year in Paris for postgraduate study. His name was known, and his scientific standing. He had friends, influential friends among leading mineralogists. Elie de Beaumont, for instance, who had been appointed Professor of Geology at the School of Mines as far back as 1829, and was a great gun in the Academy of Sciences (of which he became perpetual secretary in 1853).

On November 13th, Jackson wrote to Beaumont to tell the latter about his discovery. At this date he had never even seen an operation under anesthesia. True, the General Hospital was only a few doors away, but the staff there was in league with Morton. Why expose himself to disagreeables? Dr. Jackson was clever enough to write a convincing report without having had any personal experience. Like many scientific experts, he was an adept in getting knowledge out of books. He read Pereira's *Elements of Materia Medica* once more; looked through the reports issued long before by Dr. Beddoes' Pneumatic Institute; and revived his memories of all that he had heard and read about these matters. His memorial to Beaumont was an admirably drafted scientific paper. Every statement was supported and documented in the way a learned institution like the Academy of the Sciences would expect. A few passages from the report may be quoted:

"I ask leave to communicate through you to the Academy of Sciences a discovery which I have made. . . . I have latterly put it to use by inducing a dentist of this city to administer the vapours of ether to persons from whom he was to extract teeth. I then requested this dentist to go to the General Hospital of Massachusetts and administer the vapour of ether to a patient about to undergo a painful surgical operation."

He went on to describe how, in the years 1825–1828, when still engaged in medical studies, he had paid great attention to the results achieved by Sir Humphry Davy. This reference to Davy would show his own scientific thoroughness, and would certainly have a good effect. Then he spoke of his experiments with sulphuric ether in the year 1837. This, of course, was to establish his priority to Morton. With that end in view, he described, in a way which would give color to the belief that he was recording personal experiences, the subjective impressions aroused during the inhalation of sulphuric ether.

It was then, he wrote, that he had made the important discovery which showed that the inhalation of sulphuric ether could prevent pain. It would be well, of course, to give a concrete instance. Wells and Morton, being dentists, had talked of relieving pain during the extraction of teeth. To distinguish his own case from theirs and outdo them, Jackson decided to choose the distress of sore throat consequent upon "gassing" with chlorine. This would make a good impression, belonging as it did to the domain of internal medicine, and not to that of dentistry.

On one occasion, he wrote, when preparing large quantities of pure chlorine, he had overturned and broken a big jar of the gas and had inadvertently inhaled a large quantity.

"The next morning my throat was seriously inflamed and very painful. . . . I promptly inhaled ether mixed with air, and . . . speedily noticed that all pain had ceased in my throat, and the sensations which I had were of the most agreeable kind."

This artful penman proceeded to depict the effects of ether in terms drawn from the reports of the pneumatologists:

"I soon fell into a dreamy state, and then became unconscious of all surrounding things. . . . I suppose I remained in that state for not less than a quarter of an hour. . . . As I became conscious I observed still there was no feeling of pain in my throat, and my limbs were still deeply benumbed, as if the nerves of sensation were fully paralysed."

It was then that Jackson made his discovery.

"Reflecting upon these phenomena, the idea flashed into my mind, that I had made a discovery I had so long a time been in quest of—a means of rendering the nerves of sensation temporarily insensible to pain, so as to admit of the performance of a surgical operation on an individual without his suffering pain therefrom. I should be deeply grateful if the Academy of the Sciences would appoint a commission to study the remarkable effects of the inhalation of sulphuric ether."

Jackson's memorial was not written until after the painless amputation of Alice Mohan's leg. Matters seemed going on favorably for the discovery, but it would be a mistake for him to hurry. Anesthesia was quite young, no more than a six weeks' bantling, and the newborn are always liable to sudden illness. As a cautious man, Dr. Jackson would have to reckon with such possibilities. Dr. Warren and the General Hospital might easily have some mishap which would become a public scandal. He did not wish to expose his professional standing as a scientist to any risk—least of all in Paris and before the Academy of the Sciences. Of course he wanted to make good his claim to priority, but with the requisite caution. Caution was his leitmotif, and was never more in place than here, where the alternatives were imperishable renown and extreme discredit.

Dr. Jackson, therefore, sent his report to Beaumont under seal, with a covering letter to the effect that Beaumont was not to break the seal until special instructions followed. Thus Jackson had still a chance of getting Beaumont to destroy the report should anything go wrong during subsequent administrations of ether. Then no one would ever learn about his demand for recognition as the discoverer.

Very soon after Jackson had posted his despatch to Beaumont, Dr. Bigelow, who was a persistent champion of Morton's claim to priority, laid before the Boston Academy of the Arts and Science, and also before the Boston Society of Medical Improvement, a report upon the recent painless operation. Morton, declared Bigelow in this document, was the discoverer of the great and valuable method of ether anesthesia. On November 18, 1846, this address was published in a Boston medical periodical; and Bigelow, being energetic and businesslike, saw to it that his eulogy of Morton should be carried to Europe and the rest of the world by the Cunard steamer which sailed on December 19th.

Jackson got wind of this, and received additional information which greatly disquieted him, for it was about something which made all his precautions useless. Morton had taken steps which were likely to wreck Jackson's schemes. Having now secured his patent, he was sending specimens of his apparatus, with full instructions as to its use, to various European potentates: King Louis Philippe in France, King Leopold in Belgium, Tsar Nicholas in Russia, Emperor Ferdinand in Austria, Frederick Augustus of Saxony, William of Holland, Louis of Bavaria, Ernest of Hanover and Charles Albert of Sardinia. Someone disclosed this long list to Dr. Jackson. Soon there would be hardly a ruler in Europe, and scarcely any other man of note, to whom Morton had not sent his apparatus. Various distinguished surgeons were to receive it: in France, for instance, Velpeau, Jobert de Lamballe, Blandin, Ricord and Maisonneuve. More than this, Jackson learned that Morton had sent the apparatus to Dr. Willis Fisher, a native of Boston settled in Paris; while Edward Warren, nephew of Professor Warren, sailing for Europe on the aforesaid Cunarder, was commissioned to apply for a patent in France.

Jackson was horrified by this news of Morton's activities. If he waited any longer, his chance of establishing his claim to priority would vanish. He must act instantly. In a great hurry, therefore, he wrote to Dr. Elie de Beaumont asking the latter to open the sealed despatch forthwith and communicate the contents to the Academy of the Sciences.

Paris, of course, must be the first point of attack, being the metropolis of the world, and the Academy of the Sciences on the banks of the Seine, the intellectual forum. But Jackson did not forget the rest of the world. A leading power among intellectuals was Alexander von Humboldt, the Prussian, generally regarded as the greatest scientist of the day. The first volume of his *Cosmos* had recently been published, and was making a profound impression. The author was a confidant of King Frederick William IV and a friend of Louis Philippe. His word counted for much, both at the academies and at the courts. No doubt Humboldt, being a geologist who had traveled far and wide, must know of Jackson's own geological writings. Jackson had good grounds, therefore, for hoping that Humboldt would advocate his claims to priority both in Prussia and in France.

Nor did Jackson forget the Ottoman Empire, the Scandinavian countries or even little Sardinia. There were scientists in all of these who would be in a position to push Charles Thomas Jackson's claims to priority—noted chemists who would espouse the cause of a colleague.

Jackson's urgent missives, copies of the medical journals containing a report of Bigelow's eulogy on Morton, and Morton's numerous addresses to European potentates, all left for Europe by the same mail.

Morton waited eagerly for news. His thoughts followed the steamer which carried his apparatus and his letters across the Atlantic; he pictured the astonishment in the various chancelleries, the interest of noted professors and other men of mark; he pictured the excitement that would seize those who watched the first painless operation in the various European capitals. Unquestionably his discovery would make a universal sensation. There could not be a doubt of that.

"Do you remember, Lizzie," he said to his wife, "how at West Needham you accused me of neglecting my practice for the sake of my experiments? Now you will understand that I had good reason for what I was doing. You wait until the Cunarder gets to Europe. Then you will find that Paris and the whole world will be talking about me."

For the next few weeks, Morton could think of nothing else. He counted the days till the return mail from Europe would arrive. Edward Warren had promised to report as soon as possible after reaching Paris.

The return mail brought Morton a letter from Edward Warren. Morton tore it open and was informed that, to begin with, everything had gone well. Fisher had succeeded in arousing the interest of a number of leading authorities. Operations under ether took place, and evoked general enthusiasm. Then Wells turned up, declared he had been first in the field, with the inhalation of laughing gas. Still that mattered very little, for no one paid any attention to Wells, everyone being convinced of the soundness of Morton's claim to priority. But then something most unfortunate took place. On Monday, January 18th, the Academy of the Sciences met. The discovery of anesthesia, about which all Paris was now talking, was on the agenda. Such leading authorities as Velpeau, Roux and Serres were present. Now the unexpected happened. Elie de Beaumont read a long report from Dr. Charles Thomas Jackson, dated November 13, 1846, and in the hands of the Academy of Sciences since December 28th. Jackson claimed to have been the sole discoverer of ether narcosis. Morton was described as merely "a Boston dentist" whom Jackson had commissioned to try his discovery, first for the extraction of a tooth, and subsequently at operations in the General Hospital. All the operations in the General Hospital, so he declared, were carried out on his instructions—such was the tenor of Elie de Beaumont's address.

Had it not been for Velpeau's intervention, Morton's name would not even have been mentioned at this sitting. Velpeau, however, said that this was already an old story for him, seeing that in December Willis Fisher had informed him about the discovery by Morton, the aforesaid Boston dentist, and at the Charité Hospital had demonstrated the method on various patients. "I did not then know," went on Velpeau, "that Dr. Jackson, the Boston chemist, had been the original discoverer, and that Morton, the dentist, was merely acting under Jackson's instructions, was no more than an underling." Roux, Serres and all the others were fully convinced of Jackson's priority, and a record to this effect was made in the minutes. The Academy of the Sciences decided to appoint a special commission to discuss the method, and to pay due honor to the discoverer. Of course this would carry great weight with the scientific world, and be of the utmost importance to Morton's claims. Such was the tenor of Warren's report. But worse followed. Dr. Beaumont had declared that Dr. Jackson was the discoverer and was alone entitled to a patent. Morton must take immediate steps to insure that he would not be regarded in Paris as one who had tried to steal the fruits of another's discovery. Unless Morton acted promptly, Fisher could do nothing to help him.

These words swam before Morton's eyes, his hands trembled, and he dropped the letter. What he had been reading seemed incredible. Instead of the expected chorus of congratulations, came this crushing report. Certainly he had been right in his suspicions of Jackson, in his reluctance to apply to Jackson for information about ether. Jackson wanted to play on him, Morton, the trick which, once before, the schemer had tried to play on Morse. Well, by God, he would be foiled this time as well.

Jackson was at work in his laboratory upon a new geochemical research. He was heating a test tube, watching the changes of color that were taking place in the enclosed fluid and making notes of what he saw. Then the door burst open, Morton entered in a state of great excitement, interrupted Jackson's experiment and poured out a flood of words.

Without circumlocution, Morton began to rail at Jackson. The two men had had differences before this, but Morton had always been respectful to Jackson, as student to professor. Now he stormed up and down the laboratory, talking at the top of his voice, so that the assistants could not fail to hear.

"Edward Warren's letter, this letter, shows me how you have been trying, behind my back, to gain the credit of my discovery. It was scandalous to address such a communication to the Academy of the Sciences in Paris, when you must have known that you were lying. I won't put up with it. I shall write myself to the Academy and explain matters to Monsieur de Beaumont and his colleagues. It's all very well for you to write to Paris claiming my discovery as your own, and representing me as no more than your hodman. But you needn't think I will let you get away with it."

There seemed no end to the objurgations, but at length Jackson managed to get in a word.

"Do pull yourself together, Morton," he said quietly. "I can only attribute the unwarrantable expressions you have used to the heedlessness of youth."

"You have cheated me," shouted Morton. "You know perfectly well that you merely gave me a word or two of advice about sulphuric ether. What can have induced you to write such a string of lies to Paris?" went on the angry man, his wrath and excitement unabated.

"You are talking nonsense," answered Jackson. "I have not cheated you. My young friend Morton, you had better keep watch on what you are saying. Have you forgotten the days when you sat under me as my pupil? Can you really think me capable of such a trick as you impute? Do you think that a man in my position would have anything to gain by it? I am as much astonished as you can be at the news which has come to you from Paris, but you have hardly given me a chance to explain."

Jackson spoke with the tranquillity and restraint of a sane man trying to bring a lunatic to reason.

"There must be some misunderstanding. My old friend Beaumont certainly seems to have made a blunder. But that can easily be put right. Don't you worry, my dear Morton."

Morton had arrived in a fury, but Jackson's quietude began to disarm him. Certainly Jackson showed no signs of being a guilty man vainly trying to justify himself. His manner was that of a gentleman who merely wished to clear up an unfortunate misunderstanding with the utmost propriety.

"What you say seems almost incredible." Jackson shook his head reflectively. "Beaumont must have been carried away by his feelings. He is a great friend of mine, must have wanted to push a claim I never made and must therefore, out of the goodness of his heart, have made light of the important part you played in the discovery of anesthesia. But I am sure that Beaumont would never want to do anything incorrect. As soon as I tell him he has made a mistake, he will put matters right. I assure you, my dear Morton, that he will make Paris do you justice. At any rate, I shall write to him by the next mail, and tell him what is needed."

Morton was ceasing to think so badly of Jackson. Had he really been mistaken in supposing that his former professor had been trying to cheat?

"Wait a minute, though," went on Jackson, after a pause, in which he seemed to have been considering how best to rehabilitate Morton. "A better idea occurs to me." He spoke in a cordial and fatherly way. "I fancy news of this misunderstanding in Paris might make its way to America, and there is nothing I want so much as to avoid allowing a wrong impression to gain ground on this side of the Atlantic. The best plan will be for me to publish an article in the *Daily Advertiser,* giving a full account of the importance of your discovery—one which, I am sure, will satisfy you. It will appear on Monday morning, and that day the mail leaves for Europe. I will see to it that a copy goes to Beaumont in Paris. An article signed by me, one which has appeared in the public press, will have much more effect than if I were to write privately to my friend. Everyone is greatly influenced by the printed word. But I need not tell you how deeply grieved I am that Beaumont should have made such a muddle of things—even though he did it, I am sure, with the best intentions in the world, and because he is such an old friend of mine."

Morton did not try to interrupt, for he felt somewhat ashamed of himself.

"All will go right, you see if it doesn't," said Jackson, and he went on to ask what more news had come from France about the acceptance of the method. Next he spoke about his own recent chemical and geological researches, which had been undertaken on behalf of the state of Massachusetts.

Morton went home appeased, thoroughly convinced that he could rely on Jackson's word.

But Elizabeth was less trustful, and by Sunday morning her

repeated expressions of doubt had revived her husband's anxiety. "You are too credulous, William. It seems to me that, as before, you have let him twist you round his fingers. In fact, you behaved like a child. Don't you remember the trick he tried to play on Morse? I would never trust Dr. Jackson."

"You didn't hear what he said, Elizabeth. Had you been there, you would have been satisfied. He didn't want to write to Paris while I was there; but it was his own proposal to publish an article in the *Daily Advertiser.*"

"I would much rather have seen the article in manuscript," rejoined Elizabeth. "Who knows what he will write in it and send to Paris?"

Still, it was not the doubts inspired by his wife which drove Morton to Somerset Street on Sunday, but sheer curiosity. He was eager to read the article a day in advance. After all, this was a very important matter. The article was to make it plain to the world that he and no other had been the discoverer of anesthesia.

"What a pity that you did not let me know before you left the other day. Of course I ought myself to have thought of sending you a copy," answered Jackson regretfully when Morton turned up at noon on Sunday and said he would like to read the article. "I haven't a copy of my manuscript, which has already gone to press. I expect they are setting it up at this moment. I don't see what we can do now. Of course it is written on the lines I explained to you. Oh well, you won't have to wait long before you read it in print tomorrow. It will go to Europe in tomorrow's mailbag, and in a few weeks the whole matter will be cleared up in Paris. Till tomorrow, Morton, that's all."

It certainly seemed incredible to Morton that Jackson could have written the article in a different sense than that promised. Such was his impression after this second interview. But Elizabeth was still suspicious.

"Why didn't he show it to you?" she asked.

"I tell you, he had already sent it to the newspaper office, and naturally could not ask to have it back. I am sure he was speaking the truth."

All the same, Morton could not sleep that night. The boat sailed next morning, and the newspaper must be early on board. It would not be delivered to the Boston public until later. Still, Morton got up early, and walked along Tremont Street to ask for an advance copy as it came off the press.

Elizabeth was still asleep.

"Wake up, Lizzie, wake up! A terrible thing has happened!"

Sleepily she opened her eyes, to see her husband as white as a sheet, standing beside the bed. In his hand was the newspaper.

"Look, look!" He turned the pages with tremulous hands. "There's nothing about it, not a word. I'm going crazy. I simply can't understand."

She glanced at him significantly, and he understood.

"You were right, Lizzie, you were right. I wish I had followed your advice. I could not have believed him to be such a cheat. Nor would you, if you had heard him. Can you understand why he humbugged me in this way?"

"Perfectly well. All he wanted was to prevent your getting word to Paris by this mail. Had you written, you could have cleared matters up, and thus have spoiled his game. He wanted to make sure that the ship would sail today without conveying a word of protest or explanation from you. Well, he has succeeded. Before you can write a report and get down to the docks, the boat will have gone."

It took Morton a little time to realize the full import of the trick Jackson had played on him. Willis Fisher and Edward Warren were awaiting news from him, were expecting him to send proofs. But he, fool that he was, had been talked over by Jackson into allowing the steamer to sail without a word from him to set matters right, and justify his own claim to priority. It was four weeks before he would have another opportunity. Four weeks in which his hands would be tied. For four weeks longer the Academy of the Sciences, the doctors and the monarchs to whom he had sent his apparatus would continue to believe that Jackson was the discoverer, and that he, Morton, was a swindler trying to snatch advantages to which he was not entitled, to steal another man's thunder.

His first thought was to rush off and call Jackson to account. "I'll show him that he can't fob me off with lies! This time I won't leave the laboratory until he has declared in writing that I made the discovery, not he." Such were Morton's wrathful exclamations.

"No, William, you must not go to Jackson. Neither today, nor later. Every time you have seen him, he has humbugged you. As I have told you again and again, you ought never to have offered him that percentage. He is your most dangerous enemy, and will never forgive you for having made the discovery. Listen to me, for I understand him much better than you do. My loving intuition tells me when anyone is scheming against you, and when misfortune threatens. Don't go to him. He is your enemy, and you must treat him as such. Write a full report of the whole matter, showing that the discovery is yours and yours alone, and post it to Paris by the next mail."

Jackson fully expected that he would have another visit from Morton, that Morton would demand an immediate explanation. He waited all day, as he conned what he intended to say. Whenever the laboratory door opened, he expected the enraged Morton to burst in.

But Morton did not come, neither on the Monday, nor on the Tuesday, nor on any other day. As time passed, Jackson grew uneasy. This unexpected silence must mean something. Morton must have something up his sleeve. Had Morton an agent in Paris, who would be able to take speedy action? Had he written direct to the Academy of the Sciences? Was he preparing a report for the newspapers? Impossible to foresee what the hothead would do. A man so impetuous and so energetic might do anything.

Jackson reflected very carefully. He did not know what his adversary would do; he must be armed at every point, and prepared to rout the enemy all along the line. A new despatch to Paris would not suffice.

Well, he would trust to chance, or what is called chance, which often supplies a man with better opportunities than the craftiest design.

In the middle of February, Jackson received the usual notice of a meeting of the Massachusetts Medical Society in the rooms of the Society of the Arts and Science. Jackson meditated the possibilities, making his preparations with the skill and speed of an Odysseus, of one whose only thought is how best to overreach his enemy.

The meeting was to be held on March 2nd. The next steamer for Europe was to sail on March 1st. There was no obvious connection between the things that were to happen on these respective dates. No connection for an ordinary peaceful citizen of Boston; but an intimate connection for the schemer Jackson, whose main purpose was to defeat Morton, and who was as busy with his combinations as a spider spinning her web. Yes, for Jackson there was an intimate connection, as these two dates suited his book perfectly —the meeting on the 2nd and the mail for Europe on the 1st. His thoughts may have run much as follows:

"As a member of the Massachusetts Medical Society I shall propose reading a paper at the next meeting, and in this I shall publicly advance my claim to priority in the discovery of anesthesia. I shall invite all the notables of the city to attend, including President Everett and Professor Warren. None of them is likely to refuse my invitation. I know Dr. Warren does not like me, but he will feel that if he were to be absent he might be accused of partiality.

"On March 1st, the *Daily Advertiser* shall publish a report of the meeting, and a list of those present. No matter what Morton may write to Paris, he cannot get his letter on the way before March 1st. What weight would the letter of an unknown dentist have in Paris compared with the newspaper containing the report of a meeting at the Boston Academy of the Arts and Science, announcing that the celebrated Dr. Jackson described his discovery of anesthesia, in the presence of a number of distinguished citizens?"

A copy of the journal should be sent to Humboldt in Berlin, another should go to London, others to Constantinople, Stockholm and Sardinia. Hundreds of copies should be sent to the leading academies and medical societies of Europe, and all of them would testify to the fact that the discoverer of anesthesia had been the Boston experimental chemist, Dr. Jackson. Liston and Pirogoff, the noted surgeons; the credulous potentates who might have been ready to accept an unknown dentist's claim to this imperishable discovery—they should all be convinced of their error, and recognize that Morton was an impostor. What a splendid chance to defeat the wiles of this restless intriguer! Of course there was one little difficulty to overcome. The ship was to sail on the 1st, and the meeting was fixed for the 2nd of the month. How, then, could the newspapers contain a report of a meeting which had not yet taken place?

But an Odysseus like Jackson, skilled in all the arts of intrigue, could devise a way of evading the limitations of the calendar.

Jackson had informed the committee of the Medical Society of his intention to lecture, and the subject. He had received acceptances from all the magnates he had invited to attend. Now he betook himself to the office of the *Daily Advertiser*.

"Would you be interested," he asked the editor, "to have an anticipatory report of our meeting on March 2nd? It would be exclusive, for I do not propose to send one to any of the other papers. This will be the most important sitting of the year, for I intend to lecture upon the discovery of anesthesia, a topic the whole world is discussing at the moment, and certainly the pride of our Boston. The most noted men of science in the city will be present, including, I believe, Professor Warren."

"That would be extremely kind of you, Dr. Jackson; and I cannot but regard it as a great favor you are offering the *Daily Advertiser*. When do you think we could have the details?"

"I think the best thing would be if you were to let me write a summary myself. You see my lecture will deal with technical and scientific matters, and it would be better for everyone concerned that there should be no chance of any errors in terminology. I suppose you send a fair number of copies of the *Daily Advertiser* to Europe? Anyhow it would be well to do so on this occasion, for every alert person on the other side of the Herring Pond is eagerly awaiting authentic news from Boston about this discovery.

I recently heard as much from some of my correspondents in Paris who are members of the Academy of Sciences. Also the famous Alexander von Humboldt, who is a friend of mine, has asked me to let him know what is going on. I could compile the report so that it might appear as an advance notice in your issue of March 1st, and the copies for European notables could be addressed and sent down to the mail boat in good time. If you like I will let you have a number of suitable addresses. I think what I propose would give the *Advertiser* even more prestige in Europe than it already possesses. As our noted fellow citizen Dr. Oliver Wendell Holmes recently said to me: 'Everyone who, however remotely, is connected with this discovery receives, thereby, a title of nobility, and will become immortal.' "

"I hardly know how to express my gratitude for your friendliness, my dear Dr. Jackson," said the editor, who was genuinely touched by so much consideration and foresight. "We will count on your support in good time for the issue of March 1st. How much space shall we reserve for it?"

The newspapers of that day were sufficiently enterprising to value a scoop, although the term had not yet been coined. Everything, therefore, went as if by clockwork, and there was no hitch in Jackson's pretty little scheme. The report duly appeared in the issue of March 1st. Jackson, who wanted to make a splash, had been liberal in his demand for space. He gave a full synopsis of the lecture and described the reception of the Boston notables as if it had already taken place, not forgetting his own welcome by these distinguished persons. The impression was artfully conveyed that all of them, by their mere presence, had endorsed Jackson's claims as discoverer. This "wangle," as it would nowadays be called, was a masterpiece.

When the mail boat departed on the morning of March 1st, it was carrying hundreds of copies of the Boston *Daily Advertiser*. Few famous names among contemporary Europeans had been omitted by Dr. Jackson from the list with which he so obligingly supplied the editor.

Morton, being only a dentist and not a qualified medical practitioner, was not eligible for membership in the Massachusetts

Medical Society, nor had he received a special invitation to the sitting of March 2nd. Still, some of the members were friends of his, and they promised to report proceedings.

But there was no need to wait until after the meeting and hear what his friends had to say. On March 1st he opened the *Advertiser,* without any special interest, to glance at the news, both local and general. He could hardly believe his eyes. It contained a report of the meeting of the Medical Society, of Jackson's discovery, of its endorsement by President Everett and Professor Warren and other leading members of the Academy of Arts and Science. A report of the meeting? But the meeting was for tomorrow—or had he been asleep for a couple of days? No, there was the date on the newspaper, March 1st. What the devil was the meaning of this? Had the meeting taken place earlier than announced?

He hurried across to see Dr. Gould.

"Oh, no," said Gould, in reply to Morton's bewildered inquiry. "The meeting is for tomorrow."

"But what is the meaning of this report, then?" Morton handed the newspaper to his friend.

"I suppose Jackson sent an advance copy of his lecture to the editor."

"But the report describes the meeting as having taken place, mentions the names of those present, records the way in which they applauded Jackson as the discoverer."

Gould looked more closely at the newspaper. "Yes, my friend, Jackson is no ordinary foe, as I think you ought to have discovered already."

"No ordinary foe? I should think not!" exclaimed Morton. "No one but the devil himself could have conceived such a scheme."

But the mail boat had already departed. Jackson had taken his measures carefully, drafting his "report" to give the impression that all the auditors approved his claim. The steamer also had on board Morton's letters to Fisher and Warren, but what weight would they have against Jackson's adroit lies, published as matters of fact by a leading Boston journal?

Morton hurried off to call on Professor Warren, whom he found greatly enraged by Jackson's artifice. So was President Everett. So were all the members of the staff of the Massachusetts General Hospital, who knew that Morton, and Morton alone, had been the man with courage enough to administer ether to a patient who had to undergo an operation. Some of them advised him to collect documentary evidence in support of his own claim, and to send this to the Academy of the Sciences in Paris, accompanied by an energetic protest against Jackson's misstatement. But others, and especially Dr. Gould, disapproved of this notion.

Gould told him plainly that, since he was quite unknown in Europe, his word would not be believed against Jackson, a man with a European reputation, with powerful friends in every scientific corporation. In the Paris Academy of the Sciences Beaumont would support Jackson, and in Prussia the famous Alexander von Humboldt would take the same line. Morton could make no headway against so powerful an enemy by protests or invectives in Europe. The wiser course would be to come to terms somehow with Dr. Jackson here on the spot.

After all, in Boston the truth was known, and Jackson would not be able to get away so easily with a false story. If he continued to claim priority, there were plenty of persons to give him the lie, especially the staff of the General Hospital, who were familiar with the facts. Jackson, in earlier stages of the affair, had talked freely to all and sundry about the origin of the discovery, and could not possibly repudiate his former utterances.

"It seems to me," concluded Dr. Gould, "that by getting to work here in Boston you have the best chance of establishing your own claim to priority, and compelling Jackson to speak the truth. If you succeed here, you will produce far more effect in Paris than you could produce there by a campaign against Jackson."

At first Morton found it difficult to accept the idea of coming to terms. He was so furious with Jackson that the notion of a friendly understanding seemed out of the question. But in the end Dr. Gould's eloquence convinced him of the hopelessness of his own scheme. Compromise with the enemy was the only possible way of establishing his rights.

Gould promised to mediate, and went to call on Jackson, who showed himself perfectly willing to make terms.

Jackson said: "I have always hoped for an understanding between myself and Morton, and I have not the smallest intention of disputing Morton's claim. There is nothing I should like better than an unbiased judgment between us, a fair decision concerning our respective shares in this discovery." This plan for negotiation would keep Morton from immediate protest in Europe. He would gain time. He therefore said: "Please tell Mr. Morton that I should like a friendly understanding."

Morton had sent Elizabeth and the children to West Needham. It would be better to save his wife from the anxieties necessarily attendant on negotiations which could not fail to be acrimonious. She would pour fuel upon the flames, for she could not be expected to understand the need for compromise with this man who had important ties across the Atlantic, was on friendly terms with Elie de Beaumont, Alexander von Humboldt, and other notables.

Dr. Gould thought it expedient for Morton to write to Jackson, giving his own version of the affair. Jackson replied. The correspondence dragged on, in a friendly spirit, and it seemed as if reconciliation might be possible.

By the end of March, matters had gone so far that the adversaries began to discuss the appointment of an arbitrator. Jackson mentioned the name of a distinguished professor. Morton agreed to the nomination, but then Jackson raised objections, saying he had subsequently learned that this gentleman was on friendly terms with Morton, and could not be relied upon to be impartial. This was on March 29th. Having summoned Dr. Gould, Jackson said: "Please let Mr. Morton know that I will agree to accept the decision of any arbitrator whose impartiality will be indisputable." He knew that the next steamship would sail for Europe in three days, and presumably hoped to postpone having the matter laid before an arbitrator until after that.

Morton mentioned the name of a mutual acquaintance. Jackson said he would like a day or two to reflect. While he was "reflecting," the April steamer departed.

From day to day, thereafter, Jackson raised minor technical objections, and in this way negotiations dragged on into May.

"Still, I do not regret having followed your advice," said Morton to Dr. Gould.

Meanwhile he had received letters from Edward Warren. This gentleman had visited London, Berlin and Vienna, and his reports were most discouraging:

"All over Europe, wherever I have been, this paper [the *Daily Advertiser* of March 1st] has circulated, or its effects are felt, leading men of letters to infer that Dr. Jackson is the real and sole discoverer, because he has the sanction of the names of Warren, of Professor Everett, and of the 'American Academy.' If the Academy take no means, at an early day, to set this matter right before the world, they will be, as they have been, as directly concerned in propagating Dr. J's psuedo-claims as if they had allowed him to make that publication ex cathedra. This is a matter of the greatest moment, and should be set right at once if they desire to see justice prevail, or to give all an equal, or even a fair chance. . . . Since the report of the meeting of the Massachusetts Medical Society came to hand, Humboldt and the Vienna Medical Society are firmly convinced that Jackson was the discoverer. In Vienna people are already speaking of the administration of ether for anaesthetic purposes as 'jacksonising.'"

Matters had gone so far, then, that the method had been christened by his enemy's name! Somehow or other, it was essential to come to terms with Jackson, to make Jackson admit the truth, for otherwise the false statement would never be discredited in foreign lands.

Still the negotiations dragged on, Jackson raising point after point which concerned unessential trifles and assuredly could be swept out of the way. Meanwhile, however, May had arrived, and the Parisians continued to believe that Jackson was the discoverer of anesthesia. Morton grew uneasy. Day after day Jackson professed his eagerness for a friendly settlement. But why did he continually postpone settlement? Was it possible that his only end was to gain time while one mail steamer after another departed for Europe without any contradiction, so that in Europe Jackson's claim was more and more held to be justified?

Just before the May steamboat sailed, Jackson became so conciliatory that Morton could not make up his mind to break off negotiations when they had reached so advanced a stage. Hardly had the May steamer departed, when Jackson himself took that step. In doing so, he managed to save his face. Edward Warren had published a pamphlet proclaiming Morton as the discoverer of anesthesia. He, Jackson, had only just learned of this, and accused Morton of having instigated the pamphlet. "Morton," he exclaimed, in real or feigned indignation, "is a crafty rogue who has taken advantage of my willingness to treat with him. Well, now he shall find out that I am not to be humbugged. Europe will know whom to believe: me, Dr. Jackson, a leading man of science; or this pettifogging dentist."

"He has deliberately been protracting a decision for months. He is an intriguer, a cheat who wears the mask of a scientist," exclaimed Morton in a fury.

Thus, betwixt night and morning, the negotiators became open enemies, and were to remain enemies for life.

Jackson had a considerable reputation in Europe, was personally known, had intimates and supporters; but Morton had proofs. Would Europe allow herself to be blinded? Would personal ties triumph over truth?

Jackson was spoiling for a fight, was he? Well, he should have one. Morton believed in the power of truth, and would show Jackson that truth would prevail.

Without wasting a moment longer, by the June steamer he sent a provisional report to the Paris Academy of the Sciences, promising that detailed proofs would be despatched a month later.

Throughout June, he busily interviewed all those in Boston who had had anything to do with the discovery and its application. Many of them were reluctant to come into the open, for they did not wish to break with Jackson. But Morton, as already said, was a sticker. He overcame obstacles, drummed up his witnesses, and would leave no one alone until he had extracted written confirmation.

Laboriously he got his materials together. His desk was piled with declarations, reports of eyewitnesses, and other documents. Night after night he sifted and tested this material, determined that there should be no gaps, that doubt should be forever allayed.

When all was ready, the documents for the French Academy of the Sciences filled a dozen chests. Materials hardly less voluminous were sent to Humboldt in Prussia. With such a mass of evidence, he would surely be able to counteract Jackson's lies, and win over Europe to his side.

But life is a tricksy jade who often prefers falsehood and confusion to truth and clarity, and lends a helping hand to the liar. Life often disinherits the first-born as she allowed Esau to be tricked out of his birthright.

Morton awaited news from Paris, waited to learn of the acceptance of his claim. Many ships came and went, but the news tarried. Edward Warren was no longer in Paris, and Willis Fisher had removed to London. Morton knew of no one else in Paris whom he could ask for help. He wrote direct to the Academy of the Sciences, but received no answer. Ship after ship bore his anxious missives, but ship after ship returned bringing no reply. He began to despair. What was the meaning of it all? Was it possible that the proofs he had sent did not arouse conviction? Was there anything more to be done?

After eight months' fruitless waiting, he received a letter from Harnden, the carrier. Advice had just been received to the effect that his boxes had been held up for the last seven months by the French customs. At length an agent had been found to get them through this obstacle and receive them on deposit. The correspondent would be glad to have further instructions.

Morton had never expected such a blow as this. What a sorry trick fate had played him! He wanted to use his discovery for the advantage of mankind, to relieve pain. What did life want? All the proofs he had got together with so much diligence, and which ought long since to have secured him his rightful position as discoverer, had been lying for seven months in an out-of-the-way warehouse. Meanwhile Jackson had been free to write again and again, by every mail, and push his preposterous claims.

Well, it meant that the agent who had paid the dues and taken the cases on deposit would need to have his expenses refunded, in addition to a round sum for his trouble, before he would hand over the goods. Things were not going very well with Morton. It would take him a little while to raise the money, and a further time to get in touch with Paris and give the necessary instructions. But there were additional difficulties. Who in Paris would take charge of them for him, and make sure of their reaching their destination? Who could look after his interests so far away, when his friends had left long ago and he did not know another soul in Paris?

"I can tell you of someone over there who will help you out of this hole," said an acquaintance to whom he recounted his troubles. "A young American dentist named Brewster, who has been in Paris for a long time, and knows everybody. Write to him. Here is the address."

Morton wrote forthwith to Brewster, sending a remittance to cover expenses, and requesting his colleague to have the cases delivered as soon as possible to the Academy of the Sciences. Speed was of the utmost importance.

Surely he would have an answer before long, would hear that everything was in good order, that his instructions had been carried out. Then the Academy would soon come to a just decision.

Morton waited eagerly, expecting news from Brewster by every mail. Nothing came. He wrote again, and yet again. Losing patience, he began to reproach Brewster, asking what on earth had become of his money and his boxes. At length his tone became menacing. If he did not hear, he would take legal proceedings. Still no answer. Letters and threats passed unheeded. This went on for two years. Then, at length, came word from Brewster; but the long-expected news was even worse than the previous silence had been.

"I sent your order expecting to receive a package, but in its place comes five huge boxes. I have not opened them; the day has gone past to circulate these pamphlets. I have no

room in my house for them. I have no time to distribute
them, and if I did they would not profit anything, the cost of
storage will be heavy and useless, therefore, what shall I do
with them? Tell me by return steamer. My advice would
be to sell them as old paper."

Sell the lot as waste paper? His evidence, the proof that he
was the discoverer, not Jackson? Brewster had done nothing for
two years, had scandalously neglected to forward his proofs.

Who the devil was this Brewster? Morton knew nothing
about the man, but felt sure he must be a bad lot. Unfortunately
the acquaintance who had given him Brewster's name and address
was dead. It had been a most disastrous recommendation, but
there was nothing to be done about it now. Morton made numerous inquiries, and at length was put on the right track by a lawyer
from Hartford who was on a visit to Boston. "Brewster?" said he.
"Oh, yes, I know Brewster well enough. So they put you in touch
with him, did they? I am sorry for that. Brewster was Wells's
agent in Paris. He is still in touch with Wells's widow, and is
trying to get Wells's claim recognized."

Why had his dead acquaintance recommended Brewster to
him? What sorry tricks life was playing Morton!

Nor had any answer come from Prussia. What had happened? Had the letter to Humboldt gone astray? Morton applied to the Foreign Office in Washington, asking that inquiries
should be made, and that, through diplomatic channels, a fresh
statement of his claims should be forwarded to Humboldt. After
a little while he received an official answer. Humboldt had been
much occupied upon the affairs of his royal master. Morton's
original application had, unfortunately, been pigeonholed and had
never reached the famous scientist. Now, however, it had been
disinterred, and forwarded to Humboldt accompanied by Morton's
new letter. Humboldt had promised the American chargé d'af-
faires in Berlin to look into the matter carefully, and report on
the result to his Majesty the King of Prussia and to the Prussian
Academy in Berlin.

Well, it was good to know that Alexander von Humboldt had

at length been stirred into activity; but Morton by now felt pretty sure that life preferred confusion to truth, and promoted the destruction of those who fought on behalf of truth.

Still, being no quitter, Morton did not lay down his arms, even though the obscure will of life itself was his adversary. He would go on fighting against injustice. Against falsehood, against his powerful rival, against the slow-moving Prussian official machinery, against the spookish mishap which had kept his boxes for seven months in the Paris octroi and then handed them over to an enemy. He would go on fighting the Beaumonts and the Brewsters and their kind, whether in Paris or elsewhere; would not even shrink from struggling against the waste of irrecoverable time.

He who believes himself right must go on fighting against destiny. He will fight with the energy of a man possessed. Perhaps in the end he may win through to victory.

CHAPTER THIRTEEN

"Benefactor of Mankind"

WARREN, BIGELOW, Liston, Jobert, the great physicians and surgeons before whose eyes and under whose hands the miracle of painless operation had first been worked, were quick to recognize the value of the new method and wholeheartedly to adopt it.

Hospital authorities in general, as operation after operation was successfully performed under anesthesia, joined in the chorus of approval.

The scientific societies were less easy to convert. In their exalted environment, facts, even facts of daily occurrence, can be recognized as true only when hundreds of committees and subcommittees have sat upon them, when the resistance of misoneists has been broken, when ample inquiries have been made, when the facts have been denied and reasserted, discussed again and again at meetings, put to the vote during sittings frequently postponed. Then only, at long last, after months or years, will anything so novel as anesthesia be passed to the credit account.

When Elie de Beaumont, having opened Jackson's sealed letter, read the contents to the Academy of the Sciences at the meeting of January 18, 1847, and the distinguished Academy was first made acquainted with the new discovery, many months had still to pass in this temple of the sciences on the bank of the Seine before anesthesia could be sure of official recognition. In the interim, countless reports of successful operations under anesthesia had come to hand; doctors and patients joined in extolling the discovery; anesthesia had a "good press" and the public at large "recognized" it speedily enough. Even more remarkable things happened. Some of the most skeptical among the luminaries of science, such as Velpeau and Roux, had gone over to the side of the new method, and at several of the Monday sessions had splintered a lance on behalf of anesthesia. But among the foes of the innovation was a colossus, François Magendie, the famous physiologist. The old-time resistance of science to means for the relief of pain found expression in his words of ardent opposition to this "accursed novelty."

At this particular sitting there was rife all the ignorance, all the reactionary prejudice, all the suspicion and arrogance and scorn which, half a century before, had embittered Davy, had later driven Sertürner insane, and less than two decades ago had baffled Hickman and filled the last months of his life with gloom. The storm broke once more on the bank of the Seine, violent as ever in its pitiless stupidity, to arrest human progress, to crush human sympathy, to take a strange delight in the glorification of pain.

Magendie would not yield before "accomplished fact." Once again he railed against anesthesia, in defiance of the evidence adduced by his colleagues.

"I do not draw the moral which has been drawn by you gentlemen," he scornfully exclaimed. "I quite understand your position. You shrink from inflicting the pain essential to an operation. But pain is a natural necessity. It seems to me immoral, this desire of yours to have your patients stupefied with ether before you operate. Has anyone ever heard of making people dead drunk before operating? What is this insensibility of which you speak? It means that you reduce the patient to the condition of a corpse. You want to cut as you would cut a corpse. Is not this idea opposed to the most elementary laws of morals? I consider that the new method conflicts both with sound reason and with moral sensibility. Behind the whole matter lies this, that certain European doctors have been led astray by an American advertiser, and are now trying to enlist the Academy of the Sciences in the puffery."

But when thousands of patients had enjoyed the advantages

of anesthesia and when thousands of doctors had seen the wonders of painless cutting operations, even the most stubborn prejudices bowed before the might of fact. After the new invention had been discussed at countless Monday sittings in the Institute of France, after it had stood the test of examination and re-examination, and at length a motion for its approval had been passed, even Magendie voted for the appointment of the Ether Commission. This was to study the question as to who was really entitled to be regarded as the discoverer of anesthesia, "the most wonderful event of our age."

A distinguished French philanthropist, Baron Antoine Jean Baptiste Robert Auget de Montyon (1733–1820), three-quarters of a century before Nobel, had left in trust to the Academy of the Sciences a sum of money intended for those whom the Academy should consider justified to receive the title of "Benefactor of Mankind." Who could be better fitted to receive the Montyon prize and this exalted title than one whose discovery had done so much to relieve the sufferings of humanity by the discovery of anesthesia which would for all time save men from the agonies hitherto attendant on surgical operations? There could be no doubt that the Montyon prize for the year 1847–1848 ought to be allotted to the discoverer of anesthesia. But who was that discoverer?

"The chemist Jackson of Boston, undoubtedly," said Elie de Beaumont.

"The dentist Morton, undoubtedly," retorted another member. "He made the apparatus with which we surgeons administer ether to produce anesthesia. He gave us instructions how to use the method. The reports from Boston, the announcements of Dr. Bott in London and Dr. Simpson in Edinburgh, all speak of him as the discoverer. Surely that should suffice?"

Beaumont, who at these meetings had often noted how an apt epigram or a pithy witticism could sway his colleagues, now intervened with one in Jackson's behalf.

"Let me describe Jackson's and Morton's respective shares in the discovery. Jackson is its Columbus, and Morton the lookout man who called 'Land ho!' "

The audience laughed at the joke. But the discoverer, whichever of the two it was, had performed such great services for mankind that the Academy must not make any mistake in its award. That was why a Commission was appointed to study the question exhaustively, and to decide whether the prize should go to Jackson or to Morton. The Commission would consist of Duperrey as president, Velpeau, Rayer, Serres, Magendie, Duméril, Beaumont, Andral, Flourens, Lallemand and Roux to draft the report.

When the terms of reference to this Commission were being discussed, one of the members of the Academy pointed out that there was another name to be considered besides those of Jackson and Morton, namely that of the Hartford dentist Horace Wells. "I have in my hand a letter dated March 8, 1847, in which Wells claims priority."

The Commission was in a great difficulty. There were three claimants to the title of being the "Benefactor of Mankind" who had made one of the most important discoveries ever known.

Elie de Beaumont found it easy enough to dispose of Wells's claim. Wells had used laughing gas in his experiments, and his demonstration in Boston had been a fiasco. Besides, the substance now being extensively used during painless operations was not laughing gas but ether.

The Commission, therefore, had to decide between Morton and Jackson. This was not an easy matter. By every mail Jackson sent fresh proofs to Beaumont. Morton's witnesses were dumb ones, the numerous apparatus he had sent to Europe. Dumb though they were, they spoke eloquently enough.

Three years elapsed after the appointment of the Ether Commission; three years of laborious investigation, and eager dispute as to who was the "Benefactor of Mankind" entitled to receive the Montyon prize.

The year 1850 had begun. Surely it was time to allot the Montyon prize for the year 1848–1849? But it proved impossible to make a unanimous award either to one or to the other of the rival claimants. Determined to be impartial, therefore, the Montyon Commission, on February 25, 1850, passed the following resolution:

"Mr. Jackson and Mr. Morton were both indispensable. Had it not been for the persistency, the far-reaching vision, the courage, nay the audacity of Mr. Morton, Mr. Jackson's observations would probably have passed unnoticed and unapplied; but for the observations of Mr. Jackson, on the other hand, it is likely that Mr. Morton's ideas would never have been crowned with success. The Commission therefore recommends that the Montyon prize of 5000 francs shall be divided, 2500 francs being allotted to Mr. Jackson for his observations and experiments regarding the anesthetic effects of the inhalation of ether, and 2500 francs to Mr. Morton for the application of the method to practical surgery."

There could be no doubt that the members of the Commission had worked very hard to pronounce a just verdict. The Commission could report, the main body of the Academy of the Sciences could act accordingly, and then, it was to be hoped, resume its other labors undisturbed.

But the enmity between Morton and Jackson had by now exceeded all bounds. Neither of them was prepared to accept the award as a signal honor. Each of them could only see the devastating fact that the Montyon prize had been allotted to his rival. Jackson, who did not wish to embroil himself with the Academy, accepted the money with a crestfallen mien. But Morton's gorge rose; he protested against the decision, and scornfully rejected the 2500 francs.

For months the sum awarded to Morton lay unheeded in the cashbox of the Institute of France. Then the secretary wrote to Morton saying that his right to receive it would lapse if he did not claim the prize money. Morton replied that he did not care two hoots—or words to that effect. A prize which he, the true discoverer, was asked to share with Jackson, the unrightful claimant, was an insult.

The year 1850 drew to a close. The annual report of the Institute of France, of which the Academy of the Sciences is one of the five sections, was being drafted. "The 2500 francs for Mr. Morton is still in the treasury," reported the treasurer. The members of the Montyon Commission were summoned, and asked to find a way out, for it was impossible to describe the Montyon prize, or half of it, in the Institute's books as "rejected."

Something more than the pride and the prestige of the Institute of France was at stake. It would have been contrary to the spirit of the Montyon foundation if Morton, described as one of the "Benefactors of Mankind," were to be allowed to go unrewarded. Since the previous decision to divide the 5000 francs between Jackson and Morton, the Academy of the Sciences had received a great deal more evidence which spoke convincingly in favor of Morton's claim to be the "only genuine discoverer." The fact had made many of the members of the Commission uneasy.

"Something must be done with Morton's share. The Institute of France must discover a way of showing its appreciation of this man." After lengthy deliberations, the Commission decided that the rejected 2500 francs should be used for making a gold medal to be given to Morton.

The medal was cast. On one side it bore the head of Minerva, surrounded by the words "National Institute of France." On the other side was the inscription: "Academy of the Sciences—Montyon Prize for Medicine and Surgery—year 1847-1848.—William T. G. Morton, 1850."

All seemed now in order, but when the bill for the medal was presented, a fresh difficulty arose. The cost was a trifle less than 2000 francs. What was to be done with the surplus? The award to Morton must not cost less than the award to Jackson. The Institute could not be stingy, and make a profit at Morton's expense.

However, a way out of the difficulty was found. The goldsmith was commissioned to enrich the metal with a laurel garland in relief, using enough gold to bring up the cost to 2500 francs.

Justice had been done by the Academy of the Sciences. Not so, however, in Dr. Jackson's eyes. This afterthought of the Montyon Committee made him rabid. What had he received? A sum of 2500 francs, and he had spent a lot more than that in his attempts to annihilate Morton. What was his balance of gain?

A document, a scrap of paper, which bore Morton's name as well as his own. But Morton had a gold medal, on which stood a name surrounded by a laurel crown—and the name was not Jackson.

The thought was intolerable. Jackson could not, would not, believe that such an injustice had been committed, so he decided that the whole story of the medal had been invented by Morton. Whenever anyone spoke to him about Morton's medal, he smiled significantly, and said: "Surely you are not one of the dupes of that boaster?"

He went on to explain that Monsieur Jules Marcou, geologist to the French Government, had written him a holograph letter declaring that the Academy of the Sciences had no stamping-mill with which a medal could be made.

"No, no," Jackson went on, "Morton had the medal made on his own account by a Paris goldsmith. Yes, I know the name of the goldsmith. If the Academy of the Sciences had transformed the prize awarded to Morton for his hodman's work on my behalf, he would have a document from the Academy confirming the truth of the story. What's that you say? He has a document of the kind? You've seen it yourself? A forgery, my friend. There can be no mistake about that. Morton is a man who would stick at nothing. No, no, France knows who was the true discoverer and to whom rewards of merit are due. The French government has given me its highest distinction, the Cross of the Legion of Honor."

"The Cross of the Legion of Honor!" exclaimed Morton when he was told of this. "Don't you know that the French authorities make them by the bucketful and hand them out to the first comer? It is so trivial a 'distinction' that the best people in France won't accept it."

While the "Benefactors of Mankind" were quarreling in this unseemly way about the value of their respective decorations, London no less than Paris was discovering that it is sometimes difficult to decide who is genuinely deserving of reward. The miracle of painless surgery had aroused universal enthusiasm, and there was a widespread wish to show appropriate recognition.

Every learned society in Europe, every potentate, every medical corporation, seemed animated with the desire to shower honors and pecuniary rewards upon the discoverer of anesthesia.

Then the sources of this zeal were choked, the fervor of the congratulatory orators was damped, by the news that the identity of the discoverer was a debatable point.

Enthusiasm was robbed of spontaneity, the tones of adulation grew confused, when it seemed impossible to decide which of the rival claimants was to be praised and rewarded.

In London, where the first painless operation in Europe took place, delight over the discovery of anesthesia was so intense that a special committee was formed, and within a few days £10,000 was collected. The money was to be given to Morton. But at this juncture Jackson's agents insisted that he was the proper recipient, and the dispute between representatives of the rival claimants became so furious that the committee returned donations to the givers, and then dissolved.

The potentates who wished to thank and reward the discoverer on behalf of their subjects found the matter less difficult, being sovereigns, and responsible to no one but themselves. They merely followed the lead of their various advisers. From the Bosphorus, from Sardinia, from Prussia and from France, where Jackson's friends had influence at court, the rulers sent him orders of distinction. But from Russia and Sweden, where the courtiers espoused Morton's claim, Morton was granted orders of merit.

There were a great many sovereign states in Europe, each with its own independent ruler, and just as these differed upon numerous other questions, so did they differ as to who had been the true discoverer of anesthesia. Jackson was acclaimed on one side of the Alps, and Morton on the other; Jackson on the Bosphorus and Morton beside the Neva. All these distinctions, like the Montyon Medal and the Cross of the Legion of Honor—the Vasa Order, the Vladimir Cross, the Red Eagle, the Turkish Crescent—became fresh weapons in the hands of the infuriated adversaries.

Thus at Boston, within the bounds of the same city, were two men who could not fail to meet each other from time to time in

the streets and squares, one of them a professor and the other a
dentist, who had in former days been teacher and pupil and close
friends; they had worked together, lived in the same house, and
eaten their meals peacefully side by side. But now, because one
had given some good advice and the other had carried it into effect,
and because a great success had been secured, friendship had become enmity, esteem and well-wishing had degenerated into hatred.
The advice and the deed both proved to be sources of hatred. This
hatred grew from day to day, grew beyond the limits of the town
of Boston, even as the success spread far and wide. As success
spread, so did hatred spread across seas and continents, spread all
over Europe. The dispute between advice and deed aroused dis-
sension in the Paris Academy of the Sciences, in the London citizens' committee and in all the courts of the Old World.

The United States of America, which at first had been no
more than the smithy in which arms were being forged to compete
for the honors of the Academy of the Sciences and the European
courts, was soon to become a main seat of the ether war.

To effect the conquest of Europe, letters had to be sent, reports
to be made, proofs and counter-proofs to be fortified. Claim stood
against adverse claim, argument against opposing argument. But
in America were the claimants, man against man.

Jackson, who, with the aid of the mail boats, had been able
from Boston to spin a web entangling the learned societies and
courts of Europe, proved the doughtier champion in hand-to-hand
warfare as well. Anything was grist to his mill. At every corner
he set a snare for Morton, in every street he threw a stick between
his enemy's legs. Never would he allow his rival to escape his
claws. He recognized clearly that different tactics must be used
in Boston from those which were expedient in the struggle for
the honors of the Old World. In Boston he would get the better
of the adversary by undermining Morton's moral standing, and
try to cut Morton's financial resources. Then, when he had been
successful in these matters, he would be able to push his own
claims without fear.

Everything seemed to favor this campaign of annihilation.

Morton's original experiments had interfered with the dentist's practice. Then he had spent a great deal of time improving the inhaler. Finally Morton, who had made one of the greatest discoveries of all time, came to think he would demean himself by spending day after day upon extractions and crown, bridge and bar dental work.

The natural result was that the neglected practice greatly declined, and his income fell off. Still, he did not think this would matter, for the patent would keep him well provided with funds. On November 12, 1846, he received this document from Mr. Buchanan, Secretary of State. It was numbered 4848. Now he could begin to sell licenses for the use of his inhaler. Morton hoped that this would be sufficiently lucrative, and that he would thenceforward be able to devote himself exclusively to pushing his discovery. Although, on Bigelow's recommendation, he had made the composition of his remedy freely known to the world of science, the doctors had not taken undue advantage of this, and were willing to respect his rights as patentee.

Morton had carefully drafted a plan for the use of licenses. In a town having a population of more than 150,000 a doctor could get a seven years' license and the necessary instructions for the use of the apparatus at a fee of $200; in towns with a population of 5000 to 150,000, for $150; and in towns with a population of less than 5000, for $37. Although he magnanimously granted free licenses to hospitals, benevolent institutions, and doctors who could not pay the before-mentioned fees, he expected that the sale of licenses during the fourteen years for which the patent was valid would bring him in about $365,000.

But these careful calculations of profit were to be invalidated by the government which had granted him the patent.

Since May, 1846, the war with Mexico had been raging. The blessings of anesthesia must certainly be extended to these patriotic campaigners.

Immediately after the first successful operation under anesthesia, Morton offered to supply the inhalers to Army authorities at wholesale prices and gratuitously to instruct Army surgeons in their use. This would be the first war in history during which painless surgery was a possibility. The United States obviously could not afford to renounce this glorious priority and leave its wounded soldiers without the benefit of anesthesia. The Army command therefore enthusiastically accepted Morton's proposals, ordering that ether narcosis should be used as far as possible both in the Army and in the Navy. But when Morton asked that fees should be paid to him for the requisite licenses, the government refused.

The New York *Herald* published a report containing the decision of the military authorities. While Morton tried to console himself with the patriotic thought that those who were fighting on behalf of the Stars and Stripes would at any rate profit by his discovery, Jackson was quick to grasp the full significance of the decision.

If the government was going to use the inhalers without compensating the inventor, then anyone could do so. For practical purposes (though not as yet formally), this meant that the patent had been annulled: Jackson hurried off to Eddy's office to ask whether he was right in this supposition.

"Look here, Eddy, do you think that I shall ever get any money out of my share in the patent?" He thrust the newspaper under Eddy's nose. Eddy read, hesitated, read once more, then shook his head, saying "No." "In that case," said Jackson, "please have my name erased from the patent. I shall have nothing more to do with the affair." As he left, he called over his shoulder: "Don't forget to notify Morton of my decision this very day."

Jackson had instantly grasped that what for Morton would involve a financial collapse, might be skillfully turned to his own profit. Chance, which is always ready to aid the cunning, also gave much help to Jackson.

That evening the Massachusetts Medical Society was giving a banquet to the medical profession. Jackson asked the organizers to let him be one of the after-dinner speakers, for he had an important announcement to make.

When his time came, Jackson rose and delivered the following oration:

"Honoured colleagues, as the discoverer of ether anesthesia, I wish to make a disclosure of fundamental importance. By dishonest machinations I was induced to append my name to an application for a patent whose real purpose was concealed from me. I was told that my signature was needed to protect my claim as originator of the discovery; but I was not told that the unethical purpose of the patent was to make profit out of the sufferings of mankind. As soon as I gathered this, I need hardly tell you that I promptly had my name removed from the document. Today I take this opportunity of formally and publicly bestowing upon my fellows the free enjoyment of painless operations. The happiness of my fellow creatures and the proud consciousness that pain has forever been banned are the only rewards I ask. A gift to the medical faculty of Boston, to the doctors throughout America and to the whole world is the most valued fruit of my discovery. From the very start, that discovery has had, so far as I am concerned, no connection with any attempt to speculate upon the sufferings of man after the shameless manner of a certain dentist of this town."

During Jackson's speech, many of those present must have thought about the article in the New York *Herald*, must have wondered why Dr. Jackson had not earlier renounced his patent rights and why he chose to do so at this moment when the action of the Army authorities had made the patent practically valueless. What about this claim to be the exclusive discoverer? Was Jackson really the discoverer? Was that which he was so magnanimously bestowing on the world his property?

Still, few could resist the effect upon which the speaker had shrewdly calculated, the effect of these high-sounding words, whatever motives might be hidden behind them. The fact was that, while the state's action had lessened the value of the patent, Jackson's renunciation had destroyed its effect altogether. The utilization of ether was now free to all, and no one need bother to get a license before giving his operative patients ether to inhale. The doctors present, therefore, freed from any scruples they might have had, loudly applauded the orator.

One of those present, however, Louis Agassiz, the zo-ologist, much dreaded for the sharpness of his tongue, could not refrain from a thrust at Jackson. "You'll excuse my asking, my dear colleague, but if Dr. Morton had killed the first patient to whom he administered ether by inhalation, would you, who are now so generously renouncing profit from the discovery, also, in that case, have accepted your share of the blame?"

Still, this little thrust was soon forgotten. Jackson's "generosity" had enlisted the sympathy of the doctors in a way which helped him and did Morton a great deal of harm. For, while his seeming generosity made him the hero of the hour, he had in effect stigmatized his rival as an avaricious rascal.

Over and above this attack on Morton's moral character, Jackson was well able to use the collapse of the value of the patent in another way which would hurt Morton. His venom made him grasp at any and every means of injuring his adversary.

"What are you going to do now with your license?" Jackson asked a speculator who had acquired all the rights of using the apparatus in another state in the Union, hoping to make money in this way.

"What do you mean, Dr. Jackson?" asked the other.

"What I mean is this, that the thing for which you have paid in hard cash can really be used by everyone gratuitously."

"Do you mean to say that Mr. Morton has cheated me?"

"Well, it seems to me that what you have paid for is no longer a privilege worth a snap of the fingers. But who could have foreseen this?"

Enough said. The speculator, in a fury, rushed off to Morton and said: "You've cheated me. If you don't return my money instantly, I shall prosecute."

Various doctors and agents thronged the door of Morton's house in Tremont Street, breathing out threatenings and slaughter. All Boston talked of the matter, and one day a number of those who considered themselves aggrieved came in a body to Morton, demanding their money back. Morton had some savings, but they all went in satisfying these claims. More still was needed, so he had to borrow; when no more loans could be raised, there were still unsatisfied licensees ready to prosecute.

Yes, all Boston was talking of it. At this juncture, Jackson called upon the instrument-maker, and dropped a malicious word. "I say, my dear fellow, I'm afraid that you'll come off badly." He waved a hand at a vast number of inhalers lying on one of the counters. "Now there has been all this trouble about the licenses, no agent and no doctor will want to buy any of those. What are you going to do with them?"

The manufacturer boiled over with wrath. He had been granted a monopoly of production, and had been assured by Morton that a lot of money was to be made out of these inhalers, provided he could get plenty of them ready to meet an enormous demand. Now there were no orders, for everyone could make his own inhaler. There they lay, worthless lumber. They would all have to be scrapped.

The instrument-maker became an inexorable creditor. If any of the others were inclined to show Morton a little indulgence, he spurred them on to push their claims.

Morton could borrow no more, and there were still plenty of unsatisfied claimants. When one withdrew, another took his place. There were the agents who had traveled to different states, and there were agents who had gone to Europe. The tidings that the patent was valueless, and that the manufacturer of inhalers had sustained grievous losses, spread far and wide. Morton was unceasingly harassed with prosecutions. His life became one of unending vexation.

Behind all this, Jackson had his part to play, stirring up the discontented. Morton, at his wits' end for money, harassed day and night, could not be a dangerous rival. Jackson was well-to-do and carefree. These advantages gave him an almost invincible superiority.

Overwhelmed by his financial difficulties, Morton had had to resume dental practice. But here, likewise, the collapse of the patent had impaired his chances, for now any and every dentist could undertake painless extraction. Still, Morton had a considerable reputation as a dentist, and before the discovery had had a steadily increasing practice. He had every hope, therefore, that he would be able to work his way up again and free himself from his anxieties.

But Jackson, inveterate in his enmity, was determined to put a spoke in Morton's wheel. He managed to discover who had made the largest advances to Morton, and must have adroitly instilled the notion that Morton was about to go bankrupt. To this man and to other creditors, Jackson whispered: "You will understand that I am talking in confidence, but I think you had better make sure of your money as soon as you can."

Within half an hour after having these doubts instilled, the principal creditor turned up at Morton's office, and would not leave until Morton had given him a bill of sale upon dental instruments and library.

Jackson, inspired by hatred, was able, by these evil whispers, to induce yet other creditors to dun Morton for the prompt repayment of their loans.

Morton went on working in his office, using the instruments which were no longer his own, being in pawn to the principal creditor, while in the anteroom sat a "man in possession" representing all the creditors, and impounding the fees as they were paid.

This was a sordid and painful time, which would last until he could escape from the claws of these creditors, and have enough funds at his disposal for the perfecting of his discovery. He had a hundred new ideas of how to improve the process of anesthesia, to make the administration of ether still more dependable. Then he would show Jackson! If he only had a little free time to collect his proofs! But under present auspices he had to spend the whole working day extracting or filling teeth, while the fees which he earned went to his creditors except for a pittance reserved for his own subsistence and that of his family. Still, his day would dawn. He was sure of that, and never lost faith.

One Saturday evening, when Morton was going home weary and harassed, a messenger accosted him and, without a word, handed him a letter and vanished. Morton opened the missive, and read the following lines:

"Dear Sir,

"I have at this moment learned most singularly of a deep-laid plot to ruin your practice, and to drive you from the State. Were it not that it embraces steps intended to annoy and disturb not only yourself, but your innocent wife and children, and that, through your humane discovery you have saved my life, I should not feel justified in committing this breach of confidence which I do in making this statement. I can at present do no more than counsel you to guard the impulses of your fiery nature, and trust to Providence that all will end as well as I sincerely believe it will.

"One whom you have forgotten, but
who will never cease to remember you."

Morton was puzzled as to the meaning of this mysterious epistle. However, next Monday morning he went to his office as usual. On the stairs he met one of his lady patients, who seemed frantic with excitement.

"How could you do such a thing to me?" she asked. "How could you behave so basely to me? I simply can't understand it."

Morton tried to appease her, and asked what she accused him of.

"This is too much," she exclaimed. "Now you pretend you don't know what you have done to me." She turned on her heel and departed.

In front of the door of the waiting room was another patient who had an early appointment. Morton was a few minutes late, and made his apologies.

"Never mind about that," answered the patient roughly. "I have no further use for your services, and only came today to tell you what I think of you. You're a rascal. I wish you good morning."

Morton trembled with wrath and anxiety. What on earth had happened?

He found the waiting room packed with patients. The instant he appeared, they all began to speak at once.

"I implore you not to behave so ruthlessly. How can you think of bringing an old man like me into court?"

"Why should you treat a respectable family in such a way? It would be a disgrace I could never forget."

Reproaches, supplications, invectives, and threats—all in one breath.

There was such a hubbub that Morton found it hard to make himself heard.

"Please tell me what you are talking about. I don't understand."

"You say you don't know what we are talking about?" exclaimed one of them, showing him a receipted bill. "You are a cheat, that's all. You'd like to collect your fees twice over, would you?"

By degrees, Morton realized what had happened. Someone had been prying into his account books, and had managed to get judgment summonses sent to all his patients, whether they had paid their bills or not. They were equally furious, whether they could show him receipted bills or had been unwarrantably dunned.

Of what avail was it to try to explain? Of course he protested his innocence, declared that he would promptly apply to the court and secure the cancellation of the summonses, which had been issued without his knowledge. His patients would not believe him; and in Boston it was regarded as unpardonable for a professional man to take legal proceedings against a defaulter.

They would not listen to reason. They did not credit his asseverations of innocence. No patients would have anything more to do with a dentist who had behaved so badly. They departed in high dudgeon, determined never to cross his threshold again.

Morton's waiting room remained empty. One morning, when he came to the office, he found his assistants had not come. On his desk was a letter to the following effect: "We regret that we cannot any longer endanger our reputations by working for a dentist whose very instruments are in pawn, and who has tried to collect receipted accounts."

Within a day or two, Morton found a new plate on the doorpost: "Painless extractions and painless crown and bridge work on the most advantageous terms. Second Storey. 9 A.M. to 6 P.M." His favorite assistant had started independently in the rooms above.

Morton was ruined. There was no longer any hope of escaping his pecuniary difficulties by a lucrative practice. Nor could he look to friends for help, since they were falling away. What was he to do?

Such few friends as still remained faithful to him advised Morton to apply to Congress for a grant. His discovery had been of the utmost value to the soldiers in the Mexican campaign; ether was being administered for operations in every American hospital; surely Congress would be willing to reward him? The General Hospital endorsed Morton's petition, the staff signing a cordially worded declaration that he was the true discoverer of anesthesia.

Jackson, who kept himself fully informed of everything his victim did, took prompt action.

Next morning Morton received a letter from Jackson's lawyer, asking the dentist to be good enough to call and discuss an important matter.

"Mr. Morton," said the lawyer, in a civil tone of well-assumed regret, "it would be superfluous for me to recapitulate all that has happened in the past. Enough for me to say that from various cities I have received information regarding a number of details which are thoroughly substantiated. The publication of these would be most unfortunate for you. I am not empowered to show you this correspondence, but you must know to what it refers. For my part, rest assured that I attribute these indiscretions, if they were committed, solely to your youth and inexperience. Still, sir, what am I to do when my clients urge publication?"

"Excuse me, sir," replied Morton, "but I really do not understand what you are driving at."

A third person was present at the interview, a young man who had not previously said a word. The lawyer now turned to him. "Please explain the affair to Mr. Morton." Morton recognized him as a student whom he had seen once in Jackson's laboratory. This gentleman explained that he knew someone who had collected a lot of evidence highly damaging to Mr. Morton, and intended to publish it within a few days. The nature of the evidence and to what it referred were purposely left vague.

"Of course," resumed the lawyer, in a conciliatory tone, "it is still within our power to prevent this publication, which might prove extremely disagreeable to you. I am confident that Dr. Jackson could be induced to intervene in your favor. It is a great pity that you should have chosen this particular moment in which to quarrel with him. If I could bring about a reconciliation, I am sure that Dr. Jackson would persuade this gentleman, whose name must not now be mentioned, to renounce the publication of his evidence. I do not think there need be any difficulty about the proposed reconciliation. You would merely have to acknowledge that Dr. Jackson gave you advice of outstanding importance as concerned ether. In that case, you and he could live at peace together. In your own interest and in that of your family, I strongly advise you to come to terms with Dr. Jackson."

Another proposal for an understanding with Jackson! Morton had had more than enough of such attempts.

He had purposely refrained from interrupting the lawyer, wishing to induce the latter to declare himself, for he was convinced that Jackson's main purpose must be to prevent the petition to Congress. Despite the pretty periphrases, this was nothing but blackmail, and Morton was not a man to be intimidated by such methods.

"As far as I can understand, sir," he coldly rejoined, "you have merely invited me to your office in an attempt to threaten me into compliance." He went on drily: "I shall not allow myself to be browbeaten by any such extortion. You have addressed yourself to the wrong man. Do what you like, but I shall never admit that Jackson was the discoverer. If you'll let me give you a piece of good advice, it is that you should warn your client against taking the action he proposes. But I do not think Dr. Jackson will dare."

Without another word, Morton left the office.

Dr. Jackson did not dare. The last thing he wanted was to have his bluff called, and to find himself the defendant in a libel action. His attempt at intimidation had failed, but there were other possibilities, better ones perhaps, and certainly less dangerous.

The "material" might be put about anonymously. What a pity he had not thought of that at first! It would be enough to let a word drop here and there, to make a few allusions, vague hints, pronounce a few doubtful phrases, say: "I could an if I would. . . ."

In truth, this scheme went as if by clockwork. Those who had burned their fingers in the matter of the patent agency, the assistants who had deserted Morton, the ex-patients who had been offended by the issue of judgment summonses—one and all were eager to pass on any scandal against Morton that was whispered in their ears. Thus an anti-Morton atmosphere was created, although no one knew by whom it had first been breathed.

Directly Morton tried to meet these rumors face to face, asking people to tell him whence they had derived this or that unfavorable report, the gossip vanished into thin air—to be started anew, the instant his back was turned. He proved powerless against the might of rumor.

But this unceasing contest with the intangible, the dispute on behalf of his rightful claim, lawsuit after lawsuit, material cares, and now social ostracism—were more than he could bear.

At length poor Morton had a complete nervous breakdown. His doctor ordered absolute rest, avoidance of anything that might vex or excite him. The advice was good, but it could not be followed. It was impossible for him to remain inactive. Jackson had compiled a scandalous memorial about him, running to many hundred pages. It had been manifolded, and one of the copies would certainly go to Washington. Morton must compose a counterblast, must leave no stone unturned to defeat Jackson's calumnies.

Still, there was one place where he could get away from this turmoil and recover some peace of mind. He still had his country house at West Needham. Bowered amid friendly hills, meadows and gardens, it was his last refuge. There he would hide with wife and children, regain poise and find consolation and repose of mind.

When, after a walk, he came home tired, he was cheerfully

greeted by his wife and children, who ran out of the porch to meet him.

One evening, however, he saw that the porch was empty. Overwhelmed by anxious premonitions, Morton quickened his steps. When quite close, he saw a stranger doing sentry duty in front of the house.

"What is your business here?" he asked.

Instead of answering in words, the stranger showed him a writ signed by the sheriff. The house had been seized by his creditors. He no longer had a roof over his head.

CHAPTER FOURTEEN

The Conscience of
the Nation

AT THIS juncture, however, Morton's destiny underwent a sudden change for the better—precisely because of the poverty into which Jackson's intrigues had plunged him.

Hatred can think only of destruction, seeing naught in the world but hostile elements: the pitilessness of creditors, the harshness of colleagues, the vengefulness of the litigious, the base pleasure in gossip, the treachery of assistants, the delight of the envious in dragging a great man down from his pedestal. Hatred believes that it will be enough to feed the flames of destruction, to go on providing them with fuel, and the game will be won and the adversary ruined.

But hatred miscalculates, forgetting compassion. At first this may take only the form of a chance word, scarcely audible amid the chorus of antagonism, envy and gossip; but, by degrees, the voices become more numerous, grow louder, until the weapons of hatred are blunted.

"Poor fellow," one would say, on hearing how Morton was being driven to ruin.

"Yes, indeed, poor fellow, he has been badly treated," another would answer.

That was all. Casual remarks, a passing utterance and an assenting rejoinder. Two friends have exchanged a word or two. Nothing more.

But the words "poor fellow" have been spoken. Words are

living things, which breed their kind, grow and gather strength. Compassion spreads.

"I am satisfied that Dr. Morton has been a loser of several thousand dollars directly or indirectly through this matter," said Burnett the apothecary.

"It is well known that Dr. Morton, instead of profiting by his discovery, has suffered in mind, body and estate, in consequence of this time and toil he has consecrated to it," exclaimed Oliver Wendell Holmes indignantly.

At a meeting of the staff of the Massachusetts General Hospital, Dr. Bowditch said: "Certainly Morton deserved a better fate than to be crushed by the burden of debt. We must not look on idly and allow this to happen."

"Bowditch is right," said another. "Who can judge better than ourselves the value of Morton's discovery, we who avail ourselves of it day by day to relieve our patients of pain. It behooves us to bring the matter before Congress and urge for a substantial recognition."

Congress was busied with matters concerning the Mexican War, and the affair of Morton's petition had been shelved. Now, however, Professor Warren and Dr. Oliver Wendell Holmes joined in agitating on Morton's behalf.

They and other memorialists declared that William Thomas Green Morton, a citizen of the town of Boston, had been a benefactor to all mankind. In days to come, posterity would be unspeakably grateful to him for his discovery. Beyond question, the thanks of future generations would be the most striking testimony to Morton's success. But his contemporaries and fellow citizens owed him a more immediate recognition. It was obvious that money alone could be no sufficient return for all that he had done on behalf of mankind. Still, steps must be taken to insure that he should immediately be freed from the miseries of poverty. This concerned the honor of our country and that of mankind at large.

Washington was much busied with clearing up the mess left by the war and with the election campaign of Zachary Taylor who, as brigadier general, had been mainly instrumental in defeating the Mexicans and was shortly to be elected twelfth president of the

United States by the vote of the southern Whigs. These matters loomed very large on the political horizon, and meanwhile the Benefactor of Mankind was in danger of death from starvation.

"Unless help comes soon, it will be too late. Morton finds it hard to get a crust of bread to gnaw. His situation is pitiful," reported a doctor to the trustees of the General Hospital. "We cannot wait for Congress to act. Poverty does not wait. We ourselves must act, and instantly, if we are to save him."

Morton was practically penniless at West Needham. His furniture had been sold. A few cherished possessions were packed for removal. Whither? Morton did not know, but he could no longer stay in the house which had been seized by his creditors. Elizabeth wept, the children whimpered. He himself, ill, underfed, crushed by his misfortunes, stared apathetically out of the window. Wearily he contemplated the landscape, looked at the familiar hills and woods, feasted his eyes on the garden which had once been his own.

A carriage drew up at the gate, and six men got out. They were in formal attire, wearing frock coats and tall hats. Morton recognized them. They were the trustees of the Massachusetts General Hospital.

"Mr. Morton, we have come—" began the spokesman, then hesitated and stopped. So much moved was he by the sight of Morton's poverty and despair that words failed him. Without trying to resume, he silently handed Morton a silver box, on the top of which were engraved the words: "For William Thomas Green Morton, who has become poor in a cause which has made the world his debtor." With trembling hands Morton opened the box, and found that it contained ten rustling hundred-dollar notes.

"This is a tribute from our hospital, Mr. Morton," the speaker said in low tones, "in recognition of your most valuable discovery." Morton shook hands with them all, himself unable to speak, but full of a gratitude stronger than words.

It was like a dream, for something more had happened than the unexpected arrival of a thousand dollars to help a man in the hour of utmost need—though that was miraculous enough. But now, not only were his wife and children saved from the immediate pressure of want, not only could he pay the duns something on account and get a few of his possessions out of pawn, not only would they be able to stay on in the house for a time: more than that had happened, for Morton had reached a turning-point in his career. The darkest hour had passed and the dawn had come. Sympathy can change the world no less than hatred can.

". . . become poor in a cause which has made the world his debtor." Personal sympathy had led the trustees of the General Hospital to label their gift with these words. Soon, however, the phrase was to become a public plaint which would echo round the world.

One day someone said at Washington: "Congress recently voted huge sums of money for arms and ammunition. Are we, who are thus willing to pay heavily for the means of destroying life, to grudge paying for that which mitigates human suffering?"

Another: "Look at Europe. Great Britain, France, and all other enlightened nations have rewarded munificently such services to humanity. The British Parliament bestowed upon Jenner the sums of ten thousand pounds and twenty thousand pounds for the discovery of vaccination. The world has as yet produced but one great improvement in the healing art deserving to be ranked with that of Jenner. It would be unworthy of our greatness to undervalue a benefactor to mankind which is the peculiar glory of science, of our age, and of our country."

Soon similar remarks were being voiced on every side. "How does America show gratitude to her great son who has brought our nation imperishable glory? She allows him to die of starvation. Not merely does the government withhold honorable recognition, but actually profits by the discovery, and infringes the patent which it previously granted to Morton. That is worse than ingratitude; it is a crime."

Hundreds of people were repeating the charge: "The government is misusing this benefaction. That is worse than ingratitude; it is a crime."

"Have you heard? Out of compassion, the Massachusetts General Hospital has had to intervene and help Morton, because the government did nothing to help. To help? No, to reward, to reimburse, to make good the losses sustained through robbery by the government."

Everyone in Washington was talking about the scandalous way in which Morton had been treated. "All civilized nations know how to recompense their great citizens—all except the United States of America. Only America is capable of robbing a discoverer of the fruits of his discovery and leaving him to perish. This is a scandal involving the whole nation."

The clamor grew and grew. The conscience of the nation had awakened.

When Zachary Taylor became president on March 4, 1849, the Whigs rose to power, and the Whig party now espoused Morton's cause. Daniel Webster, their greatest and most finished orator, devoted his eloquence to the affair. Congress was urged on by the unanimous voice of the nation. Morton must be compensated for the disasters he had sustained and must be rewarded for his discovery.

The government had infringed Morton's patent. Well, that had been done and could not be undone. But the government, being conscience-stricken, would make a national grant to Morton, in compensation for the wrong he had sustained.

For two years Morton's petition had been ignored. But now, when the conscience of the nation had been stirred, when the pride of the nation had been stimulated, there was a general desire to make up for lost time.

In Washington, Morton was received as a national hero. People thronged to shake hands with him. Everyone acclaimed him. Congressmen vied in entertaining him, and asked him to demonstrate his method. Daniel Webster gave a dinner party in honor of Lajos Kossuth, leader of the Hungarian insurrection, then in Washington. At this banquet Morton was one of the honored guests, and his discovery, the pride of America, was one of the main topics of conversation.

The granting of a suitable reward to Morton was now under discussion in Congress. The eyes of the world were riveted on Washington. The debates about Morton's petition assumed historical importance. The conscience of the nation was making itself solemnly heard in the popular assembly, that the world might learn how America rewarded discoverers. In Congress the orators tried to outdo one another in their tributes to Morton's discovery.

Jackson had never foreseen anything of this sort. He had assembled Morton's creditors for the hunt and had believed that his merciless incitements would drive Morton to despair and sweep a rival forever out of his path. But now this miserable dentist, whom he had thought to destroy, was being honored as the hero of the nation.

Day after day Jackson received tidings of Morton's success at Washington, read the enthusiastic speeches of congressmen and senators, heard that Morton had been entertained by the famous Daniel Webster, that Morton had been highly honored at the Kossuth banquet, read the report of the subcommittee which was considering Morton's petition, and learned that Congress intended to grant Morton a testimonial amounting to $100,000. Jackson found it impossible to sit quiet in Boston, and went to Washington to see how far matters had gone and whether he could pull any strings which would interfere with the award.

Was he to give up the game? Was he to accept defeat? Was he to look on idly while Morton received $100,000 for what he had by this time seriously come to regard as his own discovery?

No, he would never allow Morton to snatch the fame, the honor and the money which were due to him, Jackson, the real discoverer. He refused to accept the fact that destiny was working against him, and continued his endeavors to guide fate's hand. Only to outward seeming did he remain inactive. While Morton was being fêted in Washington, and the committees were still considering the question and making arrangements for the award, Jackson did not let the grass grow under his feet.

He had secured the signatures of 143 dentists and doctors in support of his own claims. Dr. J. N. C. Kees and Daniel F. Black, one of the disappointed patent agents, swore affidavits to the effect that they had heard Morton acknowledge Jackson as the true discoverer, and that he himself had merely tried to turn the discovery to practical account and make money out of it.

Jackson felt sure that in his portfolio he now had sufficient material to blow Morton's claims out of the water. Why, then, did he not bring his big guns into action? Why did he remain silent when Morton's ship was running before a fair wind? He was silent because he had formed an insidious plan which must not be disclosed prematurely.

To set rumors circulating, to show his "materials" to one person and another, had sufficed in Boston to shatter a man's reputation in a small circle, to drive Morton the dentist out of his place in Boston society. But now Jackson had to deal with a man whose name was revered by a whole nation. It would not suffice, here, to approach individuals privately, on a small scale. The shameful defeat of Morton must be a big affair, and as public as his ascent to glory. The explosion should take place before the distinguished and honorable public which now acclaimed him. When orators were rising one after another from their places to extol the conquest of pain as the greatest benefaction ever worked on behalf of mankind, when the announcement was being made that the government had decided to reward the discoverer with an honorarium of $100,000—at this solemn moment when everyone was expecting to hear the name of Morton, they should hear, instead, the name of Jackson. It was then that the senators and representatives who could not do enough to extol Morton, that the government which was ready to vote him so large a grant, should learn that Morton was only the name of an unworthy impostor, of a rascal who had shamelessly misled Congress, and that the man to whom the honor and reward rightfully accrued was no other than Dr. Charles Thomas Jackson, the true and only discoverer of anesthesia.

The Thirty-third Congress was about to vote the award to Morton when, at the appropriate moment, neither too soon nor too late, Jackson's claim to the discovery was announced, and the comprehensive material with which it was supported was produced with the indispensable affidavits.

In actual fact the decision had to be postponed, the award deferred, while a special committee considered Jackson's claim, and decided who had really been the discoverer.

But, by a strange fatality, whatever Jackson undertook against Morton recoiled on his own head. For the moment, indeed, Jackson might seem to triumph, but in the end Morton proved victorious.

The machinations by which Jackson had thrust Morton into the abyss of poverty were the beginning of Morton's recent unparalleled ascent. The same thing was now to be repeated.

So far, Jackson was victorious. His protest prevented Morton's being granted honor and pecuniary reward. Congress had to undertake another long and tedious investigation. But, to Jackson's extreme annoyance, the House subcommittee immediately applied to the Massachusetts General Hospital, and asked information from Professor Warren, Dr. Hayden and Dr. Bigelow. Let the doctors who had seen the first applications of the discovery, and who had witnessed the first painless operations, give their account of the matter. Experts, chemists and surgeons, were appointed, since the essential thing was to decide, after full examination, what the discovery really was. The results of the investigation which took place on Jackson's own initiative were fatal to Jackson's claims.

The doctors of the Massachusetts General Hospital reported that they had never heard of the use of ether by inhalation as a means of preventing the pain of surgical operations until, in October, 1846, it was suggested by Dr. Morton. The most that Dr. Jackson's claim amounted to was that he made Morton certain proposals which the latter was able to use at the last moment in furtherance of earlier successful experiments and laboratory work.

Jackson's advice was purely hypothetical, they held, and might be compared to a ticket in a lottery in which Morton, through courage and enterprise, was able to win the great prize. The discovery was exclusively Morton's. For the real discoverer is a man who openly demonstrates practical use. Before Jenner, many milkmaids in Gloucestershire knew that cowpox would safeguard them against smallpox, but it is not the milkmaids whom we honor for Edward Jenner's discovery of vaccination. Jackson never made any claim to the discovery until Morton began to be recognized as the discoverer. Nay, Jackson declared Morton to be a rash fellow who was likely to have a patient's life upon his conscience. The staff of the Massachusetts General Hospital was, however, of opinion that when Dr. Jackson offered to dispose of his share in the pecuniary advantages of the discovery for the sum of $500, he renounced forever his title to be regarded as the discoverer, for it seemed unthinkable that the genuine discoverer would abandon his birthright for a mess of pottage.

Hitherto it had only been one man's word against another's. Morton had his proofs and his witnesses, and Jackson had others. Amid this conflict of evidence, Jackson was able to push his claim with some chance of success, false though that claim might be.

But now Jackson, by coming into the lists before Congress, had conjured up an inquiry which was to settle the matter once for all. The result was to be a formidable indictment of Jackson.

Dr. Bigelow sent the House subcommittee a memorial pointing out that if Dr. Jackson had really succeeded, as he declared, in discovering anesthesia as early as the year 1842, that is to say four years before Morton's demonstration, it was hard for him to explain having kept the matter secret for so long a time. Why did he not come forward with this immense benefaction? Why did he not announce it to all the world? The world could excuse Dr. Jackson only by the assumption that he did not possess any accurate knowledge about the importance of ether for surgery, so that his inaction was due, not to indifference, but to ignorance. Had it been otherwise, he would deserve punishment rather than reward for having needlessly withheld from mankind for four long years the means of saving human beings from intolerable pain.

Senator Stephen A. Douglas of Illinois spoke in the Senate as follows:

"My colleague in the other House [Mr. Bissell] who is a regularly educated physician, as chairman of the select committee thoroughly examined the matter. The report of the select committee produced entire conviction on my mind that Dr. Morton was entitled to the credit of this discovery."

A memorial abundantly signed by the staff of the Massachusetts General Hospital and the members of the Massachusetts Medical Society was presented to the Senate and the House of Representatives. It was couched as follows:

"The undersigned hereby testify to your honorable body that, in their opinion, Dr. William T. G. Morton first proved to the world that ether would produce insensibility to the pain of surgical operations, and that it could be used with safety. In their opinion, his fellow-men owe a debt to him for this knowledge. Wherefore they respectfully ask a recognition by Congress of his services to his country and mankind."

A bill had also been presented to Congress, "An act to reward by a national testimonial the discovery of the means of producing insensibility to pain in surgical operations and other cases of suffering." The sum of $100,000 was specified. There was to be a judicial inquiry as to the rival claims of Wells, Jackson and Morton. If Morton were given the award, he should surrender his patent.

Should this scheme be adopted, Jackson's game would be lost. But Jackson protested in the most energetic terms, saying that the staff of the Massachusetts General Hospital, upon whose recommendation the report was based, was of a prejudiced group who were all in league with Morton. Besides, these gentlemen were utterly unqualified to decide about a discovery of such enormous scope.

Jackson demanded that new and unprejudiced expert opinion should be secured. The foreign world should be consulted, Monsieur Elie de Beaumont of Paris, the famous Alexander von Humboldt of Prussia. They were the men whose opinion was worth hearing, and their opinion ought to be heard before Congress decided. Besides, it was no longer a question of a reward payable to this man or to that, but of the honor of the whole nation.

"Think, gentlemen, for the eyes of the world are today directed toward Congress. The discovery about which you have to decide is, indeed, the pride of America, but the subject under discussion concerns the welfare of the whole human race. You have to settle matters for the present and for all future generations. Bear that well in mind."

Jackson tried to make out that he was exclusively concerned with the establishment of the truth and with the honor of the nation. He was ready to make a fine gesture, was ready, for the sake of truth, to renounce any idea of pecuniary reward. Surely that would show Congress what sort of man he was. He stood above the battle, and was magnanimous enough to renounce the proposed award; while he was faced by a man who thought only of his $100,000, an avaricious dentist with an unsavory reputation.

That was how Jackson tried to represent his side of the case. But his fine gesture of ostensible unselfishness did not work, and the proposed renunciation of the award failed to ring true. The government felt uneasy about its infringement of the patent it had granted. The award would relieve it of the pricks of conscience— and, besides, it was a matter of American prestige. In rewarding great discoverers, the United States could not afford to lag behind other countries.

The occasion was now at hand when it could show how the New World honored its greatest sons. Congress had no intention of allowing this national demonstration to be frustrated. It wanted to reward the discoverer, wanted the country's generosity to be fully disclosed, wanted to pay the $100,000 award. What else had they been discussing all this time? Now Dr. Jackson came along and, with his "fine gesture of renunciation" expected to make Congress eat its own words.

He would renounce the sum of $100,000 which the government was willing to pay the discoverer? It was inevitable that such extravagant generosity should sound suspicious to grown-up Americans with sound human understandings and Puritan hearts. Was it to be supposed that there was anything paltry in accepting a proper reward for one's achievements, or something grand in refusing a fine honorarium?

The Puritans, who were on such intimate terms with the Almighty and were closely acquainted with His commandments and His wishes, had always regarded money-getting as a sacred affair. Jackson was a heretic who professed to have no interest in

$100,000, but only in truth. Congress saw through the fine gesture.
A man who was so ready to refuse $100,000 which the nation was
prepared to give must be a man whose claim to priority as discoverer was ill-grounded.

No, Congress was far more inclined to believe the man who
was ready to accept the award, and thereby to give additional evidence that he was the genuine discoverer.

By an overwhelming majority the House decided that William
Thomas Green Morton was the discoverer of anesthesia, and was
fully entitled to the award.

A few days later the following appeared as an editorial in the
Boston *Daily Mail*:

> "The Ether Discovery.—The following was telegraphed to
> the 'Transcript' and 'Journal' on Monday evening:
>
> *"'Washington, March 15th. The committee in the
> House have decided upon awarding $100,000 to Dr. Morton
> for his discovery of ether. Dr. Morton has caused the arrest of
> his competitor, Dr. Jackson, for libel.'*
>
> "The statement is false in many respects. Dr. Jackson has
> *not* been arrested for libel, although it is true that a majority
> of the committee have decided to recommend an award of
> $100,000 to the discoverer of the anæsthetic properties of sul-
> phuric ether. It is rumored that the committee were *Morton-
> ized.* . . . Morton has no more claim to this discovery than
> the Fiji mermaid; his entire merits in the premises are precisely
> the same as those of a thief who enters a person's house, and
> finding some valuable article, attempts to appropriate it to his
> own use and behoof on the ground of *discovery*. The attempt
> to pull the wool over the eyes of members of Congress is in
> perfect character with the unblushing impudence of the in-
> dividual."

Morton was powerless against the anonymous reports Jackson
had so busily circulated in Boston. But now the calumny appeared
in black and white in the columns of the Boston *Daily Mail* and
the newspaper could be called to account.

When an action for libel was threatened the *Mail* declared that
the item in question had been supplied by Dr. Jackson.

All that Dr. Jackson had hitherto secured by the public attempt to discredit Morton had been a postponement of the decision of Congress. Now, however, he had exposed himself to an action for libel and defamation of character and was threatened with arrest. Next day in the Washington and Boston papers he could read the unwelcome item:

"We learn that before the close of the present session of Congress a resolution will be passed to the effect that Dr. William T. G. Morton is to receive an award of $100,000 for his discovery of ether narcosis. We understand that Morton is bringing an action against Dr. Jackson for libel and defamation of character."

CHAPTER FIFTEEN

Ghosts

ROM WASHINGTON, Morton returned to West Needham, happy and cheerful. The University of Maryland had granted him a doctor's degree "honoris causa." Over and above this, he was bringing Elizabeth the best of news. Beyond question Congress would grant the award. The matter would be settled this session, perhaps within a very few weeks. Jackson's last protest had been ignored, Jackson's claim had been disclosed for what it was—totally unfounded. There was no obstacle in the way of future happiness. Life was about to begin afresh for Morton, his wife and the children. He would be able, henceforward, to devote every energy to perfecting his discovery.

But at that same moment Jackson was on the way to Hartford excogitating another scheme, a sound scheme, one that would assuredly succeed. Jackson, too, was full of hope.

Wells's widow and her little sons were at Hartford. Jackson intended to call on the lady and say: "You live here impoverished and full of sorrow. Your husband has been forgotten; he is dead and buried; no one troubles to think about him. But it was he, he alone, who made the first experiments leading to this great discovery which has liberated mankind from the pain of operations. Still, who bothers about that now? Mr. Morton has received all the honor which properly belonged to your deceased husband; Mr. Morton will pouch the money to be voted by Congress, while you, the widow of the real discoverer, starve at Hartford.

"Well, I, though not impoverished, am otherwise in much the

same case as yourself. I, too, played a leading part in this discovery. I was the first to think of using inhalations to annul pain during surgical operations. It was I who thought of using ether for this purpose. But my share was merely theoretical. It was your husband who introduced anesthesia by inhalation into practice. I can bear witness to that. Who better? Your husband came to see me before his first essays in Boston, and talked the matter over with me before his first public demonstration. I am in a position to assure the world that it was Horace Wells and not Morton who ventured upon the original experiments.

"Morton, indeed! I know what a simpleton he was in these matters; that it was from your husband he first learned of the possibility of such experiments; and that later he came to me, who had been his teacher, to glean a little information about ether and its administration. He was an ignoramus, was and is a rascal, a thief who stole what he claims to have been his idea from his former partner, Horace Wells, and from myself.

"Two persons, and Morton was not one of them, bestowed this great idea upon mankind—your late husband, who was the unfortunate victim of circumstances, and I. What has been our reward? A thief is to receive the $100,000 which should rightfully come to us, and the silly world gapes with admiration while the rascal pockets his takings.

"As to the money, I am fairly well off, and should not lift a finger if I alone had been despoiled. But what I cannot endure is that the widow of my late friend Horace Wells, a widow with little children, should live in penury at Hartford while a usurper of fame and money battens on unrightful gains. The wretch Morton hounded your poor husband into the tomb that his partner's mouth might be closed forever, and Morton believes that his calumnies will clear me, likewise, out of his path. But I am not so easy to silence, and I have a keen sense of duty. I intend to take vengeance for the wrong done to Horace Wells, and to restore the credit of the dead inventor. In a word, Mrs. Wells, I have come, unsolicited, to offer you my help in this difficult matter."

Of course it was not an easy task which Jackson had set himself, but he had become a monomaniac. Although by the light of reason he must have known that he was not really the discoverer of anesthesia, hatred and ambition overpowered reason and, in the emotional sphere, he was convinced that he was the sole discoverer. Now he was going ostensibly to abandon this claim, and admit that another had played a no less important part than he.

Only by feigning this admission could he hope to save the situation. What the ties of friendship, his materials and his witnesses, his "noble renunciation" of the claim to pecuniary reward, his previous restless activities, had not been able to achieve, he hoped to achieve with the aid of a ghost from the tomb.

In imagination he foresaw the triumph over Morton that would result from the production of the specter of Wells. He would conjure up Wells, and the phantom should walk before Congress. How would the congressmen, even those who had most heartily espoused the cause of Morton, be able to resist the might of this phantom? Of course, he, Jackson, would have to pay a long price. He would have to share his claim with another, but that other was dead and the dead are not exacting. The dead Wells would not dispute his title to have been the only begetter of the discovery in the ideal world; the dead Wells would ask no more than that widow and children should enjoy this unexpected legacy of $100,000.

At Hartford all passed off as Jackson had hoped. Mrs. Wells was profoundly touched by the unselfish way in which this distinguished man was prepared to relinquish any claim to the anticipated grant from Congress, asking no more than the recognition of his intellectual priority. Her husband, after all, had not lived and worked in vain. Even though poor Horace had perished so miserably, his name would be restored to honor. He had always been devoted to his wife and children, and would have asked nothing better than that they should be enabled to live highly respected and free from pecuniary cares. This would be the work of the generous Jackson, who vowed that he would leave no stone unturned to secure their rights for the wife and children of his deceased friend.

To the poor widow, Jackson must have seemed an angel from heaven. She herself need take no trouble. Jackson would do everything to push the late Horace Wells's claims. Indefatigably he collected materials, reconstructed the story of Wells's experiments, interviewed the Hartford doctors and patients who had been interested in the matter, compiled an exhaustive report, and (most important of all) engaged a lawyer named Truman Smith who was a senator from Connecticut.

Jackson was a past master in the art of playing upon the avarice and vanity of others and turning these powerful instincts to his own advantage.

He could not have found a better instrument. Truman Smith was a lawyer. "Sir, I want to entrust you with a case through which you ought to be able to earn substantial fees. It is a claim for $100,000." Truman Smith was also a senator. "Senator, if you push this affair successfully through Congress, it will secure you much renown. A great injustice has been done to a dead man and his heirs. You will demand expiation. The victim was a citizen of Connecticut, a man who practiced here in Hartford, made the greatest discovery of all times, and has been robbed of the honor which should properly have accrued. Not of honor alone. Congress, as you are doubtless aware, proposes to make a special award for the discovery, and intends to give it to a citizen of another state. A Massachusetts man is to have the money and the fame which rightfully belong to the late Horace Wells of Connecticut. I think you will agree that this is a matter of the first importance, and that by taking it up you will not be neglecting your own interests."

Neither as lawyer nor as senator was Truman Smith the man to throw away such a chance.

There were fine opportunities for distinction as well as for earning a fat fee. The appeal to local patriotism would undoubtedly make a hit. Connecticut was jealous of Massachusetts, Hartford of Boston. These Bostonians had always suffered from swelled head. Now they were trying to ascribe the discovery of anesthesia to a Bostonian when it had really been made by a Hartfordian—being, as usual, convinced that all good things came from Boston, that Boston was the intellectual center of America and the hub of the universe, that Boston had been the fount of this stupendous discovery. Boston this and that, Boston here and Boston there; always Boston, Boston, Boston. Well, Massachusetts and Boston should be taught that Connecticut and Hartford counted for something, not only in the United States but also in the wider world of discovery. Truman Smith was a politician to the tips of his fingers, and recognized a fine slogan when he heard one. "I am fighting for the honor of Connecticut, for the immortal fame of Connecticut."

Jackson was of the utmost help to the Senator in preparing this campaign. His diligence, his ceaseless activities, made him worth a whole staff of skilled clerks; his encyclopedic knowledge was equal to any test; while he showed marvelous adroitness in discovering witnesses against Morton and for Wells. It was a genuine pleasure for Truman Smith to have a man like Jackson as collaborator.

The session of Congress was drawing to a close. All the preliminary formalities had been fulfilled. The day had come when the grant to Morton was up for final action in the Senate. Senator Shields rose to make a last eloquent speech concerning the importance of the discovery. Senators Mallory and Badger were to make seconding orations.

Truman Smith listened with close attention. When Shields insisted upon the magnitude of the discovery and upon the fame that it would bring to the United States of America, Truman Smith nodded approval. Hardly anyone in the chamber was more firmly convinced than Truman Smith that this much was indisputable. Senator Douglas spoke, and his peroration was: "The award should be made to William Thomas Green Morton."

When Senator Truman Smith's turn came, his sonorous voice rang through the hall: "I denounce this attempt to filch money from the Treasury as an outrage upon the rights of others, and a most abominable imposition on this Government. I agree with the honorable gentleman from Arkansas that the discovery is a great boon to humanity, and is the pride of the United States of America. But Morton was not the discoverer. I believe that this Morton is a rank impostor—that there is no justice or truth in his pretended claim. I demand in the name of justice and right, to have an opportunity to come before the Senate, and tell the story of the wrongs of the poor widow and defenseless children of Dr. Horace Wells; wrongs which they have suffered at the hands of this man, Morton, who has attempted to rob their husband and father who has descended to the grave, of a discovery, which is one of the most extraordinary made in modern times."

Truman Smith's voice quivered with indignation, and his whole body shook. Every word, every glance, every movement, disclosed his moral indignation at a wrong which cried to heaven, a wrong now being perpetrated against a dead man. An amazed silence followed, as he looked round the hall.

Senator Badger from North Carolina was the first to recover his composure and rise to answer Truman Smith. "I know not, Mr. President, what private griefs the honorable Senator from Connecticut has; but certainly something or other seems to have stimulated him into a very undue excitement on this occasion. The honorable Senator demands an opportunity of making out a case —for whom? For clients of his."

Senator Badger's insinuation was almost enough to rob Truman Smith of his success. The next to speak was Senator Brown from Florida, who advised the Senate not to be diverted by this intervention from carrying into effect a resolution which had already been passed in the House. Congress was being made mock of. It was five years since Morton's petition had been lodged. What had become of the generosity of the nation? To wait five years and then dismiss so well-grounded a petition would shame the United States of America in the eyes of the world. The Paris Academy of the Sciences had granted Morton a gold medal; the Tsar of All the Russias had bestowed on him the Cross of the Order of St. Vladimir; the King of Sweden, the Cross of the Order of Vasa. Morton was a citizen of the United States. What had the United States done for him? It had waited five long years before granting a reward to this most distinguished of its sons. Careful and detailed inquiries had shown beyond the possibility of dispute that Morton was the discoverer of anesthesia, and it would be most unjust to withhold this long overdue reward from a man who had been impoverished by his discovery.

Truman Smith found himself up against an extremely stubborn opposition, but he did not lose courage. A skilled debator, he ignored Senator Badger's and Senator Brown's disrespectful and incredulous remarks and tranquilly proceeded to marshal his arguments.

"I am speaking, sir, on behalf of a dead man. A dead man who, but for my aid, would be defenseless."

He spoke reverently, and the solemn words echoed through the hall. For the time being, protest had been disarmed. After an oratorical pause, Smith went on:

"The honorable gentleman who has just spoken appealed to foreign examples, to Paris above all. Permit me, then, to read you a passage from a Parisian newspaper, in defense of the claims of another than Morton, and let me say before doing so that I take no shame in appearing before you as the advocate of one who has been shamelessly victimized."

Then, his voice vibrating with emotion, Truman Smith read as follows: " 'While a young, unlucky man who had done so much to free mankind from the curse of pain perished by his own hand with a clouded intellect in some corner of the New World, another, undeserving of the fame he had snatched, was enjoying the credit which properly accrued to the prematurely deceased Wells.' "

In ringing tones, Truman Smith went on: "Here, gentlemen, I represent a dead man who claims justice from you. Reverence the dead."

The ghost walked. No one ventured a word. The newspaper extract from Paris, a trump card, had won the trick. While the ghost walked, what living senator dared dispute his pre-eminence? Smith went on:

"The last speaker was bold enough to declare that no one would contest the rightfulness of the claim of Mr. Morton of Massachusetts to be the discoverer of anesthesia. I venture, however, to ask Congress to grant me leave and time in which to produce witnesses and additional evidence. I can bring dentists and surgeons from Hartford, and I can adduce opinions from foreign medical societies which will all confirm my statement that the late Horace Wells of the state of Connecticut was the true discoverer of anesthesia."

The orator paused, and then resumed:

"I feel assured that Congress will allow me to defend the interests of a dead man, and will not hastily decide this matter without allowing the widow and orphans of the unhappy Wells to push their rightful claim."

"Yes, Wells's heirs must be given a chance of putting their side of the case," said one.

"The dead man's claims must be investigated before Congress decides," added another.

Mallory intervened: "We have been discussing this matter for five years. How much longer will it be before we make the award?"

"We must not ignore the interests of a dead man. No one could assume such a responsibility," came the answer.

"Hear! Hear! No one can shoulder such a responsibility"— this from several voices.

In short, the award was postponed and a senatorial subcommittee was appointed to investigate the claims of the deceased Wells. Truman Smith received instructions to produce his proofs.

The letter written by Brewster which had arrived after Wells's suicide and had been opened by the widow could not immediately be found. It had passed from hand to hand as proof that Wells was the discoverer, and had somehow gone astray.

"We must get this letter," insisted Jackson. "It is of vital importance."

Again: "I have written to my friend in Paris asking for copies of the paragraph written by Wells and published in *Galignani's Messenger;* also the minutes of the meeting of the Paris Medical Society. I expect they will arrive by next mail. They are indispensable to our case."

It would certainly take weeks to get all the requisite materials together. Every delay would strengthen Jackson's position and weaken Morton's.

A month passed when, by January 21, 1852, Truman Smith had his materials ready to lay before the subcommittee. They filled about a thousand pages, and in a fortnight the session of Congress would close.

How were the members of the subcommittee to examine all this material in a fortnight and then report to the Senate? How, at the tail end of the session, was that body to decide between the claims of Morton and Wells, and make a definitive vote?

The "Mortonists" might clamor as much as they pleased. It was of no avail. The whole question was adjourned to the next session.

The "Mortonists," however, took advantage of the interval to work on behalf of their protégé. Although Truman Smith had secured an oratorical success on the floor, when the members of the subcommittee came to examine the material evidence in favor of Wells's claim it proved to be slender. Wells was disclosed to have been nothing more than a hard-working, aspiring and at first promising young dentist of Hartford, lacking the talents required to push so great a discovery to a successful issue. In the end he had become a chloroform addict and had committed suicide. Was this unhappy fate, dramatically adduced by Truman Smith as one of his "exhibits," really sufficient ground for challenging an indisputable truth—the truth that not the deceased Wells but the living Morton had been the discoverer? No, among all the relevant "exhibits," death could not outweigh living truth.

Wells had repeated the experiments with laughing gas made long ago by Davy and more recently by Hickman; he had undoubtedly had the courage to try the gas on himself and had had one of his own teeth extracted under its influence; but his public demonstration had been a fiasco, and after it he had let matters rest.

Here was the letter Wells had written to Morton about the patent; here was Dr. Hayward's written report of a conversation with Wells in which the latter had admitted that he was not the discoverer; here were the opinions of the staff of the General Hospital, wholly adverse to Wells's claims. No, it was impossible to regard Wells as the discoverer, even though his ghost had been made to walk before Congress. No doubt everyone with a feeling heart must sympathize with his widow and his orphaned sons, but sympathy cut no ice here. Sympathy must not induce Congress to make an award to Wells's widow which properly belonged to the living Morton.

Truman Smith's proofs ran to 270,000 words. But in the end all these words were effectively counterpoised by five: "Morton is the true discoverer."

"I feel no interest or wish in this matter, except that the truth may be arrived at, and right and justice done; and that I may discharge faithfully the duty which the Senate has imposed on me, by endeavoring to attain it, and present it. And it is but fair to say that Dr. W. T. G. Morton first discovered a safe, certain and efficient anesthetic, and that he is entitled to whatever honor and reward are due to the discoverer." Such was the unanimous report of the Senate's subcommittee.

No one could doubt that, next session, Congress would make the award to Morton.

But Truman Smith did not lose heart. "Make your mind easy, Dr. Jackson. We shall win through."

Truman Smith was a skilled orator, but Jackson could not accept this confident assurance. Morton had recently visited Hartford to show those who championed Wells's claims the letter Wells had written him; to give his own account of Dr. Jackson's persistent animus; and to insist that Jackson himself, in Boston long before, had spoken with the utmost contempt of Wells's experiments. Morton actually possessed written proofs of this last assertion. Nay, Morton had even been able to produce a letter in Wells's own handwriting publicly accusing Jackson of trying to filch the credit of the discovery. Yes, Morton had shown these documents to Mrs. Wells! Jackson was outraged at this attempt to turn the poor woman against her unselfish adviser and benefactor.

All the same, Jackson could not but be aware that the ground was quaking beneath his feet. He felt he would make a mistake if he continued to devote himself to pushing Wells's claims. That could be left to Truman Smith. His own cause must not be allowed to stand or fall with that of Wells. There were other ways of checking the exuberance of the Mortonists in Congress.

Jackson was a subscriber to the leading scientific periodicals of Europe and America. He read them assiduously, taking note of any scientific innovations, and especially of advances in medicine, chemistry and geology. For years he had been accustomed to cut out and classify in his file-books the items in which he was mainly interested. This extensive collection was given exceptional value by Jackson's marvelous memory, which enabled him, even after the lapse of years, to put his hand upon any item he wanted.

"James," said Jackson to his assistant, "if I remember aright, a few years ago I made a clipping about a man who claimed to have been the first that ever administered ether to a patient. Where was it? Some place in the South, I believe. A report of a meeting. . . . I've got it! It was the account of a meeting of the Medical Society of Georgia. Half a minute, and I shall remember the year. Yes, it must have been in 1849. Just look up that cutting, please."

Jackson had hit the bull's-eye. It was really a report from Georgia, in the year 1849. After a little search, the assistant found what was wanted.

A doctor from Athens in Georgia had reported to the Medical Society of that state how, in the year 1842, four years before Morton and Jackson applied for their patent, he, being then a country doctor in Jefferson, had successfully performed operations under ether anesthesia, but had not published his results.

"I know that I delayed the publication too long to receive any honor from the priority of the discovery, but having by persuasion of my friends presented my claim before the profession, I prefer that its correctness be fully investigated before the Medical Society. Should the society say that the claim, though well founded, is forfeited by not being presented earlier, I will cheerfully respond, 'So mote it be.'"

When Jackson had first scanned this report, some years before, it did not seem to him of much importance. Like most New

Englanders, he regarded the South as a vestige of the eighteenth century which persisted in modern civilization like an enclave, and in his eyes a southern country practitioner was an antediluvian whose name was not worth bearing in mind. Besides, how presumptuous it was for this Southerner to proclaim himself the first who had used ether. He himself, Jackson and no other, had been the first to use ether. He had begun his experiments as far back as 1838. No Morton and no southern general practitioner was in the field before him.

Still, he had cut out the item as a matter of routine and filed it in the appropriate place. Now, when disinterred, it seemed to him worthy of more attention.

"So this Dr. Crawford Long of Athens, Georgia, operated under ether in the year 1842? That is extremely interesting," said Jackson to his assistant. "Only because he lived in a one-horse town down south, cut off from the scientific world, has no one heard about the matter. Still, it is plain that Morton was not the first to administer ether for operative purposes. We New Englanders are far too ready to ignore the South. I have often said as much. Great things go on there and pass unnoticed; most valuable scientific experiments; things which the whole Union ought to be proud of, but never hears about. We let the South with its magnificent estates fall into decay; we leave men as noteworthy as this Crawford Long utterly ignored. But all America shall hear of him. He was the very first to turn my discovery to practical account, and he, therefore, is the only person besides myself entitled to rank as the discoverer of anesthesia. A country practitioner in Athens, Georgia, Crawford Williamson Long by name. Most interesting, James!"

A few days later, Dr. Jackson set out for the gold mine of Dahlonega.

"You know," he said to his friends before starting on this journey, "since gold was discovered in California and the first consignment of the precious metal reached Washington, one might fancy that the whole of the South and the West had been transformed into gold-fields. News is continually coming to hand of some fresh strike, and the government has gone crazy about gold.

As state geologist I have been commissioned to visit Dahlonega and sample the gold mines there. A most interesting affair."

He broke his journey at Athens, to which Dr. Crawford Long had removed from Jefferson some time ago. He had been fully rewarded for the shrewdness which had led him to abandon operations under ether when they threw the whole neighborhood of Jefferson into excitement, and the population threatened to lynch him. He had now a very good practice. Having done well at Jefferson, and put by money, he was able to establish himself in Athens where, while still carrying on medical practice, he made a supplementary income out of the drugstore in which he had invested his savings. He was now what used to be called a "warm man," and, like every well-to-do Southerner of his day, he had a plantation of his own and was the owner of a number of Negro slaves.

Life jogged along easily for him, amid his threefold activities as man of business, doctor and planter. When he got home from his rounds, the children ran out to greet Daddy and pat his horse. He joked with them and told Caroline all that had happened. He was no longer the dandy he had been before marriage, but was still carefully dressed, his clothes being made by the best of the local tailors.

Week followed week, one much like another, and he had plenty of leisure for archery or croquet. He enjoyed the usual amusements of the southern gentry, and would not have thought an evening well-spent on which he had not had his customary game of whist.

During these years, his quiet life had only once been disturbed, and that for no more than a few days. One December evening, in the year 1846, he was fluttering the pages of the *Medical Examiner,* by the reading of which he tried to keep up-to-date with what went on in the medical world. Suddenly a headline attracted his attention: *"The first painless operation."*

"The first!" he contemptuously exclaimed, out loud, so that Caroline looked up from her needlework.

"What is it, dear?" she said.

"Just listen to this. It says here in the *Examiner* that in

October an operation was performed at the Massachusetts General Hospital, and it is described as the first painless operation. What about my operations at Jefferson in 1842? That tumor I cut out from Venable, and the nigger boy's finger I amputated?"

"You ought to have published your results, Crawford. I always told you so," said Caroline.

"Oh well, dear, you know what happened. Those idiots at Jefferson regarded me as a sorcerer. I was losing my practice, and I might have been lynched if there had been an accident. It seemed best to lie low and say nothing. But now someone has got ahead of me."

"Well, it's not too late, after all," said Caroline. "Write this evening to the *Medical Examiner* to say that you performed painless operations more than four years ago."

Certainly, thought Long, it would not be difficult to prove his priority. He had the entry in his ledger stating that he had removed a tumor for Venable under ether. Then there were plenty of eyewitnesses. The most important detail in the report of the *Medical Examiner* was that the discoverer, a Boston dentist, having applied for a patent, was keeping secret the nature of the substance which he used. If Long were now to announce in the columns of the *Examiner* that some years earlier he had given ether to prevent pain in surgical operations, it would be plain that he had been the first to perform painless operations.

How circumstances altered cases! What in Jefferson had boded disaster now seemed to hold great promise for the future.

Long sprang out of his rocking-chair, got his materials together, and sat down at the writing table to compile a report to the *Medical Examiner*. He had written no more than the date when there came a knock at the door. An agitated farmer entered:

"Please come at once, Doctor. My wife is in labor."

Of course Long had to go instantly. It was a tedious and difficult confinement. He was detained all night. When he got home, his waiting room was full of patients. Next day his business affairs needed attention. So it went on until he had missed his chance of sending an article in time for the January number. Oh, well, February would do.

But the January issue of the *Medical Examiner* dashed Long's hopes. He learned how Morton, the Boston dentist, had, before a subsequent operation, announced that the vapor he administered was that of pure sulphuric ether. Long's disclosure of his knowledge that the remedy was ether would now be out of date.

Then in the February number of the *Medical Examiner* came an article which made Long feel he might just as well drop the matter. A Hartford dentist named Wells had been beforehand with Morton in having one of his own teeth painlessly extracted under laughing gas. Who could tell how many claimants would come forward? Long was not a New Englander with the push characteristic of those Yankees. He was a southern gentleman who would not try to elbow his way to the front.

Above all, being a modest country practitioner (modest in the most literal sense of the word), he began to think it was unlikely that such a man as he could really have been the first to make so important a discovery. Plenty of others probably had done what he had done at Jefferson nearly five years ago. To claim priority, to wrestle for it, would give him a great deal of trouble. He had an assured income, led a comfortable life, savored his game of whist every night. Why bother?

Later some well-intentioned friends induced the Medical Society of Georgia to ask Long about his experiments with anesthetics. Long supplied the information for which he was asked, but (as previously explained) declared, with fine candor, that it was likely enough any claim he might have made to priority would be forfeited because he had not published his results at the time and pushed his claim earlier. He would leave that matter to an enlightened medical profession, and would be content with the decision, whatever it might be.

Thus, of all those who were concerned with the discovery of anesthesia, Long was the only one whose life was unperturbed by vexatious disputes about priority.

Unperturbed for a time, at least, until March 8, 1854. On that date a stranger with black hair and sparkling eyes called to see Dr. Long.

"Dr. Long is on his rounds," said the assistant, "but perhaps I can help you, sir."

"No, no, I am not a patient," said the stranger. "There is nothing the matter with me. I want to speak to Dr. Long personally about a very important affair." He walked up and down restlessly, awaiting Long's return.

At length the clatter of a horse's hoofs was heard in the street.

"There he is," said the assistant to the stranger, who ran out to see Long dismounting, and presented his visiting card.

Long took it and read: "Dr. Charles Thomas Jackson, Legion of Honor, state geologist, chemist and Master of the Mint."

"Have you a few minutes to spare, Dr. Long?" inquired the visitor.

"What can I do for you, sir?" replied Long.

"I have come," said Jackson, "to have a talk with the man who was the first to use ether during a surgical operation."

"Come in, sir, come in," said Long, most cordially.

"I want to help you to your rights," said Jackson, after, in Long's office, he had carefully examined the materials his host put before him. "It all seems most convincing, and the only thing which puzzles me is why you have never laid them before the public."

Long explained his reasons, and Jackson was quick to recognize that Long was of a very different type from himself, and would need pushing to the front.

"I am sorry you did not write to me long ago," said Jackson. "My extensive connections in Europe would have enabled me to bring your claims to priority before the Paris Academy of the Sciences, and had you and I joined forces we could have insured recognition from the world. I think you must be aware that I, too, had a good deal to do with this discovery, but in case you are not, I will explain."

Jackson went on to give an account of his own theoretical and practical connection with ether, indicating that he was in the field a considerable time before Long.

Having skillfully led matters to the point at which he could hope to win over Long to his own schemes, he went on: "Of course,

I did not, like you, undertake actual operations." Jackson favored Long with a winning smile. "In that matter I must certainly grant your priority. Though, sir, even as regards practice, the idea occurred to me as far back as 1838. I experimented on myself, too, at that date. We were both of us rather backward in making our knowledge public. But let me ask you, my dear sir, if it does not seem intolerably unjust that the fame which properly belongs to you and me should be snatched by an interloper, an obscure and petty Boston dentist? Is it not worth our while to take the wind out of this impostor's sails?" Now that a famous and highly respected scientist, a man who had been in Paris, a man thoroughly well versed as to what went on in the great world, a man who knew all about experiments with ether, came and assured him that he, Long, had been the first to perform a painless operation— new vistas dawned. How excited Caroline would be!

As has been explained, this country doctor was of an extremely quiet disposition, hesitant and procrastinating rather than a fighter. Still, he was a clear thinker and thoroughly straightforward. If he really was the first in the field, if he really was the discoverer of anesthesia, it was he, Crawford Long, not Morton or Wells, but also not this Dr. Jackson.

If he had really been the first to perform a painless operation under ether, such was the fact. He did not need any help in advocating his claim to priority, and he did not need to share that claim with another. Unquestionably Dr. Jackson was a distinguished scientist, a man with a great name. But he would not share his claim with another merely because that other had a great reputation. If he was the discoverer, his priority was not merely a claim but a fact, and facts are stubborn things. Long therefore answered Jackson with all due respect, but in a way which could not be misunderstood, that in view of what Jackson himself had said he had no intention of sharing with anyone his priority as discoverer.

In Hartford, previously, it had been a bitter pill for Jackson to swallow when, in order to form an alliance with Mrs. Wells, he had had to renounce his own claim as sole discoverer of anesthesia. He did so only because the annihilation of Morton was nearer to his heart than even his own (unfounded) claim to priority. Now it seemed that he could not push his determination to annihilate Morton unless he actually renounced even a partial share in the discovery. This was a pill still more bitter.

No one could deny that he had experimented with ether; that he was early aware of the pain-allaying properties of ether; and that it was he who had advised Morton to try ether upon his patients. Even Morton did not and could not dispute that. Was he now to have his whole claim to a share in the discovery wiped out of existence? Was he to admit that this southern country practitioner was the discoverer? That seemed almost too much. Still, his venom toward Morton overpowered every other feeling. If only he could convince the world that Morton had no claim to be regarded as the discoverer of anesthesia, if only he could prevent Congress from granting Morton the proposed reward—to secure these ends would be worth such a sacrifice as was now demanded, for the annihilation of Morton had become Jackson's chief, nay his only, purpose in life.

"My one desire is to insure that justice shall prevail," said Jackson hoarsely. "I stand above the battle, and have no personal interest in the matter. This conversation with you, sir, and the proofs you have shown me, have fully convinced me of your rights. Truth is my sole concern. You can count upon my dispassionate help. Press your claim, sir, and you can rely upon Dr. Charles Thomas Jackson, state geologist, Montyon prizeman, Chevalier of the Legion of Honor, to declare before the whole world that you, and you alone, are the actual discoverer of anesthesia."

This momentous interview made a complete change in Long's life. His quiet study became a busy office. Long, his assistants, Caroline, his whist partners, even his patients, were equally interested in the affair, writing letters to friends in Washington, and doing whatever they could to push the claim. Jackson, the helpful Jackson, guided the campaign. He set the pace, and all threads passed through his hands. Vanished was the former rural peace. The doctor's whole circle, the town of Athens, everyone in the neighborhood, was keenly interested in the affair, talking about Dr. Long, "our Dr. Long," who had made one of the greatest discoveries of all time, but had hitherto refrained from making it public. Now a stranger, a most distinguished scientist with a lot of orders and decorations, had come all the way from Boston to Athens seeking out Dr. Long, and persuading him to take action.

"Did you see this Dr. Jackson? Have you heard of him before?" the citizens of Athens asked one another.

"I understand he is on friendly terms with European monarchs. He is one of the greatest men of learning of our day."

Dr. Jackson had become the talk of the town; and with him, of course, Dr. Long.

"I always knew there was something exceptional about our doctor; now it is plain that I was right and that he is a man of mark. But I wonder why he did not come to the front before? Why has he held his tongue all these years?"

"Oh, that's the sort of fellow he is. Truly great discoverers are like that, modest and retiring. Dr. Jackson, when he was here, told someone that the greatest discoverer in England, the famous Dr. Jenner who discovered vaccination, said nothing about the matter for twenty years. Very likely our Dr. Long would have waited twenty years had not this great man from Boston given him a push."

"I understand that this famous Dr. Jackson has asked our senator to bring the matter before Congress. Dr. Long is too modest ever to have thought of such a thing. But this is of prime importance for the state of Georgia. It will attract attention throughout the Union. Dr. Jackson said that it was necessary to push Dr. Long's claim, and that people in Washington must understand how great a man we have here in the South. Of course this Jackson is a Yankee, a Bostonian. But he is not like most Yankees. He is a celebrated man, wholly devoted to scientific pursuits, and an honorary member of various foreign academies. He has received numerous distinctions from European monarchs."

The general opinion in Athens was that the public recognition of Dr. Crawford Long as the discoverer of anesthesia would be of vast importance to the state of Georgia.

At the opening of the new session, Senator Truman Smith was to make another call upon his oratorical talents. The day was approaching when Congress would infallibly vote that the tribute for the discovery of anesthesia must be made to the Boston dentist, William Thomas Green Morton, unless Smith intervened.

But at this juncture, when all were devoting their best energies to making sure who had in fact been the discoverer, Senator Dawson from Georgia rose to protest against the claim of any northern state, whether Massachusetts or Connecticut, to the glory of having given birth to the discoverer of anesthesia. That honor belonged to the South. The discovery had taken place in the state he had the honor to represent, in the state of Georgia.

Senator Dawson waved his hand toward a pile of papers on his desk, but he did not propose to make any detailed use of these. Like the senator from Connecticut he could, of course, ask the committee to toil through a thousand pages of manuscript, but it would be enough for him to take two papers from his well-filled portfolio. Having made this preamble, and selected his exhibits, without bombast and in an ordinary tone he read them to the Senate.

One of them was a receipted account of the year 1842, showing that a student named Venable of Jefferson had paid Dr. Long two dollars for removing a tumor under ether anesthesia. The sober testimony of this receipted account disinterred from many years back produced quite as strong an impression as had Truman Smith's impassioned obituary oration about Horace Wells.

Like Truman Smith, Dawson knew how to make oratorical pauses. He waited until the impression aroused by his reading of the receipt had subsided, and then proceeded to his next exhibit. Here, likewise, his manner was restrained, in marked contrast with the perfervid style of Truman Smith. Nor did he use many words. It would be enough, he said, to introduce the letter he was about to read, which was signed Charles Thomas Jackson, by explaining that Dr. Jackson, the famous experimental chemist and geologist, had written it to him. The Senate would remember that Dr. Jackson had claimed priority over Morton in the discovery of ether anesthesia, believing himself at that time to be the first in the field. That assumption had been justified until, one day, Dr. Jackson was informed that, years before either he or Wells had made any public demonstration of the value of anesthetics, Dr. Crawford Williamson Long, then of Jefferson, Georgia, had successfully performed operations on patients rendered insensible by the inhalation of ether. In the letter he was about to read to the Senate, Dr. Jackson frankly acknowledged that he had been mistaken, but declared he found it necessary to bow before the truth, and to abandon his claim that he had been the original discoverer of anesthesia. That honor belonged to Dr. Crawford Long of Georgia.

Senator Dawson now read Dr. Jackson's actual words. These were clear and precise, and the effect was no less remarkable than had been that of Truman Smith's oratory when he called up from the tomb the specter of Horace Wells. Dawson, in conclusion, said that all southern gentlemen would gladly acknowledge how perfectly correct throughout had been the attitude of Dr. Jackson, the New Englander.

Truman Smith was as much surprised as if a bomb had burst beneath his feet, and privately he took Dr. Jackson to task. Jackson replied: "My dear Senator, I myself was completely unaware that this unknown country doctor in Georgia had stolen a march on us all. Naturally this came as a great shock to me, but my sense of justice compelled me to bow before the might of truth. Besides, there was no longer any possibility of pushing my claim and that of the heirs of Horace Wells."

The faded receipt from the year 1842 had no less effect upon Congress than had had the ghost called up from the Hartford grave. Obviously before a decision about the award was made, Long's claim must be carefully examined by the subcommittee.

Once more, then, the decision was postponed. Jackson's new scheme was working better than he had anticipated. Congress was perplexed by these ghosts from the tomb, these specters from the past. Confusion was heaped upon confusion. Perhaps yet more claimants would appear?

Certainly the examination of the Venable account would not take the subcommittee so long as had the study of the Wells dossier running to one thousand pages of manuscript. But before the members had got to work upon this matter, another document was put in, likewise from the South.

This came from Georgia, too, in the form of a passionate protest against the recognition of Dr. Long as the discoverer. The claim was preposterous, and Senator Dawson ought to have known better than support it, since the true discoverer was another Georgian, Dr. Wilhite who, when still only a medical student, had, three years before Dr. Long, anesthetized a Negro boy with ether. The award, therefore, ought to be made to Dr. Wilhite, and nobody else.

Long's supporters denounced Wilhite as an impostor; the partisans of Wilhite took up the cudgels, and a fine battle began to rage in Georgia.

At this juncture another Richmond appeared in the field, from Connecticut this time. It is true, said the supporters of this new claimant, that the discoverer of anesthesia had been a Connecticut man. Not Horace Wells, however, but Dr. E. E. Marcy, a native of Hartford. Marcy had advised Wells. More important still, whereas Wells had merely experimented with laughing gas, Marcy had used ether. It was Marcy who had substituted ether for laughing gas. There was a young man prepared to swear that in 1845 Dr. E. E. Marcy had removed a tumor from him painlessly, under ether. Dr. E. E. Marcy therefore claimed the award.

Then Senator Hale produced a seventh claimant, another ghost. Like Wells, he was in a strong position, being dead and having left orphaned dependents. "I do not know whether it will have any influence upon the votes of Senators tonight; but there is a gentleman in this chamber now who has informed me," said Senator Hale, "that neither Dr. Morton, nor Dr. Jackson, nor Dr. Wells, had anything to do with the original discovery of this principle; that it was discovered and applied to practice in the city of New York by a young physician who is now in his grave; (that if there is any merit belonging to it at all, it belongs to him,) and if there is any meritorious reward due to anybody, it is to his orphan sister, if the subject is postponed until December, he can by irrefutable proof establish that fact."

Congress did not know what to do. The news that the matter still hung in the wind was calling up claimants all over the place. A number of "jump-up-behinders" appeared on the stage.

Now voices came from abroad. All due respect must be paid to the United States' generous determination to reward the discoverer of anesthesia, but surely it would be a mistake to be led astray by local patriotism, and to claim for America an honor which did not really belong to the New World at all. No doubt inhalation of ether for anesthetic purposes was first practiced in the United States of America, but there the use of ether was merely a transplanted growth. If the subcommittee increased the scope of its investigations, it would find that Robert H. Collyer of Jersey had been the first to use inhalation, in this case of alcoholic vapor, to reinforce mesmerism for the production of insensibility.

Dr. Robert H. Collyer brought the message to America. His first experiments were made in London, in the presence of a chemist named Turner. Four years later, while on a visit to his father (who had settled in New Orleans), he was called to see a Negro with a dislocated hip, and, having given the man the vapor of rum to inhale, he had been able to reduce the dislocation without causing the patient any pain. Then, in 1842, in Philadelphia, by the same method he had painlessly extracted a tooth from a certain Mrs. Allen. Subsequently he had demonstrated the method in Boston, where Morton, Jackson and Wells were mere imitators.

"It is true," wrote Collyer in his memorial to Congress, "that I administered neither laughing gas nor ether, but alcoholic vapor. But surely this makes no difference to the question of priority? Whether alcoholic vapor or laughing gas or ether vapor is used to produce anesthesia can have no more bearing on the question of priority than whether wood or coal is used as fuel to generate steam."

It was true enough that England and not the United States was the place where anesthesia by inhalation was first discovered, but not true that the discoverer was Dr. Robert H. Collyer, native of Jersey. There could be no doubt, said the friend of yet another claimant—another ghost—that the original discoverer was a far worthier man than Dr. Collyer. The very first to discover the pain-allaying effect of the inhalation of vapors or gases, the man who demonstrated his method before scientific authorities in London and in Paris, the mightiest dead in all the world, had been named Henry Hill Hickman.

Dr. Thomas Dudley, a friend of the Hickman family, advocated Hickman's claim to priority, appealing to the affection and justice of mankind. He recalled the fact that Hickman, who had died as long ago as 1830, had, in the 'twenties, first conceived this brilliant idea, which had been despised and rejected by an ignorant world, so that Hickman had died unrecognized. Surely it was the duty of posterity to recognize this claim from the past? If the United States Congress intended to honor the discoverer of anesthesia, no worthier candidate could be chosen than the prematurely deceased English doctor, Henry Hill Hickman.

These claimants both in America and in Europe were all trying to make out that they, or the dead on whose behalf they intervened, had, with their inhalations, discovered the general principle of conquering pain. But what about the mesmerists who had first performed painless operations? There were plenty of persons still living in India and in Scotland who could testify to this. Nay, the first who had ever made a successful use of mesmeric anesthesia for operative purposes was himself still living. Esdaile was his name, and he had devoted his whole career to the task. Now, in retirement at Sydenham, he heard of the intention of the United States Congress to honor and reward the discoverer of the method of painless operation.

Immediately Esdaile addressed an indignant memorial to Congress. He did not ask for any reward, but begged Congress to proclaim the fact that mesmeric anesthesia had been the first successful method of inducing painlessness for the purposes of surgical operations, and that it had been practiced successfully far earlier than anesthesia by the inhalation of gas or vapor.

As if all hell had been let loose, claimants were appearing everywhere. The living and the dead seemed to have entered into a conspiracy to deprive Morton of his reward.

Perhaps this spectral dance would have scared any other man. A less resolute champion than Morton would have laid down his arms in view of so satanic a confusion. But Morton had always been a sticker. Morton was assured of the justice of his claim. He would fight death and the devil, and would go on fighting until he had routed all the other claimants.

But when Congress came down to hard pan, it did not appear that these multifarious claimants had any more serious title than Jackson with his "advice" to Morton or the representatives of Horace Wells with their too voluminous dossier. In rapid succession the committee passed them in review:

"Mr. Wilhite, for a joke you held a flask of ether under a Negro boy's nose. He went sound asleep. Is that all?"

"Dr. Marcy, what was the name of the patient on whom you performed the first painless operation? You have forgotten? That is rather unfortunate."

"Dr. Robert Collyer, will you be good enough to let us see the evidence which shows that you performed a painless operation? Oh, you were attacked by bandits when crossing Mexico and robbed of your proofs? Thank you, Dr. Collyer, that will suffice."

"Please inform Dr. Esdaile that the Committee of Inquiry, after due consideration, has decided that mesmerism is now regarded as out of date, and that his claim to priority cannot be seriously considered."

"Will you please report upon the Dudley-Hickman application?"—"Having examined the material put in, all I am able to ascertain is that Henry Hill Hickman, guided by the previous experience of Sir Humphry Davy, recommended the inhalation of laughing gas to render surgical operations painless, and that he devoted a good deal of time and energy to advocating this idea. Unfortunately, however, he did not get beyond the stage of experiment upon animals, and did not try laughing gas on himself."

"What about Long? Was not Long the first to operate under ether?"—"Certainly. His operations in Jefferson, Georgia, were made as long ago as 1842. But he did not bring the matter before the public. Of what use, then, were his experiments to the world at large? Had he died, meanwhile, he would have taken his discovery to the grave with him, and no one would ever have been the wiser."

After the most careful study of all the claims, the subcommittee came to the conclusion that Dr. William Morton was alone entitled to be regarded as the discoverer of anesthesia. Maybe others before him had said that laughing gas and ether would allay pain. But no one else had said so often, so loudly, and so clearly that this was so, and thus forced a hearing. Who other than Morton had publicly demonstrated anesthesia and proved its efficacy?

Although the others may have conceived the idea of anesthesia, although others might have made this experiment or that, the plain fact that Morton alone ventured to put the idea into sustained practice was enough to justify Morton's claim to priority. He alone proved what for his predecessors had remained mere hypotheses. He alone had the courage to force publicity and to take the risk of a possible mishap. Not one of all those who were now candidates for the honor and glory or for the pecuniary reward, or those dead men whose representatives were pushing their claims, would have been able to say, had the experiment of October 16, 1846 miscarried: "Hold me accountable for the disaster, for I am responsible."

Prior to October 16, 1846, no one knew that painless surgery was a practical possibility, to be achieved with certainty and without danger by the inhalation of ether. It was from the operating theater of the Massachusetts General Hospital that anesthesia began its triumphal march round the world. Thus, at long last, was confirmed the accuracy of the statement made by Congress eight years before: "Morton is the sole and exclusive discoverer."

"But if that be so," said Senator Mallory, at the next meeting of the subcommittee, "the award of $100,000 will rightfully accrue to Morton. I recommend, therefore, that we come to a unanimous decision and secure the speediest possible payment of this sum to Dr. Morton."

"What's the hurry?" asked several members of the subcommittee. The fine gesture of recognition had been frustrated long since by the multifariousness of the claims. Time was now of little moment. The main thing was to insure that no mistake should be made.

More deliberations. Further sittings. Postponement after postponement. More discussions. When the time for a decision came, it was impossible to secure a clear majority on behalf of Morton. There were too many doubters, too many who were afraid that if the award were made to Morton, complaints would be voiced that the nation had honored an unworthy suitor, that the reward had been paid to the wrong man, that Wells's widow was starving in Hartford, that the real discoverer was at Athens, in New York, in England, was someone other than Morton. Why should we expose ourselves to the risk of such accusations? The subcommittee could not come to a plain and straightforward decision, and the last sentence of the report ran: "The committee has no hesitancy in saying, that to the discoverer, the highest honor and reward are due: but to which of these persons the discovery should be awarded, the committee is not unanimous."

Morton was weary of waiting and made a personal appeal to Congress: "Whatever floating notions may have crossed men's minds from the earliest ages, tending to the same end, it must be conceded that the world is no richer for them until it fell to my lot to devote all my energies and sacrifice all my means to its attainment. Now it is fully attained. What was the dream of the philanthropist and the half-formed conjecture of the scientific speculator, has become a household fact. To me alone, of all the world, this result has been fraught with suffering instead of comfort. Of pecuniary sacrifices I will not speak; but surely it was not to have been anticipated that this discovery should have made me the target for the most malicious and envenomed assaults. There are wounds which are sharper than those of the surgeon's knife, and which—

'not poppy, nor mandragora,
nor all the drowsy syrups of the world'

can make us feel less keenly. These have been my portion. I trust that the reward is at hand. I look to you for justice; nothing more, nothing less."

The answer to this appeal took the form of words, brave words —the very words that he had heard when Congress had put the question of his reward upon its agenda. Then these words had been a promise; now they were uttered as his sole compensation. Meanwhile eight years had sped, eight years of hopes and disappointments, expectation and agitation. Always words, words, words, the everlasting refrain about his discovery having been the greatest achievement of America, the pride of the nation, something that would earn the eternal gratitude of his country.

Morton was sick of it all. Shaking the dust of Washington from his feet, he returned home to the loneliness and peace of West Needham. Perhaps he would stay there for the rest of his life, in rural retirement, seeking to forget the torment of these eight years of fruitless waiting.

What little funds he had been able to get together had been carefully invested in a small undertaking which was to provide a livelihood for himself and his dependents. He had gone "back to the land," and would seek solace in agricultural pursuits. He kept fowls, went in for pig-farming and dairy-farming, made butter and cheese, tilled the soil, planted orchards, grew flowers and vegetables.

The farm thrived. His flowers, his vegetables, his fruit, his cereals, his pigs and his poultry were exceptionally good, and helped him to forget. He seemed himself to have become a part of nature, to grow peacefully side by side with flowers and fruit, crops and livestock.

At the close of a local agricultural exhibition, the Agricultural Society of Norfolk County gave a banquet to the farmers of the neighborhood. Morton was invited. To his astonishment, he found that he had been placed at the head of the table. There was the usual farming talk about land and prices, about weather and crops, food and drink. At the end of the meal, a speaker rose and, on behalf of the Agricultural Society, ceremoniously announced that Norfolk County Fair had decided to express its appreciation of the most industrious farmer among them, and to reward him to the best of its ability. All looked at Morton, as his name was pronounced as the chosen recipient of this honor, and he rose, as was proper, to listen.

"Mr. William Thomas Green Morton," said the speaker, "is hereby granted by Norfolk County Fair a prize of $75 for the best dairy produce; a further prize of $20 for important economic improvements; a further prize of $10 for having the finest pair of farm horses; a further prize of $5 for the best breeding sow; a further prize of $5 for the cow Beauty, and a further prize of $3 for his admirable geese." There was vociferous applause; Morton was congratulated; a toast was drunk to his health; and until dawn was at hand the company continued to extol him as the ablest farmer in Norfolk County.

The recognition and the rewards which Morton had hoped for as a benefactor of humanity who had made the greatest discovery of the age were now bestowed upon Morton by his neighbors as a successful farmer, who had produced the finest dairy produce, the best breeding sow and the most beautiful cow in the neighborhood. Sic vita!

CHAPTER SIXTEEN

─────────────────────────────────

Inferno

─────────────────────────────────

A MAN had conferred a wonderful boon on his fellows, by freeing them from the pain of operations. This was a turning point in human history. Destiny would not be content to allow such a man to vegetate in a retired country life. The existence of the Benefactor of Mankind must not end with growing fruit and vegetables and with raising hogs. For him a peculiar fate must be reserved, and, if he were denied a triumph, he could at least be the hero of a tragedy.

That this tragedy might be fulfilled, destiny summoned Dr. William Thomas Green Morton from his rural seclusion, back into the world for further struggles—and for further disappointments.

Morton rose at dawn. He went out to look after his livestock, contemplating each beast and congratulating himself on his prosperity. From the stalls he went into the garden, an unfailing source of delight. What a joy it was to him to contemplate in the early sunlight his fruit trees, his vegetable plots, and his flowerbeds! They were all coming on nicely. While he was busy in the orchard, grafting, the postman came by and looked over the hedge, saying: "A letter for you, Doctor; a letter from Washington."

Morton opened it, and was much excited by the surprising contents.

Shields, the senator from Illinois, who had always enthusiastically espoused his cause, wrote that although the scheme for a national award to Morton had been shipwrecked because there were so many other claimants, a good many members of Congress were of opinion that it was absolutely incumbent upon the United States government to confer some sort of pecuniary recognition upon Dr. Morton for his discovery. Next week there would be a motion to buy Morton's patent rights. This would at any rate provide some sort of compensation for the government's infringement of its own patent. Since Jackson had renounced his share in the patent, no one could deny Morton's exclusive right. Thirty-three senators and one hundred and eighteen congressmen had pledged support. Morton should come to Washington without delay.

That morning Morton grafted a fruit tree for the last time. Never again was he to know another peaceful morning.

Must he really leave West Needham, where he had found happiness? Must he go back to the turmoil of Washington where, perhaps, the fulfillment of his dreams would bring yet greater happiness? Washington lured him by its promise of recognition and reward, by all on behalf of which he had fought for more than ten years. It could assuage him for past torments. Yes, he must go, since his discovery was in question.

"You have done a great deed and your life belongs to it," Dr. Bigelow had said to him in the early days. Bigelow was right. The idyll of West Needham was finished.

The opening of the debate in the Senate, when a motion was introduced proposing that the United States government should buy the patent, was a tribute which before Morton scarcely any private citizen had ever received.

The motion was proposed by Senator Shields of Illinois: "It has been stated that this is one of the greatest discoveries of modern times. I believe it is."

"I have been through the Massachusetts General Hospital, where I saw every form of disease and suffering. I went into the dissecting-room, and I confess my blood almost ran cold as I looked at the instruments of torture, as they appeared to me; but I was assured by the physicians attending upon that hospital that, by the use of this remedial agent, patients were insensible to the operation," said Senator Hall.

"Yes, indeed," interpolated Senator Walker. "I have seen a member of my family suffering under the surgeon's knife, lying

in a calm and peaceful sleep, and yet undergoing one of the most
torturing surgical operations in the world. I felt at that day, rising
in my heart, the feeling that if God should ever give me the opportunity of manifesting my gratitude to the person who had made
this great discovery, I should do so. The opportunity is now offered. Whether the Senate will sympathize with me or not, I
know not, but it is now for them to speak."

Amid a general shout of approval, Senator Mallory from
Florida rose and said: "If the question be asked, what is the character of the service rendered? what is the utility of the discovery?
the response comes from thousands of our fellow citizens, in every
walk of life, whom gratitude has made eloquent. It comes from
the lowly couch of the poorhouse patient, and from the aristocratic mansion of the millionaire; from feeble woman in the pangs
imposed upon her first disobedience, and from the stern, strong
man, writhing in agony. It comes from your battlefields, from
your military, naval, and civil hospitals, from your gallant sailors
and soldiers tortured by wounds and amputations. By hundreds,
people used to commit suicide, so much did they fear the surgeon's
knife. But all this is now past. The knife has lost its terrors, the
appearance of the surgeon is hailed with joy, for he not only
banishes pain, but substitutes for an anguished frame the happy
dreams of a joyous spirit."

"Yes," put in Senator Brown, "for more than two thousand
years the world has been in search of this discovery. It is the most
important boon, I think, which has been given to mankind for
many centuries."

Many other senators heartily supported the proposal.

"Nor must we forget," said one of them, "that the State
adopted Morton's discovery, using anesthesia for the benefit of our
army and our navy. The State granted Morton a patent, and then
infringed that patent. Is it not then right and proper that the
State should undo the wrong it has done?"

If there were any dissentients, surely they should have been
moved by Senator Borland's appeal, which now followed: "I will
briefly sum up. This discovery is a most valuable one to the human
family at large. This idea which we are thus using, not only

prolongs human life, and protects our soldiers and our sailors, and all in our public service from immense suffering, but it is saving, in that mode of treating diseases, thousands upon thousands of dollars every year. . . . We are making use of his property to our great benefit, and he is receiving no compensation whatever for it. The papers before me show that he is the individual entitled to compensation for the use of his property. . . . Then, sir, I ask if this is not a proper occasion for the continuance of this practice?"

"Senator Borland is right"—thus many were disposed to chime in. "It would be unworthy of our great nation to leave uncompensated the man who has made the greatest discovery of the century, a discovery which is a lasting glory to science."

Such were the tributes with which the last act of the drama opened.

But if Morton was in a sense compensated, by these tributes, for his ten years' martyrdom, he was but temporarily uplifted so that the tragedy of his subsequent disappointment might be greater. Since he was raised on a pedestal, the crash which followed did but prove the more overwhelming.

For now the opposition entered the lists. "I denounce this attempt to filch money from the Treasury as an outrage upon the rights of others, and a most abominable imposition upon this Government. . . . Sir, there is that family in destitute circumstances; and I assert that the real discoverer is now in his grave. Will the Senate act upon this matter in this *ex parte* manner? Will they proceed to render judgment against the widow and the orphans, without hearing what they have to say for themselves? I shall ask for an opportunity to be heard in defense of them.

"This individual never sold a patent right, and never pretended to sell a patent right; and, I repeat again, that the mere idea of ascertaining the effect of an old and known article is the subject of contempt and ridicule all over the northern country. Why does not this patentee assert his rights? If he has got any rights under his patent, why does he not sue somebody for their violation? He has never instituted a suit. He has never pretended to enforce the patent in any shape or form. The physicians, surgeons and dentists, all over this continent and all over Europe, are using sulphuric ether as an anesthetic agent, and he has never demanded a penny from them. He knows well enough that he could not recover a penny of damages, if he were to sue them for a violation of his patent rights; I do not care who makes any assertion to the contrary. In my own State, in every State of this Union, it has been administered, I have seen it administered to patients in this city. Why does he not institute a suit against somebody?" [1]

Such were the arguments of the opposition, and they proved victorious, for a considerable majority voted against the proposal, on the grounds that Morton had not taken the trouble to protest against the infringement of his patent.

"The greatest of all discoveries."—"A blessing to mankind and the glory of a nation."—"The discoverer must be honored and rewarded."—Such had been the congratulatory and approving words of Congress eight years before, when the proposal to reward Morton had been under discussion. But nothing came of that proposal. Who had been to blame for the failure? Surely not the government? The government had never refused recognition to the discoverer. Congress had described him as "the greatest son of the nation," and had again and again been ready to award him $100,000. Congress had never stinted its approval of Morton. Year after year, Congress had given a great deal of time to the discussion of the matter. The government could not be held accountable for the fact that, after all these years, Morton's hands were still empty. False claimants, living and dead, had appeared, and had thus sown confusion. Why reproach the government?

The discovery was beyond the scope of reward, but the government had been ready and willing to compensate the discoverer for the infringement of his patent. The government, when proposing to buy the patent, had been most cordial in its praise, declaring again and again that the discovery had been a blessing to mankind, that it was the glory of the nation, and that the discoverer must be both honored and indemnified.

Nor was Congress to blame if Morton remained unrewarded. There had been no lack of generosity. The only reason for with-

[1] Truman Smith.

holding compensation was that the patent had become worthless. That was not the fault of the government, but of Mr. Morton himself, who had failed to protect his patent by bringing its infringement before the courts. Of course this was tantamount to saying that the one who suffered injustice, not the one who committed it, was to blame—but thus the weary round went on.

Why had not Mr. Morton gone to the front? Why had he not taken steps to prevent the army surgeons and naval surgeons from using ether that operations might be painless? Why did not force his way into the operating theaters of the hospitals and snatch the ether flask from the anesthetist's hands? Why had he looked on inertly when his discovery was being used for the benefit of soldiers, sailors and hospital patients? Why had he not made energetic protests against the infringement of his patent? Was it right that the government should pay through the nose because the discoverer had neglected to pursue his rights? Was it proper to ask the government to buy a worthless patent?

Extremely obscure is the meaning of life, obscure to the point of absurdity. How was Morton to understand all this? What did destiny want of him?

Morton had discovered a means for achieving the conquest of pain. The government had granted him a patent in due form. This justified him in issuing licenses which would assure him an income and enable him to provide for his wife and children. This would put him beyond the reach of anxiety.

Then the government had infringed his patent and deprived him of the hoped-for gains. Why? The infringement had been for the welfare of wounded soldiers, for the benefit of the country. Hospitals and private practitioners were quick to follow an example set by the government and to infringe his patent. They all infringed it, and his chance of making money out of his discovery was gone. Why? This was done to alleviate the pain of poor patients. Was he to protest, to interpose a veto?

He had been quick to realize that his discovery was of far wider significance than a mere instrument to make money for a Boston dentist. It could subserve a much more important purpose. He recognized, on his own account, that the discovery must be used for the welfare of all mankind. That was why he had acted as he did, making the use of his discovery free to all, that no sufferer should have to do without it. He had grasped, likewise, that he must renounce private advantage, private happiness. He had risen to the stature of his discovery, aware that the Benefactor of Mankind must be, not petty, but unselfish. He had fallen on evil days, had become impoverished, but, fully alive to the fact that poverty, persecution and suffering were often the lot of the great, he had borne them without complaining—all for the sake of his discovery.

When the United States subsequently honored him with the most exalted tributes, held out to him a reward of $100,000 and then did not give him so much as a cent, he still understood that one who has conferred great benefits on mankind must be prepared to go empty away.

But now the country had again lured him out of his retirement, had showered praises upon him, had talked about compensating him for the infringement of his patent—and had then refused to do so because he had not withheld his discovery from the suffering, because he had renounced personal advantage, because he had been compassionate, and had behaved with the magnanimity which was appropriate to the greatness of his discovery . . . because he had proved himself a worthy Benefactor of Mankind. But that it should be made a reproach to him that he had done these things, and that for this reason his claim to compensation should be rejected—this was really more than Morton could understand.

At West Needham was a quiet garden, and an orchard where fruit trees thrived and bore good fruit. His beasts grazed in the pastures; "Beauty" was going to have a calf. Poultry and vegetables were in good shape, and promised to make provision for his wife and children. There would be another county fair soon, where he probably would be honored again as a successful farmer. At West Needham he could enjoy the calm of the mornings, and the peace of eventide. There he could find tranquillity. Back, back from Washington to the petty joys of a farmer's life.

"Dr. Morton, it would be an unpardonable blunder for you to withdraw at this juncture, to leave everything here in the lurch. Do not give up your cause as lost.

"The assignment of a national reward must be left to the magnanimity of the government—but compensation for the infringement of a patent granted by the government and then infringed by the government is a matter of plain duty. If the government will not do it spontaneously, the government must be forced. You have an indisputable right to compensation, Dr. Morton. You must no longer beg; you must demand.

"Thirty-two senators and one hundred and sixteen congressmen are prepared to support your claim and fight vigorously on your behalf. But don't bother about Congress any more. Apply direct to the President of the United States. He will see that you get your rights. You must do this for the sake of your wife and children, and not heedlessly abandon your rights."

Senator Shields, Senator Mallory and Senator Borland all gave him the same advice. "You must on no account go home at this juncture. Fight the thing through. Insist upon your rights."

That the tragedy of a life should be fulfilled there was needed, not only the assaults of adversaries, not only the ingratitude of the world, not only poverty and derision—not only all these hostile forces—but also the blind folly of the hero, who was tempted by his friends, and yielded. What despair and disappointment might never have achieved, this mistaken but well-intentioned advice achieved. The sorest wounds were the wounds with which he was wounded in the house of his friends.

"Don't forget that you are in the right, Dr. Morton." Such was the plea of the tempters. The tempters continually assured him that he was within his "rights." The appeal was always from his friends. "Two-and-thirty senators and one hundred and sixteen congressmen are ready to fight in your behalf"—"Do not give up the cause as lost." The tempters awakened hope; reminded him of his duty to his wife and children. In all friendliness, the voices spoke as they would have spoken if their design had been to thrust him into the abyss.

Destiny would not allow Morton to shake the dust of Washington off his feet, and seek the refuge of his farm.

No, his friends in the Senate and in the House urged him to stay and fight valorously for his claims. They would help him through. They assured him that the State would be compelled to grant him his plain rights. Was he, not only to abandon his own cause, but to leave his friends and helpers in the lurch?

Morton wrote to the President of the United States, using the words advised by persons who were well informed about such matters.

"The undersigned," he wrote in his petition, "holds a patent. From motives which must be apparent from the nature of the subject, and relying upon the justice and magnanimity of the government, he has not hitherto exercised his legal rights by suits at law for damages or injunctions to prevent the use of a discovery which has happily proved so beneficent to humanity. Nor would he now take any such steps, but that his forbearance is sought to be turned to his disadvantage, and objection is made to granting compensation by an act of Congress, on the ground that he ought to enforce his right under his patent against the officers of the United States using his discovery in the military, naval, and marine service, and against all persons violating the same. He therefore with great reluctance respectfully asks the government either to buy the patent or else to discontinue the use of ether."

The leading authorities in the Army and the Navy were glad to give him declarations in support of his claims, and authorized him to append their names to his petition.

"In compliance with your verbal request, I have to state," wrote Staff Surgeon General Lawson, "that at the present moment it is believed that no surgical operation of importance is performed by the medical officers of the army without the aid of some anesthetic agent. Although the discovery of this new therapeutic effect of sulphuric ether has led to the introduction and employment of other anesthetic agents, this does not in any way militate against the merits of the original discovery, which I regard as one of the most important and valuable contributions to medical science, and to the relief of suffering humanity."

Thomas Harris, Senior Surgeon of the Navy, in his reply to Morton, described the latter's discovery as the most important philanthropic contribution to the welfare of America, and concluded with the words: "It is earnestly hoped that our Government, with a similar appreciation of this great acquisition to medical science, will stamp their sense of its importance, by a substantial acknowledgement which will remunerate you in some measure for the toil and vexation attendant on your struggle for success."

Destiny, having vowed his destruction, continued to nourish his hopes. The President's favorable reception of his petition naturally convinced him that he had been right to follow his friends' advice.

Since 1853 Franklin Pierce, a New Hampshire Democrat, had been president of the United States. He lent a most gracious ear to Morton's petition, saying he would do his utmost to insure that the injustice which had been done to the "greatest son of the nation" should be adequately atoned for. He would personally intervene in Morton's behalf.

In 1829 an English scientist named James Smithson had made a bequest similar to that of Montyon in France nine years earlier. He left the sum of £105,000 to the government of the United States in trust "to found at Washington an establishment, under the name of the Smithsonian Institution, for the increase and diffusion of knowledge among men." The bequest became operative in 1835, and in 1838 the United States government received from the Court of Chancery of Great Britain the sum of $515,169, and, with the aid of further resources, the Institution was duly founded. The famous John Quincy Adams played a considerable part in the affair; and in 1846, the year of Morton's discovery, the noted physicist, Joseph Henry, became secretary of the Smithsonian Institution.

That all objections to the governmental compensation of Morton might be averted, President Pierce now commissioned the Smithsonian Institution to draw up an unprejudiced opinion regarding the scientific value of the patent, and also concerning its value to mankind and to the country. The Army and Navy authorities were likewise to be consulted. President Pierce was determined to be sure of his ground.

He instructed the senators and congressmen who were interested in Morton's cause as follows: "Gentlemen, assure Dr. Morton from me that his position is extremely favorable. All expert opinion supports his claim. He need merely have patience while certain formalities are arranged."

The profits of the little farm at West Needham had been enough to enable Morton to keep his wife and children in modest comfort and, by degrees, to pay off his debts. But the expenses of this long stay at the seat of Federal government, during the tedious consideration of his cause, were considerable. Of course, there was no lack of usurers who would have been ready to finance Morton had he applied to them. But as soon as it became generally known that the President of the United States was personally in favor of Morton's claims, the moneylenders spontaneously came to Morton with offers of help.

Morton hesitated for a while; but his friends, men of mark, assured him that the prospects were most auspicious, and that it would be madness to refuse the proffered help. To begin with, therefore, he obtained a sum of $4000 on his note of hand, and then gave another promissory note for $2000 more. What could these sums matter when it was only a question of fulfilling a few formalities, and then everything would be in order? The recognition of his patent rights would assuredly bring in more than ten times that amount, since there was considerably more at stake than mere compensation by the Union.

Far away in Russia, the Crimean War was raging. The Russian Army was using his method of anesthesia. No one had paid him a cent on this account. England had introduced ether anesthesia into the colonies. Morton's friends assured him that if the United States compensated him for the infringement of his patent rights, this would be a precedent, and would induce England, Russia and other States to give additional compensation.

Morton was already planning, as soon as matters were settled at Washington, to visit Europe and there represent his claims. Never before had there been such chances of success. His hopes ran high.

He signed another note of hand for $4000.

Meanwhile a year ran by. Expert opinion was in Morton's favor. The formalities were practically complete.

When Mr. Witte, who was one of the President's friends, called on Franklin Pierce on March 22, 1855, to urge the signing of the treasury order which would insure the payment of compensation to Morton, the President said: "Come again tomorrow, my dear Witte. I shall have all the documents in hand by then, and shall sign the order in good time."

When Witte turned up on March 23rd, at about ten, the documents lay on the President's desk.

"Good morning, Witte. Now we'll deal with your protégé's affair, and see that he gets his rights. This man who has done such good service to our Army and Navy has certainly needed a great deal of patience. Sit down, my dear Witte, while I see that I have all my documents. Yes, here is the report of the Smithsonian Institution; also the report from the Massachusetts General Hospital. Both quite in order. Here, too, is the opinion of the Chief Surgeon of the Navy. Morton could not have a better testimonial."

While fluttering his papers, the President picked up his pen, prepared to sign his approval.

"Yes, and here is another testimonial, one from the Army command this time. Splendid. Couldn't be better." Still holding the pen, he said, "Just listen," and read aloud: "Although the discovery of this new therapeutic effect of sulphuric ether has led to the introduction of other anæsthetic agents, this does not in any way militate against the merits of the original discovery."—"Yes, everything is in order." Laying the authorization on the top, he prepared to sign. The point of his pen was already in contact with the paper, ready to write the name that would acknowledge the justice of Morton's claim and make him happy at length. One could hear the creaking of the pen, as Pierce began to write. One, two, three letters had been formed. Then the pen ceased to move. Next the President put down his pen, and scanned the document once more, the testimonial from Surgeon General Lawson. He read it again aloud: ". . . other anæsthetic agents, this does not in any way militate against the merits of the original discovery." Again he read: ". . . does not in any way militate against the merits of the original discovery." But wait a minute: "Other anæsthetic agents." After a moment's reflection, he turned to Witte, and said: "There is a point which is not yet exactly clear to my mind, as to whether the patent includes all anesthetic substances—for instance, chloroform, and to prevent any more doubt, I think it will be better to refer it to the Attorney General."

He saw that his friend was a trifle concerned, that Witte's face was somewhat clouded.

"Don't you worry, my dear Witte, the matter is of trifling importance. Still, I think I had better get more precise information about this chloroform. We shall have the opinion of our chief legal authority within a very few days. Morton's claims will not be endangered by a little delay. You can tell him from me that the matter is as good as settled. You have seen for yourself that everything lies ready for signature on my desk."

While the Attorney General was studying the question whether Patent 4848 covered the use of chloroform, spring passed into summer, summer into autumn, and autumn into winter. Soon the gardens of Washington bore witness to the advance of a new spring; flowers were sprouting, the trees were turning green, the birds were tuning up.

"A whole year has passed, Mr. President," said Witte, "and the matter is still unsettled."

"I will write today to the Attorney General, and hurry him up," promised Pierce. "Come early next week. We're sure to have an answer by then."

At West Needham, too, spring was on the way. The sunlit mornings were peaceful and pleasant. But the owner of West Needham was detained in Washington.

"Dr. Morton, your notes of hand are overdue. The matter of compensation has been hanging in the wind for more than a year. You keep on telling us that everything is as good as settled. Why does the President go on putting off his signature to the document? When will it be definitely approved?"

"Mr. Witte, what is happening? Is the President going to

sign?" asked Morton impatiently, when Witte came to see him after the audience previously recorded.

"Have patience, my dear friend; only a little more patience. The President has written to the Attorney General urging a prompt answer. The Attorney General has replied that he must have more light upon the matter before he can give a formal opinion."

"I really don't understand," said Morton. "What the devil has chloroform to do with my discovery?"

"I fancy some other difficulties may have cropped up, but I do not think they will prove insuperable. The last time I saw Mr. Pierce he told me he hoped that everything would soon be settled to your best advantage. Have patience, my dear friend, a little patience."

"Dr. Morton, our patience is at an end," said the money-lenders. "We advanced you considerable sums in the belief that the matter of compensation for your patent would speedily be settled by the President. Again and again you fobbed us off with new assurances, but what we want is the cash. We have given you a long rope, but really we must ask you to settle up. No more excuses or expectations please. Why don't you go and see President Pierce, and ask him how the matter stands? If everything is in as good shape as you imply, he will surely grant you an audience? Anyhow, Dr. Morton, if the matter is not settled by the end of this month, and you cannot redeem your notes of hand, we shall be reluctantly compelled to attach your property at West Needham."

Witte managed to arrange for Morton to see President Pierce. The latter was most encouraging. He had been on the very point of approving the compensation to Morton, when a trifling technical difficulty arose. Yes, it was a great pity, really a great pity. The chloroform question no longer stood in the way, but other little matters had intervened.

"Can you explain to me, Dr. Morton, why you never took legal proceedings when all the world was infringing your patent? If only you had done that, there would not be the smallest difficulty about granting your petition."

"Mr. President, I did not wish to withhold the advantages of my discovery from any patient who had to undergo an operation."

"That was very fine of you, Dr. Morton, very fine indeed. But still, as you can easily understand, this makes it rather difficult to grant your petition. Just as did some of the congressmen, so the Attorney General considers this weakens your claim. You really ought to have brought a suit against someone, for infringing your patent. I am giving a great deal of time and thought to this matter. I am fully aware that you deserve reward or compensation of some sort for your discovery; I know quite well that it is our duty to recognize you in some way—if only we can agree upon a form to which no legal objections could be raised. In fact, I think I see a way out of the difficulty. Why should you not now undertake what you previously neglected to do? That would put everything in perfect order. Don't you think so?"

The President went on to expound his notion in greater detail. Morton was, *pro forma,* to bring a suit for infringement of his patent. Since he could not take proceedings directly against the United States, the best thing would be for him to sue some doctor or surgeon in the government service for having infringed his rights. Then the government would step into the breach. There could be no question that the suit would be decided in favor of Morton, and the validity of the patent would thereby be legally established. The legal advisers of the government, however, were of opinion that before any sum could properly be paid to Morton as compensation, some such legal decision in favor of Morton must be secured.

"As you can see, my dear doctor, we have given very close attention to your claim. Follow the advice of the legal luminaries, and everything will go well."

Morton was fully convinced that the President, the leading figure in the United States, meant well by him, and sincerely desired to get his petition out of the blind alley in which it had become entrapped. Surely Franklin Pierce's kind and reassuring words ought to have contented him? Yet they inspired him with deep anxiety, and he was in two minds when he came away from the White House.

The fact was that he had been only half-hearted when, yielding to the advice of his friends in the House and the Senate, he had stood upon his rights and petitioned the President. Still, he had yielded to temptation, and the tempters continued to whisper in his ear. The President himself had now become one of them, asking: "Why hesitate? Go ahead, and bring a suit." The senators, the congressmen, all his friends and supporters sang the same tune: "Follow the President's advice. He wishes you well. Undoubtedly the most reasonable course, nay the only possible course, will be to sue. Don't go on thinking about it. Do what President Pierce advises. Everyone who has your welfare at heart gives you the same advice," said the tempters. "You cannot, at this juncture, withdraw your hand from the plough."

Yet he found it hard to decide on bringing a lawsuit. His wish had been to devote his discovery to the general advantage of mankind. Was he now to bring ether into the law courts? Was he to withdraw his discovery from its proper field, that of the relief of pain, and trail it through the courts? It seemed intolerable that he should have to go into the legal arena, and sue there about the price he was to extract for the relief of suffering.

"But the President and the others have all given you the same advice. They would not urge you to do anything unethical. They alone fully understand the legal technicalities involved, the legal obstacles in the way. The lawsuit is a mere formality." The tempters always found fresh arguments to overcome his inward reluctance.

Conflict raged in Morton's mind. Before he could finally decide, he must return to West Needham. He needed rest after all these agitations and tensions. The long succession of hope and disappointment had shattered his nerves. At home, perhaps, far from the fret and worry of Washington, he would be able to think matters over quietly. He would confer with Elizabeth. She would advise him for or against bringing the lawsuit. In the quiet mornings on the farm, he would regain mental peace, and find energy to continue the struggle.

"I am going home for a few days' rest," he told the friends who implored him to hesitate no longer. At West Needham he found a situation with which previous bitter experience had made him familiar. Elizabeth was in tears. His furniture was being seized. "Men in possession," sent by the moneylenders, sat in the dining room wearing their hats, and issuing orders. The sheriff was at their backs.

For two days the bailiffs had been there. The usurers had heard a rumor that Morton's case was not going well. They knew that other vultures would gather round the carcass, and wanted to be first in the field. Hence the seizure. The creditors were there as well as the bailiffs and the sheriff. The creditors said:

"You seem surprised to see us, Dr. Morton. You think we ought to have waited a little longer before taking this peremptory action?" They spoke harshly: "It is months and months since your notes of hand became due. Again and again we have believed your assurances that all would be well. A few weeks back you declared that the matter was about to be settled. We waited until, three days ago, you told us the result of your audience. What did you communicate to us? Nothing at all. You had nothing to say, because, apparently, the President had had nothing to say to you. You are a litigant, that is all, and likely to be an unsuccessful one. We need our money back, and cannot wait any longer because you have 'good prospects.'"

To emphasize their words, they showed him the list of goods they were about to seize.

Morton went out into the garden, and thence to the barn. Nothing here belonged to him any more. "Beauty," who had been given a prize at the show, the other pedigreed animals, the trees in the orchard—all, all had been pledged long since. Even the morning calm from which he had hoped so much seemed to have vanished, as if the usurers had levied on that too.

They followed him into the garden, where they continued to pester him with reproaches and questions:

"So that is all you possess? This is your famous model farm? How do you think you will ever be able to redeem your notes of hand? There is not enough here for two of the notes, even if we sell everything without leaving you a stick of furniture and bring all your farm stock under the hammer. How do you propose to pay the third one, and the overdue interest? With fresh notes of hand, we suppose?"

Within a week Morton's furniture, estate and farm stock were to be sold by public auction. After the sale, he would still be over head and ears in debt, and he could see no prospect of ever freeing himself from the burden. What would happen to Elizabeth and the children? Without his home at West Needham, without a farm, without the remotest possibility of earning the necessaries of life, what would become of himself and his family?

This was no time for troubling about conscientious scruples, those that had troubled him before he left Washington. Circumstances alter cases, and the need for daily bread came first.

The principal creditor was a man whom Morton had known for a long time, and was more approachable than the others. The debtor had a private talk with him. Since Morton had already made up his mind to follow the President's advice, he would perhaps be able to persuade Mr. Stone that here was a last chance worth taking.

"Listen to me, sir," he said, "and trust me once more. If you can help me out of my present hole, you'll get all your money back in the end. President Pierce has personally advised me to bring an action against some employee of the government, and has led me to believe that if I do so the government will, in the end, buy my patent. I did not start a lawsuit before leaving Washington, I could not make up my mind to do so. I came here to think matters over and discuss them with my wife. But now I have decided to bring the suit, which I expect to win, and if so I shall be able to clear off all my debts. Tomorrow let us go back together to Washington, where you will be able to convince yourself that I have been speaking the truth. Have a talk with your own lawyer as to my chances of winning litigation which the President himself has advised me to bring. Meanwhile give me a further loan, a last one, that I may leave my wife and children in funds, and have enough to start the suit. You have nothing to gain by proceeding to extremities, and reducing me to beggary. I am not simply advising you to throw good money after bad when I ask you to extend me a little more credit which will almost certainly enable me to settle all my obligations and more. What I own here in West Needham will remain pledged to you, but, meanwhile, my wife and children will be able to go on living here so that, without needless anxiety, I can devote my best energies to the litigation."

Mr. Stone was skeptical at first. "We have waited too long already," he objected. In the end, however, he said he would have a talk with the other creditors.

"You still trust him, Mr. Stone? He is only a litigious fool. I think we had better save what we can out of the wreck."

"But the President has actually promised that if he brings the action and wins it, the government will buy his patent. Since we have waited so long, let us give him one more chance, which is a chance for ourselves as well. We shall get very little out of selling him out, and the loan he asks for does not seriously increase our risk."

The others were stubborn, and insisted upon the auction.

"Very well, then, I will take all the liabilities upon myself," said Mr. Stone. "I don't know why, but I can't help thinking that the man will get his rights."

Mr. Stone bought the other notes of hand, took the furniture and the farm with its livestock in pledge, renewed the bills, and advanced Morton an additional sum to enable him to begin the trial.

Once more, then, Morton was spared the worst. He was not going to be sold out immediately. Well, he must get to work energetically in Washington, and engage the best lawyer on behalf of his suit.

Mr. Witte and his other friends assured him he was taking the right course. Experienced lawyers were confident he would win his case.

Morton was being asked to bring the suit only for form's sake, that the government might be enabled to rally to the defense of the accused doctor, and compensate him for damage. It was decided to make Dr. Charles A. Davis of the Naval Hospital the defendant.

Jackson heard what was in the wind, and called on Davis.

"My dear sir, why on earth have you agreed to act as defendant in this suit? Why should you allow yourself to be subjected to this publicity, when you had every right to use ether as you did? Morton was not the first to use ether in operations. You ask Dr. Crawford Long whether he did not operate under ether anesthesia four years before Morton applied for a patent. I can assure you that Dr. Long would never have objected to any of his colleagues using it. He would not have dreamed of doing so, being a reputable physician fully aware of his professional responsibilities, and knowing that every medical discovery must at once be made publicly available. Then this unprincipled tooth carpenter forced his way into medical ranks, and wanted to use anesthesia as a source of profit. It is most unfortunate that persons of standing should ever have been found in the United States to tolerate such unscrupulousness. But you and I, who are conscientious practitioners, must not allow such a scoundrel to feather his nest by using a medical discovery in a purely business spirit and as a means of private profit. I am sure that after a moment's reflection you will be convinced that you are making a serious mistake if you allow yourself to be used as a pawn in this game of Morton's."

Dr. Davis was profoundly impressed by Jackson's words. His colleague was perfectly right, and he must not allow himself to be used as the tool of a money-grubber. If Morton should win his case, this would mean that no other doctor would be free to use ether. It would never do to become confederate in such a scheme.

"Your arguments are perfectly sound, Dr. Jackson. But the action is already under way; I don't quite see what I can do."

"There is plenty for you to do, Dr. Davis. I know that Dr. Long is on our side, and that he will be ready to testify to having been the first to use ether as an anesthetic. He will swear, moreover, that, as the original and genuine discoverer, he was ready to allow any of his colleagues to administer ether for operations. No decent practitioner could take any other line."

"Are you sure we can rely on Dr. Long?"

"Absolutely certain. Dr. Long is an old friend of mine. I know what he thinks about this sordid business, and I will have a talk with him without delay. But there are others among our professional colleagues, quite a lot of them, who will share our point of view. I am convinced that American medical practitioners, as soon as their eyes are opened—always excepting the clique of the Massachusetts General Hospital—will refuse to countenance such attempts to chaffer with human suffering, and will energetically protest. Everyone concerned about the honor of our profession will rally to its defense against Morton's skinflint methods. It is our joint business to safeguard one of humanity's most sacred treasures, the healing art which exists for the help of every sufferer. We doctors must not allow ourselves to be led astray by the politicians. Politics has one standard, and medicine has another."

"Do you really think, Dr. Jackson, that we could be successful in such a course? You must not forget that Morton has the backing of many senators and congressmen. These politicians have a lot of influence."

"My dear sir, justice always prevails, even against politicians, even against those who sit in the seats of the mighty. We shall fight with pure hearts to prevent an avaricious man turning to his own advantage what belongs to mankind. We shall win, and the United States—nay, mankind at large—will be grateful to us for having rescued ether anesthesia from the claws of a greedy vulture and preserved it for the general advantage of our species. I believe in my mission, and all I ask of you is that you protest against this improper action which has been brought against you. I will see to the rest, and let me assure you that you will find me a man of my word."

Yes, in one sense Dr. Jackson was a man of his word.

"I am sorry to have to tell you," said Morton's lawyer, "that your suit against Dr. Davis makes no progress. The accused intends to produce 'important material' received from Dr. Crawford Long to show that your whole claim to the patent is invalid. The court intends to summon experts to examine Long's material before hearing our case. I am afraid we have a long and arduous campaign before us."

Dr. Jackson called on Burnett, the apothecary.

"What did I always tell you about Morton? I sized him up from the first. Now he has dropped his mask, and disclosed himself as a hard, avaricious, unfeeling man of business. Yet it is this Mammon-worshiper to whom the University of Maryland has given an honorary degree. Why, even the President has promised him support! Congress described him as the Benefactor of Mankind. Certainly the rascal got ahead of me there. The matter has become a public scandal. The cheat has led the government by the nose. Surely this might have been avoided, and would have been avoided if people had listened to me."

Jackson visited others besides Burnett: the secretaries of the medical societies, the dentists; he buttonholed acquaintances in the street, and used the same sort of words and phrases he had used to Burnett.

Then he went to Washington, for a few days, on some geological affair—or so he said. Really he went to lobby, repeating to everyone the same tirade: "What did I always say?" etc., etc. On the way home to Boston, he broke the journey at Baltimore, and spent some profitable hours in the corridors of the university. Then his "geological business" led him to New York, for the doctors there must be kept informed how a fleecer and cheat was trying to fleece the government.

When lobbying at Washington, when talking to the secretaries of the medical societies, to university professors, officials, drugstore keepers, doctors and dentists in Boston, Washington, Baltimore and New York, his accusing voice was incessantly heard: "What did I always say about Morton? A money-grubber. A man of business with no bowels of compassion. Yet our senators actually give their support to such a rascal."

He was never weary in ill-doing, and unfortunately his words did not fall on deaf ears. There are always so many who are glad to hear that one reputed to have done a great deed is really a scoundrel.

"Have you heard what Morton is up to now? It's really too bad, this action he is bringing against Dr. Davis of the Naval Hospital. No one with a grain of decency would do anything of the kind. Even if the government did grant him a patent, it is most unethical of him, this attempt to prevent his colleagues' using his discovery for the welfare of all the sick without exception.

Only a man devoid of human feeling would try to turn such a discovery to his own profit."

Such were the opinions voiced on all hands, in Washington and in Boston, in Baltimore and in New York—wherever the case of Morton versus Davis came up for discussion. And it was almost universally discussed. The doctors especially were outraged by the course Morton was taking. Even the most moderate among them considered that it was "incompatible with proper medical feeling for any professional man to impose restrictions upon the use of a discovery intended for the relief of human suffering." Most of them went so far as to demand that Morton should no longer be regarded as a member of the medical confraternity and should be deprived of his title to practice. "We do not want any such rascal in our ranks, a man who fights for a patent, and insists, in cold blood, that no one shall be allowed to relieve pain without paying for authorization."

Only the staff of the Massachusetts General Hospital would not heed these malicious distortions, having faith, not merely in Morton the discoverer, but in Morton the human being. They knew him, and fully understood the circumstances which had led him to bring the suit against Dr. Davis. He was a man embittered by ingratitude, who could find no other expedient for promoting his cause. They answered in very plain terms when the representatives of the Medical Society tried to enlist them against Dr. Morton.

"We have not modified our opinion of Dr. Morton by one jot or tittle," replied Dr. Bigelow. "What we say of him today is precisely what we said ten years ago, inscribing it on the casket given to him by the General Hospital: 'He has become poor in a cause which has made the world his debtor.' We know his achievements, we know him personally, and we shall therefore be loyal to him. He may have made a mistake in bringing this action against Dr. Davis. But why does no one ask who led him into this lawsuit? Why does no one blame Congress for having refused to compensate Morton for the infringement of his patent, alleging as the reason that he was not entitled to compensation because, for years, he had allowed everyone to use his discovery freely? Was it not Congress which reduced him to despair; and

was it not the President of the United States who advised him to
bring this lawsuit?"

"You seem to forget, Dr. Bigelow," said the representatives of
the Medical Society, "that a doctor should listen to no voice but that
of his own conscience. Morton's lawsuit is utterly out of keeping
with professional ethics. What Congress may have decided about
the matter of patent rights is no concern of ours as medical practitioners, nor are the views of the President. These things have
nothing to do with the case. It does not behoove us as doctors
to pass judgment on what Congress or the President of the United
States may have decided, but it does behoove us to pass judgment
on the behavior of a colleague who was accepted into our corporation because of a discovery he made and who is today entitled to
style himself Doctor of Medicine. The course of action, by the
outcome of which he is now overwhelmed by debts, was so dis-
graceful that we must protest in the strongest terms against his
remaining a member of our honorable company. You, Dr. Bigelow, and all the members of the staff of the General Hospital, must
surely agree with us upon this point?"

Bigelow replied: "Ten years ago, when the first amputation
under anesthesia was about to take place, we could not agree with
your view of Mr. Morton's conduct. Nor can we agree with you
today. You must follow your own judgment about his alleged
infringement of professional standards. But we who performed
the first painless operation with the aid of his discovery do not feel
competent to judge him; we are too greatly indebted to him; and
our only attitude toward him must be one of profound gratitude."

Owing to the position taken by the staff of the Massachusetts
General Hospital, it was impossible to secure in Boston a majority
of doctors to censure Morton.

It was otherwise in New York where, regardless of Morton's
great services to the profession and to mankind at large, and paying
no heed to the peculiar circumstances which had led him to bring
suit against Dr. Davis, but thinking only of the strict obligations of
"professional ethics," there was passed upon the offender a judgment which was equivalent to a sentence of professional death.

At its headquarters in New York the American Medical Association declared that Dr. Morton, by bringing actions against fellow practitioners and against charitable institutions on the ground that they infringed his patent, had put himself outside the pale of an honorable profession. Since Dr. Morton's behavior was unworthy, and since he had taken out a patent for anesthesia, the Association strongly protested against the proposed reward.

The tragedy of Morton's life, to which were added the accusation of his enemies, the ingratitude of the world, poverty and neglect, and all the other forces which can be centered upon a devoted head, was now to be consummated when a misguided public opinion turned against him.

Thanks to the decision of the American Medical Association and to the general anger aroused throughout the medical profession of the United States by the ill-advised lawsuit against Dr. Davis, there had been produced in the general public a state of mind in which any rumor about the scapegoat—however petty and untrustworthy—might find credence. The harvest season had come for Jackson's schemes. The slanders he had for years been busily spreading about Morton now bore abundant fruit.

"Did you ever hear those stories about his younger days?"

"I say, has anyone told you how he cheated his creditors?"

"Yes, those games he was up to with his promissory notes!"

"I know, and I have been told that he made his way into the hospital by means of forged papers."

"That medal of his is faked."

"He has no genuine right to call himself a doctor."

"I believe in some of the hospitals he snatched the ether bottle out of the doctor's hands while an operation was going on."

"Yes, he's a skinflint."

Thus did one speak to another; and everyone, believing it, was eager to pass on the word. Buzz, buzz.

These cruel slanders reached Morton's ears in his retirement at West Needham. The place was no longer his own, for he was no more than the unwelcome guest of his creditors. Still, he had hoped, there, in the bosom of his family, to creep into hiding.

"Papa, papa, come to the window. Some of the boys from the

other farms are bringing us an enormous doll!" shouted his youngest daughter, as she seized him by the sleeve and pulled him to the window.

A number of unlicked cubs, shouting and laughing, were approaching the house. They carried a sort of scarecrow, dressed in a frock coat.

"But Papa—that is meant to be Papa!" the little girl suddenly screamed as she got a clearer view.

Morton staggered, and almost fell. Yes, this puppet was meant for him! The whole neighborhood was going to burn him in effigy, before the very eyes of his own children.

"Lizzie," he said to the little girl, "come away from the window, do."

"No, no!" screamed the child. "What are they going to do with you, Papa?" She banged on the window with her little fists, and then shrieked in terror: "No, no, don't let them!" She burst out crying.

Outside the window, the effigy had been tied to a tree, and now the hooligans were setting fire to it.

Their howls of derision, their invectives, their foul abuse, penetrated every corner of the house.

The whole neighborhood had assembled and was greedily watching.

Yes, calumny and disgrace had followed him to this last refuge. Even the countryfolk of West Needham had turned against him, and were publicly disgracing him before his family.

Now a despairing letter came from Elizabeth's mother. Many people had lately written to Mr. Whitman, saying the most horrible things about his son-in-law. "Your father is ashamed to leave the house. The newspapers are full of the scandal. How could William do such things?"

Letter after letter brought bad news, telling of fresh accusations, of additional calumnies. Elizabeth was afraid to show her husband the mail.

"He was criticized on all sides for taking out the patent," wrote Morton's widow long after his death. "Abuse and ridicule were showered upon him by the public press, from the pulpit, and also by prominent medical journals. . . . In those days I feared to look into a newspaper, for what wife does not feel more keenly unjust aspersions on her husband than he for himself. Then, too, the world's way—jealousy, malice, and envy, was new to me." [1]

Why had Congress rejected his demand for compensation? Why, notwithstanding the President's approval, had his petition never got beyond the Attorney General? Why had the government, in the end, refused to pay him so much as a cent? Simply because he had not bothered about his rights under the patent, allowing the Army, the Navy, the hospitals and private practitioners the free use of ether, instead of taking steps to interfere and ruthlessly defending his rights. That was the reproach which had been leveled against him; that was why his claim for compensation had been rejected. Well, what was happening now? Now people rallied against him because he had tried to defend his rights under the patent, because he had brought suit against a doctor in the government service. He was described as a close-fisted patentee, an unconscionable rogue, simply because he had acted on the advice of distinguished senators and the President of the United States in the hope of defending his rights. What a muddle life was! He could not understand. It had become intolerable.

At length he had a nervous breakdown. After crying spells and fits of despair, he was so profoundly exhausted that he had to take to his bed. These paroxysms came again and again, at shorter intervals. His health was already much impaired by years of trouble and anxiety, but now his condition had grown positively dangerous.

"I have become," wrote Dr. Morton to a medical friend, "a perfect sensitive plant. I am chilled by the slightest changes of weather; a little extra fatigue brings on a spasmodic action. . . . My nervous system seems so completely shattered, that a trifling surprise or sudden noise sends a shock all over me. I am so restless that I cannot lie or sit long in any position, by day or night. Then convulsive pains seize me suddenly, without any premonitory warning or apparent cause, and my limbs are instantly drawn up by the intensity of the cramps, which rack me so that I cannot prevent

[1] Elizabeth Morton in *McClure's Magazine*, September, 1896.

screaming until I fall exhausted. . . . My eyes feel heavy and painful, and neuralgic pains, like the pricking of needles, dart from them to all parts of my head; similar shocks or pains often rise from the lower portions of the back. . . . After the subsidence of one of these attacks, my limbs tremble, and I feel dizzy, weak and despondingly sick. The disorder has not diminished for the last four years, but seems rather to increase in the frequency and severity of the attacks."

Such was the letter penned by William Thomas Green Morton, the hero of the struggle against pain.

What had become of all the praises, of all the brave words about his being "the pride of the nation," and "America's greatest son"? They had been voiced years ago, in Congress, the forum of the United States, which had described him as "the Benefactor of Mankind." Had they been wholly forgotten? Would nothing be left him other than shame and disgrace?

Oh, no. The words of praise and recognition were to be uttered once more, publicly and ceremoniously, in the same sonorous phrases. They were to be uttered once more—that the cup of mockery might be filled.

When the suit against Dr. Davis was held up indefinitely, owing to the machinations already described, since there seemed little or no prospect of Morton's ever receiving compensation from the government, Mr. Stone, the moneylender, grew impatient.

Morton's lawyer had advised him to bring an additional lawsuit against a private company, the "New York Eye Infirmary," which was making Morton's inhaler for export, on the ground that it was thereby infringing his patent rights. Perhaps this would give the other proceedings a jog.

The case came to trial before a jury, with Judge Shipman presiding. The judge raised the question whether Morton's patent was a valid one, and upon hearing the argument decided that the patent was invalid and dismissed the case. Morton's counsel moved for a new trial. On December 1, 1862, Judge Shipman denied the motion and delivered the following opinion: "A discovery is not patentable. . . . It is only where the explorer has gone beyond the domain of mere discovery and has laid hold of the new principle, force, or law, and connected it with some particular medium or mechanical contrivance by which, or through which, it acts on the material world, that he can secure the exclusive control of it under the patent laws. Sever the force or principle discovered from the means or mechanism through which he has brought it into the domain of invention, and it immediately falls out of that domain. . . ."

This last and most crushing blow, dealt Morton by Judge Shipman's decision that the patent which had been granted by the government was primarily invalid, was accompanied by the high-flown terms of commendation for the discoverer.

There had been no lack of such words in the past from the various orators in Congress when his claim to compensation had come up for discussion, nor were they to be lacking now when the patent was being formally declared invalid, so that the unhappy inventor was to be definitively ruined.

"Before dismissing the case," read Judge Shipman's opinion, "it may not be amiss to speak of the character of the discovery upon which the patent is founded. Its value in securing insensibility during the surgical operation, and thus saving the patient from sharp anguish while it is proceeding, and mitigating the shock to his system, which would otherwise be much greater, was proved on the trial by distinguished surgeons of the city of New York. They agreed in ranking it among the great discoveries of modern times; and one of them remarked that its value was too great to be estimated in dollars and cents. Its universal use, too, concurs to the same point. Its discoverer is entitled to be classed among the greatest benefactors of mankind. But the beneficent and imposing character of the discovery cannot change the legal principles on which the law of patents is founded. . . ."

In a word, by the decision of December 1, 1862, the patent which the government had, in 1846, granted to Dr. W. T. G. Morton, was formally annulled.

In the shipping quarter of Boston, a pawnbroker named Frederick T. Johnson carried on business. He opened his shop at nine o'clock every morning, and there was always a long row of persons waiting to pawn their goods. One after another, those who had been waiting thrust their possessions through the little window for Mr. Johnson to appraise; articles of clothing, or things that had, perhaps, been their most valued trinkets; men and women, young and old, weary and restless hands thrusting in one thing after another, while the pawnbroker valued the pledges, and handed out whatever he thought fit to lend.

"Hurry up, please, for others are waiting," said Mr. Frederick T. Johnson impatiently, as a fresh pair of trembling hands appeared at the little window, and slowly, reluctantly, unfolded a small object wrapped in silver paper. At length there was exposed to view what appeared to be a gold medal. The pawnbroker tested it with aqua fortis. Yes, it was gold. He weighed it, and named the amount he was prepared to lend.

"Can't you give more, sir?" inquired a tremulous masculine voice. "I know that medal cost a lot more."

"I can give you only the bare value of the gold," answered Johnson shortly. "Take it or leave it."

"All right," said the voice, disconsolately.

Meanwhile the pawnbroker had been reading the remarkable inscription, and said: "What right have you to pawn this medal? I must know how you got possession of it," he said harshly.

"It belongs to me, was given me by the Paris Academy of the Sciences. Here is the original document sent me when I received it," answered the voice, almost in a whisper, as if dreading to be overheard.

The trembling hands produced a document, and passed it in.

Mr. Johnson examined it, looked up, and said in amazement: "Are you really the person described here as the Benefactor of Mankind? Are you absolutely obliged to pawn this medal?"

"Yes, it is the last thing of value I possess, and I can no longer buy a morsel of food for my wife and children. We have nothing in the house. I have no choice."

Describing this scene later, Mr. Frederick T. Johnson was wont to say that though he had been a pawnbroker for many years, and a great many "last possessions" had passed through his hands, he had never been so much moved in his life as when Dr. Morton pledged this gold medal which had been given to him as a Benefactor of Mankind.

A commercial traveler from Boston who dealt in agricultural implements told young Edward Warren that on one occasion in the winter of 1863 business led him to West Needham. There he saw a remarkable-looking broken-down man, with threadbare clothing and wasted features, standing beside a small handcart laden with wood. He was arguing with the baker's wife, trying to get some bread in exchange for his wood, which had been gathered in the forest. His children had had nothing to eat for days.

When the bargain had been struck, and the man had wheeled his handcart away, the drummer, who had overheard the conversation, asked the baker's wife who the bargainer was.

"Oh, that was Dr. Morton. He is in a bad way, a very bad way indeed. Everything he possessed came under the hammer, so that often he has not a bite of bread in his house. His only piece of luck was that when the house was sold some of his friends bought it, and they allow him to live on there rent-free—otherwise neither he nor his family would have a home."

CHAPTER SEVENTEEN

Three Men

RS. HARRIET BEECHER STOWE's *Uncle Tom's Cabin* was
published in the year 1852 at the very time when Congress was celebrating the discovery of anesthesia. The
book, like Morton's achievement, was destined to give a strong
impetus to advance the humanization of the world. The author,
writing crudely, touchingly, melodramatically, gave a lurid picture
of the horrors of slavery in the United States—an account that was
not free from exaggeration. Mediocre though it was in literary
style, this description of the "peculiar institution" of the southern
states was destined to prove one of the three or four books which,
besides the Bible, have been strongly influential in determining the
destinies of mankind. It plumbed the abysses of human sentiment.
Mrs. Stowe's art and imagination enabled her to stir her readers'
passions, which welled up from obscure depths to produce an outbreak of furious indignation. The modern world, aspiring toward
democratic progress, had always felt the persistence of slavery in
the South to be inhuman and intolerable. Here so striking a picture was given that brains were fired, hearts convulsed and consciences could no longer rest.

Nevertheless the three presidents before Lincoln, their supporters, most of the congressmen and many other professional politicians remained, for a long time, unmoved. This was the period
when American political life reached its nadir. Walt Whitman,
the great singer of freedom, in his *Origins of Attempted Secession,*
describes, in biting terms, the corrupt administrations that prevailed
under Millard Fillmore, the feeble compromiser Franklin Pierce,

and his successor James Buchanan, the thirteenth, fourteenth and fifteenth presidents of the United States. It would be hard to find in political literature utterances more scathing than these: "History is to record those three Presidents and especially the administrations of Fillmore and Buchanan as so far our utmost warning and shame. Never were publicly displayed more deformed, mediocre, snivelling, unreliable, pulp-hearted men." Writing about the conventions that were held between 1840 and 1860, Whitman exclaimed:

> "Whence the delegates of the politicians? Whence the Buchanan and Fillmore conventions? Who are they personally? Office-holders, office-seekers, robbers, pimps, exclusives, malignants, conspirators, murderers, fancy-men, post-masters, custom-house clerks, contractors, kept-editors, spaniels, well trained to carry and fetch, jobbers, infidels, disunionists, terrorists, mail-riflers, slave-catchers,—spies, blowers, electioneers, body-snatchers, bawlers, bribers, compromisers, lobbyers, spongers."

Under Zachary Taylor, twelfth president (1849–1850), the question of slavery had already been forced into prominence by the Fugitive Slave Law, included in the Omnibus Bill of 1850, which secured to slaveholders additional facilities for the recovery of runaway slaves. This written law remained a dead letter, for it conflicted with the unwritten law of humanity. But an armed conflict had become inevitable, although the presidents and many influential statesmen tried to postpone it as long as possible by means of every conceivable compromise. American industry and commerce were on the upgrade. Railroads were being built. In California gold was discovered. "Big business" was beginning, and the businessmen of the North felt it would be a calamity to interfere with such encouraging prospects by a fratricidal conflict with the slave states of the South.

But during the decade that followed the publication of *Uncle Tom's Cabin,* the young men of the North, whose brains and hearts had been seared by its account of the wrongs of slavery, had grown to full manhood, and were capable of bearing arms. They could no longer endure what they spoke of as "the disgrace of slavery."

Rufus Choate was perfectly right when he said that *Uncle Tom's Cabin* had, betwixt night and morning, created two million Abolitionists—two million men who were determined that slavery should cease. The center of the movement was in Massachusetts.

The train was laid for civil war, and all that was needed to fire it was a sufficient political cause. The start was furnished by the secession first of six states and ultimately of eleven to form the Confederate States of America. The Civil War began in April, 1861.

It was through the personality of Abraham Lincoln that the war acquired its moral significance and its overwhelming impetus, for Lincoln speedily became the most outstanding figure in American history. These virile words about slavery he uttered before he became president: "I hate it because of the monstrous injustice of slavery itself. I hate it because it enables the enemies of free institutions with plausibility to taunt us as hypocrites; causes the real friends of freedom to doubt our sincerity."

As president, on September 22, 1862, he issued the famous proclamation which declared that on January 1, 1863, all the slaves in the secessionist states would become free men. The fortunes of the war were fluctuating until, in March, 1864, Lieutenant General Ulysses Simpson Grant was appointed commander-in-chief of the Union Army.

The war was a long and bloody business. Whitman, who volunteered as an army nurse and served two years at the fighting front, gives a terrible description of the conditions of the wounded:

"Outdoors, at the foot of a tree, within ten yards of the front of the house, I notice a heap of amputated feet, legs, arms, hands, etc.,—about a load for a one-horse cart. Several dead bodies lie near, each covered with its brown woollen blanket. . . . The house is quite crowded, everything impromptu, no system, all the wounds pretty bad, some frightful, the men in their old clothes, unclean and bloody. . . . The results of the late battle are exhibited everywhere about here in thousands of cases, (hundreds die every day) in the camp, brigade, and division hospitals. These are merely tents, and sometimes very poor ones, the wounded lying on the ground, lucky if their

blanket is spread on a layer of pine or hemlock twigs, or leaves.
No cots, seldom even a mattress. It is pretty cold. . . . The
camps of the wounded. . . . Oh, heavens, what scene is this?
—Is this indeed humanity—these butchers' shambles? There
are several of them. There they lie in an open space in the
woods, from two hundred to three hundred poor fellows—the
groans and screams—the odor of blood, mixed with the fresh
scent of the night, the grass, the trees—that slaughter-house!"

As the year 1864 advanced, the Confederates were driven from
their western position, and the campaign entered upon a dramatic
phase. General Grant began his movement against Richmond.
The Battle of the Wilderness, the Battle of Spottsylvania Court
House, and the crossing of the James River, took place in quick
succession. Grant "fought it out along this line all summer."
There was hardly a day when the guns ceased roaring. Fierce and
formidable struggles, demanding terrible sacrifices. The dead and
wounded were lying about in heaps. The wounded could not be
brought under shelter, for no shelter was available. There was a
shortage of ambulances, of orderlies, of medical men. There was
a shortage of everything.

John H. Brinton of Philadelphia records that, on the morning
of July 2, 1864, at the headquarters of the Army of the Potomac,
an aide entered General Grant's tent and said to him that a stranger,
a civilian doctor, wished to see him for the purpose of obtaining
an ambulance, for his personal use in visiting the field hospitals.

"The answer of the general was prompt and decided:
'The ambulances are intended only for the sick and wounded,
and under no circumstances can be taken for private use.'

"This response was carried, and given, to the waiting applicant, a travel-stained man in brownish clothes, whom at the
distance I [Brinton] thought I recognized. I went to him and
found that he was Dr. W. T. G. Morton. I asked him to wait
a minute, and returned to the general. On repeating his request, I received the same answer.

" 'But general,' I ventured to say, 'if you knew who that
man is, I think you would give him what he asks for.'

" 'No I will not,' he replied. 'I will not divert an ambulance to-day for anyone; they are all required elsewhere.'

" 'General,' I replied, 'I am sure you will give him the wagon, he has done so much for mankind, so much for the soldier—more than any soldier or civilian has ever done before; and you will say so when you know his name.'

"The general took his cigar from his mouth, looked curiously at the applicant, and asked, 'Who is he?'

" 'He is Dr. Morton, the discoverer of ether,' I answered.

"The general paused a moment; then said, 'You are right, doctor, he has done more for the soldier than anyone else, soldier or civilian, for he has taught you all to banish pain. Let him have the ambulance and anything else he wants.'

"Afterward, during his stay, by order of the general commanding, he was tendered the hospitalities of the headquarters, ambulance, tent, mess, and servant." [1]

The following is an extract from one of Morton's letters, written to a friend in May, 1864:

"When there is any heavy firing heard, the ambulance corps, with its attendants, stationed nearest to the scene of action, starts for the wounded. The ambulances are halted near by, and the attendants go with stretchers and bring out the wounded. The rebels do not generally fire upon those wearing ambulance badges.

"Upon the arrival of a train of ambulances at a field hospital, the wounds are hastily examined, and those who can bear the journey are sent at once to Fredericksburg. The nature of the operations to be performed on the others is then decided upon, and noted upon a bit of paper pinned to the pillow or roll of blanket under each patient's head. When this had been done, I prepared the patient for the knife, producing perfect anæsthesia in the average time of three minutes, and the operators followed, performing their operations with dexterous skill, while the dressers in their turn bound up the stumps." [2]

One of the war correspondents of the Associated Press who witnessed such a scene in the Army of the Potomac wrote that

[1] Quoted by Elizabeth Morton in *McClure's Magazine*, September, 1896.
[2] *Ibid.*

nothing could show the value of Dr. Morton's discovery more dramatically and more convincingly than what went on immediately behind the fighting line. The value of anesthesia to the army was enormous. Now that the men knew that, if they were wounded, the necessary operations could be made painless, they faced the enemy even more courageously than before.

Such scenes as those just described continued to mark the advance of the Army of the Potomac.

Morton was in his element. From dawn to nightfall, and often by torchlight far on into the hours of darkness, he was at work, giving ether to those about to be operated upon. In this way he was able to save more than two thousand wounded soldiers from the terrible agony of the knife.

Thus was it vouchsafed him to use in wartime the great, the civilizing discovery by which he had achieved the conquest of pain. This enabled him to forget the wrongs he had himself suffered. He thought no more about public ingratitude or how his ears had been tickled by empty promises. Though there had been so much bitterness, though there had been so many disappointments, now, day by day, he could assure himself how unspeakable a blessing his discovery had been. Whatever might lie buried in the past, the present brought Morton full reward for having devoted his life to the cause of anesthesia.

Here are his own words about the matter:

"For myself I am repaid for the anxiety and often wretchedness which I have experienced since I first discovered and introduced the anæsthetic qualities of sulphuric ether, by the consciousness that I have been the instrument of averting pain from thousands and thousands of maimed and lacerated heroes, who have calmly rested in a state of anæsthesia while undergoing surgical operations, which would otherwise have given them intense torture. They are worthy of a nation's gratitude—happy am I to have alleviated their sufferings."

The South was engaged in a life-or-death struggle. The Federal forces were steadily advancing. The great southern generals could no longer resist the northern army. Lee's defenses at Richmond had been broken; the Federals were firmly established on the right bank of the James River; General Sherman's troops had invaded Georgia from the west, had occupied Atlanta, and were marching on Savannah. Soon the secessionist area would be completely encircled, and that would write "finis" beneath the Confederate States of America. The "peculiar institution" would be over and done with.

But the South continued to defend itself and its ancient customs with heroic vigor. These ancient usages, this distinction from the Yankee North, had been the pride of the southern aristocrats, a great part of whose wealth was invested in slaves, and who felt their very existence threatened by the invasion of this new spirit from the North.

Traditional ideals were menaced no less than traditional wealth. With slavery would fall the patriarchal mode of life and the romantic spirit which their forefathers had brought with them from England. An end would come to cavalierdom and the patrician sense of honor. What could the new spirit from the North do for these southern aristocrats? Intending to abolish slavery, on the ground that it was inhuman and immoral, the Yankees would put in its place the hardly less inhuman capitalist exploitation of a labor proletariat. To the Northerners the economic method and the mode of life of the South seemed out-of-date; but to the southern planters the system by which it was to be replaced was the self-seeking of businessmen, eager for profit and always in a furious hurry. The South detested the Yankee spirit, and would fight to the last in the hope of maintaining its beloved patriarchalism.

Georgia, one of the original secessionist states, had been throughout a leader of the southern resistance, a leader in respect to the heroic determination of its children. Among the southern officers, Crawford W. Long played his part in the medical service. He did his best for General Lee's wounded, operating and dressing wounds at the front, sometimes in field hospitals, and often—since the hospitals were few and overcrowded—under the open sky and on the bare ground. Battles are equally bloody, no matter on what side or in whose cause they are fought. The sufferings of a wounded

man were equally great whether he were a Federal fighting for
what he considered the cause of humanity or a southern soldier
who regarded himself as the heir of the Cavaliers. An ambulance
man working in General Lee's army saw the same sights as Walt
Whitman saw in the army of the North. Dr. Long of Athens,
Georgia, was as wholeheartedly devoted to his professional task of
relieving pain as was, facing the other way, Dr. Morton from the
North.

The steady advance of the Federals had become a menace to
Long's own town of Athens, to his plantation and other property,
to the future of his family. In common with other whites in the
South, he regarded Negro slaves as his rightful property, believing,
like the rest of the planters, that slavery was a God-given method
for civilizing the blacks, and that his position as slaveowner had
been imposed on him by the Almighty.

As usual in wartime, atrocity stories were current on both
sides, and the planter officers used to talk to one another about the
horrible things the Yankees would do wherever they overran the
South. When Athens was taken by the enemy, it was likely that
the town would go up in flames.

Determined to visit home before it was too late, Long, getting
leave from the front, galloped all night and awakened his eldest
daughter from her sleep. There were only a few minutes to spare,
for he must get back to his post quickly.

"You must pack up and clear out, Frances, at once, before the
Yankees get here. Go to my lieutenant's sister, who is expecting
you, and will take good care of you."

Hastening to the surgery, and opening a secret drawer in his
desk, Long took out a glass jar, the mouth of which was covered
and tied with waxed paper. Since Congress had refused to consider his application to be regarded as the discoverer of anesthesia,
he had kept all the relevant documents in this receptacle, carefully
protected from damp. Did he still hope to establish his rights?

"This is the most important thing for you to take charge of,"
he said, handing her the jar. "Don't lose it, whatever happens.
You know what it contains. When you get to your destination,
you must hide it so that no one but you can get at the papers."

He thought for a moment, and went on: "But if the enemy should capture you on the way, the game is up as far as I am concerned, for you will have to surrender these papers."

"I will die first!" exclaimed the girl, flinging her arms round her father's neck.

Long felt reassured as he rode back to the front. Frances knew how important these documents were. She was brave and devoted to her father. When she had made good her flight, with the jar stowed away beneath her petticoats, she let her hostess, a trusted friend, into the secret.

At night, when the household was asleep, the two girls stole out, carrying a spade, and made for the forest. Long's daughter had with her the jar containing the papers, and they buried it at the foot of a tree, whose position was carefully noted.

Lee's surrender at Appomattox, April 9, 1865, closed a sanguinary but heroic chapter of history. With the return of the soldiers from the front, American life resumed its ordinary course. Farmers went back to the plough, men of business to the desk, operatives to the tools of their trade. Political activities took on their customary complexion; new religious sects were founded, and Wall Street was as lively as ever. The chase of the Almighty Dollar had begun again in a country destined to become the wealthiest and most powerful in the world.

Dr. William Thomas Green Morton returned to West Needham and took up the threads of an every-day life no less gloomy and purposeless than it had been for many years—a life devoid of future or of hope. For a brief space the Civil War, with its exceptional conditions, had lifted him out of the Slough of Despond, giving his existence a meaning, enabling him to dwell for a while in the sunshine of great deeds and to participate in the practical application of his discovery. Now that brief interlude was over.

What did the sometime war-heroes who had returned to their peaceful avocations care about this enthusiast who had so suddenly emerged from obscurity, appearing at the front with his gift of ether which he held beneath the nostrils of the wounded to save them the agony of the knife?

McClure's Magazine, 1896.

Dr. and Mrs. Morton and their children at their summer home at Wellesley.

The Morton monument, erected by citizens of Boston.

For three years after the war, Morton was ignored at West Needham—except for the creditors, the duns, who continued to pester him with evidence of their invincible hatred.

Then, on the morning of July 5, 1868, he received a registered letter with the New York postmark. The envelope contained a copy of a monthly magazine, with an article advocating the claims of Dr. Jackson; more calumny, more invective. After twenty years of intrigue and slander, his adversary was still campaigning with a string of malicious accusations, shameless lies, which brought an angry flush to Morton's cheeks.

The article "agitated him to an extent I had never seen before," reports Elizabeth.

His health had been failing for some time, and this last blow was too much. As he read the pamphlet, he began to scream, louder and ever louder, as if seized with violent pain. Then he lost consciousness, and was carried off to bed, beside which Elizabeth and the doctor sat watching.

At dawn he came to himself, and, with a faltering voice, stammered almost incomprehensibly "Pack my things, Lizzie, at once. . . . I must go to New York; at once, at once. Do you understand?"

Elizabeth and the doctor tried to dissuade him, saying that he must stay quietly in bed until he was strong enough for such a journey. It would be at least a fortnight, they declared, before he could get over this attack.

"No, Doctor, I must go immediately. The matter cannot be put off."

At ten o'clock he insisted on getting up. He could barely stand, his hands trembled so that he could scarcely hold anything. Nevertheless, he tottered to his writing table, and spent several hours sorting his papers to find the materials he wished to take with him to New York where he would print an answer to Jackson's charges.

Elizabeth implored him not to go, saying: "I shall be so terribly anxious that it will be the death of me. You must take care of yourself, William. Wait till tomorrow, do; you will be better then."

"No, no, I must start at once."

"All right, then, if you must. But take me with you to New York, so that I can look after you."

"No, no. You must stay here with the children, and look after the house. Besides, I shall be better alone, for I have so many things to think over, so much to prepare."

Nothing could be done. He insisted on going. His invincible determination worked wonders, giving him unexpected strength, so that his wife and his doctor, thinking he must really be better, let him have his way.

In New York he had a new and more serious attack, so that Elizabeth was wired for on July 11th. Thanks to her assiduous care, he got better once more—but only to return to his papers. He began to compose an answer to Jackson's pamphlet and, having sent for a lawyer, talked about filing suit against Jackson. Again Elizabeth advised him to let matters rest for a time, to return to West Needham and recruit his strength.

"No, Lizzie, no, there is not a moment to waste. My rejoinder must be published instantly. I must show the world who is right, Jackson or I."

New York is almost always hot in summer, but that year the heat was altogether exceptional. On July 15th the place was like a furnace, and during the midday hours the only thing to do was to keep doors, windows and shutters closed.

One of Elizabeth's relatives had placed his carriage at the Mortons' disposal. In the evening, when it began to get a little cooler, Morton said he would like to go for a drive to Washington Heights. At eight they started, and the doctor said he would drive, that driving would steady his nerves. They were crossing Central Park, and it was getting dark, when Morton reined in the horses. He was giddy, he said, and beads of sweat gathered on his face as he drew his hand across it.

"Turn round, dear," said Elizabeth. "We had better drive home."

"No, Lizzie, I'm all right now. It was only the heat," he answered. "There's nothing the matter. We'll go on with our drive."

He twitched the reins and clicked to the horses, which started off again at a slow trot. After a while, however, he complained that his hands felt heavy and were growing weak. Then, just before the carriage reached the park gates, he pulled up and dropped the reins. Springing down from the box he stood mute beside the carriage, staring vaguely into the dark.

"William, William, what's the matter?" said Elizabeth. "William, can't you answer?"

Apparently he could neither hear nor answer. For a moment or two he still stood, then fell unconscious beneath a tree.

Elizabeth, too, jumped down, knelt beside him, shook him gently, and tried to raise him. But his body was inert, his lips were convulsively closed, his eyes open as he continued to stare into the dark.

Putting her ear to his chest, Elizabeth could hear that he was still breathing gently, and that his heart was beating. Hope gave voice to her terror, and she shouted, sobbingly, for help.

Passers-by stopped, more and more, and soon gathered to form a crowd. Among them was a druggist named Swann, who had been taking his evening constitutional when he heard the cries for help. Since there was no doctor among the crowd, he took charge. Having done what little was practicable in the way of first aid, Swann, deciding that the case was serious, made for the park gates to summon an ambulance.

Meanwhile the crowd was steadily increasing. Sinister figures were mingled among the onlookers, some of them moving to investigate the unconscious man's pockets, and Elizabeth became alarmed. From one of the pockets she herself extracted the Russian Vladimir Order and the Swedish Vasa Order, which he had brought with him to New York as evidence of his discovery, and she put them safely away in her reticule. It struck nine; it struck ten; eleven was approaching. "The horror of the situation stunned me," reports Elizabeth,[1] "finding myself alone with a dying husband, surrounded by strangers, in an open park at eleven o'clock at night. A double carriage arrived. We were driven at once to St. Luke's Hospital, where my husband was taken in on the

[1] In *McClure's*, September, 1896.

stretcher, and immediately the chief surgeons and the house physicians gathered about him. At a glance the chief surgeon recognized him, and said to me: 'This is Dr. Morton?'

"I simply replied; 'Yes.'

"After a moment's silence, he turned to the group of house pupils and said:

"'Young gentlemen, you see lying before you a man who has done more for humanity and for the relief of suffering than any man who has ever lived.'

"In the bitterness of the moment I put my hand in my pocket, and, taking out the Orders, laid them beside my husband, saying,

"'Yes, and here is all the recompense he has ever received for it.'"

Thus, on July 15, 1868, died William Thomas Green Morton, the Benefactor of Mankind, at the age of forty-nine. He perished despised and rejected, one who had never found peace but was afflicted till his last breath. His wife and his five fatherless children were left unprovided for.

S. Weir Mitchell, novelist, poet and famous physician, penned the following impassioned lines in memory of the great discoverer:

> *How did we thank him? Ah! no joy-bells rang,*
> *No pæans greeted, and no poets sang;*
> *No cannons thundered from the guarded strand*
> *This mighty victory to a grateful land!*
> *We took the gift so humbly, simply given,*
> *And, coldly selfish—left out debt to Heaven.*
> *How shall we thank him? Hush! A gladder hour*
> *Has struck to him; a wiser, juster power*
> *Shall know full well how fitly to reward*
> *The generous soul that found the world so hard.*[1]

Among the ruined Confederate officers who returned to their desolate homes after the war was Dr. Crawford W. Long. He found it hard to accommodate himself to the changed circumstances. The old days of ease and comfort and the evening whist

[1] From "The Birth and Death of Pain," *The Complete Poems of S. Weir Mitchell,* The Century Company, New York, 1914, p. 416.

parties had vanished. Of course there was still the drugstore, and there was still medical practice. But he was getting on in years, was less able to endure the fatigues of extensive country rides and those of business life. Gray, indeed, were the prospects for the future. He was a discouraged and gloomy old fellow, continually asking himself: "What will become of us all?"

Immediately after peace had been signed, however, his daughter drove off to see her friend the lieutenant's sister, and the pair of them, revisiting the forest with a spade, dug up the glass jar.

"There, Father," she said proudly, "I've brought you back your precious documents."

But poor Crawford Long was past consoling. Nervously, hastily, he took the jar from her, without vouchsafing a word of praise to the disappointed girl, who watched him stow away his treasure in another hiding-place.

On one occasion, when Dr. Long had completely surrendered to his fears for the future, Caroline tried to console him, saying: "Have courage, Crawford, the day will come when you will be recognized as the discoverer of anesthesia."

"What's the use of talking like that?" he answered irritably. "Never let me hear the word 'anesthesia' again. I am sick of it."

All the same, the old gentleman, when he thought no one was watching, would steal off to the lumber room, and there spend hours turning over the contents of a battered trunk. Here he kept the affidavits, Venable's receipt and the other proofs of his experiments upon the use of ether. Then his wife and children would say: "Father is attacked by the old fever." But when he came back from the lumber room, they would pretend not to notice that anything had happened, and no one asked where he had been. It would have been thought bad form to allude to the matter.

"My father," writes Frances, "was a man who bore disappointment and sorrow uncomplainingly, keeping them secret in his soul lest others be made unhappy."

One winter evening in the year 1878 a knock came at the door, and a farmer entered.

"Doctor, please come at once; my wife is in labor, and she can hardly bear the pains."

While Long was examining his obstetrical bag to see that all was in order, the husband went on: "My poor, poor wife! Even you, who are used to it, will find her screams almost intolerable. I doubt if she will live through, this time.—Doctor, I have been told that in the towns, the big towns of the North, they give women something at these times which relieves the pain. Can you do anything of the kind?"

Long looked up and did not answer for a moment; he was thinking things over. Then he heard the farmer's imploring voice once more:

"I beg you, Doctor, do try to relieve her. When our little Ellen was born, I thought the pains would kill her. You must do something for her."

Long could not resist this pitiful plea.

"All right, wait a moment," he said. "I will bring along something to relieve her."

Going into the dispensary, he took a small bottle from one of the shelves. The farmer had driven over in a wagon, and now he whipped up his horses.

The agonized shrieks of the farmer's wife were audible long before they reached the door. The doctor went to the poor woman's bedside, and said encouragingly: "I am going to give you something which will take away all the pain within a minute or two." She looked up at him trustfully. Opening the bag, he took out the bottle he had brought, and a sponge. Unstoppering the flask, he poured on the sponge some of the fluid it contained. The powerful, aromatic smell of ether pervaded the room. Dr. Long was about to thrust the saturated sponge beneath his patient's nostrils, when his hand began to tremble, and he dropped both sponge and bottle. A moment later, he himself fell across the bed. Death had struck him down as he was about to administer the ether.

It had been a long night, and dawn was near. For many hours Dr. Charles Thomas Jackson had been seated at his writing table, looking through accumulated records, thousands of pages; reading and making notes; underlining critical passages; writing reports to the newspapers, composing lengthy letters—all this work having to do with an undying controversy.

Although he was now an elderly man and could not see very well by artificial light, although his stiffening fingers were no longer those of a ready penman, he spent his nights in the study of his documents instead of seeking his bed.

His hatred was inextinguishable, had become a monomania, gave him no rest. Day and night he was striving to crown his life-work—which was, to annihilate Morton's claim to have been discoverer of the anesthetic qualities of ether.

Surely he had done enough, and more than enough, to achieve this end? Almost every mail brought newspapers, other periodicals, scientific reports, from all parts of Europe and America, to Jackson's house. All of them had to be scanned for references to the discovery. The errors must be contradicted, and well-substantiated counter-proofs must be sent to the respective editors.

Five summers had passed since, in the year 1868, Jackson had published a new article upon the ether question. At that time he hoped to settle the matter once for all, to show the world "what really happened," and "that Morton had had very little, practically nothing, to do with the discovery of anæsthesia." This article was full of concentrated venom. Directly it was published he sent a copy to Morton, who was to be shown how impossible it would be for him to make headway against Dr. Jackson. He had expected the article to produce a powerful effect, and in truth the effect was even more powerful than he had anticipated. So annihilating did it prove that his adversary's tongue and pen were silenced for ever. Morton's excitement on reading the pamphlet and preparing to answer it led to fatal apoplexy.

The hated rival was dead, and no longer in a position to contradict Jackson. But, as had so often happened during this long and unhappy ether campaign, when fate vouchsafed Jackson a victory this was but a temporary success, for his weapons were soon turned against him. Hardly was Morton dead and buried when his powers as adversary seemed intensified—as if rank weeds were growing out of the tomb, invading Boston, spreading far and wide across land and seas, to cover the whole world.

For in every journal, from whatever quarter it came, embittering Jackson's life, he found flattering references to Morton. Morton was the discoverer. Morton was the Benefactor of Mankind. Not long before, at a meeting of the Medical Society (which from the first had been opposed to Morton), one of the speakers had declared: "While Dr. Morton was still alive, we failed to recognize his greatness. Now, when he is dead, we know that he alone was the discoverer of anæsthesia." Physicians, men of science, after-dinner speakers in London, Paris, Berlin and other capitals, joined in the hateful chorus.

Jackson's struggle against the memory of the dead was a far more arduous one than had been his long and fierce campaign against the hindrances and difficulties which for years had been imposed by the living Morton, with his ambition, his counter-allegations, his documents, his Orders of Distinction and his friends in the Senate and the House of Representatives.

It seemed almost beyond human power to expunge Morton's name from the mind of the world; to nail every lie to the counter; to deal with every mention in periodicals far and near, in speeches and reports. This was an expensive business, cost Jackson unending spells of work and kept him out of bed night after night; and though he had the seeming advantage of having outlived Morton, every year of this "advantageous" survival brought Jackson more trial and more torment.

Even the intensified hatred of a lunatic could not cope with this Sisyphean task. Would he never succeed in rolling the great stone uphill? Would he ever be able to erase the name of Morton from the memory of mankind?

When doubt and despair seized Jackson, he turned to drink, which could inspire him with fresh hope, renewed energy. Amid the mountainous piles of journals, letters and other documents there now always stood the whisky bottle, to which he had frequent recourse.

Dr. Charles Thomas Jackson had taken to drink. His state, which had formerly entrusted him with important geological investigations, cashiered him as a chronic alcoholic. Still, what did that matter? He had no time to spare for scientific research. His energies were exclusively devoted to the one task of undermining the dead man's reputation.

In the middle of July, 1873, he had nearly finished a new pamphlet. A few pages more, and the manuscript would be ready for the press. This would be a final settlement with the enemy, clearing up all the misstatements that had been made since Morton died five years before, rectifying the erroneous proclamations of Morton as the discoverer, the errors of periodicals, orators and resolutions.

As usual, Dr. Charles Thomas Jackson had been at work till dawn, amid frequent potations. At length he dropped into a drunken sleep. Awaking late in the afternoon, his limbs still heavy from the effects of alcohol, he rose, went straight out of the house and made his way toward Mount Auburn Cemetery.

Today, a weekday, had been fine and calm. The sun was sinking behind the trees, and only a few visitors had come to pay their respects at the resting places of the dead. Jackson strolled unheeded among the tombs. Then he suddenly caught sight of an aspiring monument—Morton's! What had led him hither? He could not tell. His brain was clouded by a long succession of sleepless nights, and by the effects of the whisky in which he had indulged throughout the years since Morton's death.

Standing before the monument, he read the chiseled inscription:

WILLIAM T. G. MORTON
Inventor and revealer of anæsthetic inhalation,
By whom pain in surgery was averted and annulled;
Before whom in all time surgery was agony,
Since whom Science has control of Pain.
Erected by the citizens of Boston.

The sun was dipping behind the horizon, yet it seemed to Jackson as if it had suddenly risen to the zenith and was shining down on him with resplendent energy. Not one sun alone, but hundreds of them, shining from the zenith upon the monument, and bringing out the words of the inscription. That's what the sun was shining for, having no other purpose than to make the inscription brighter. It was not the sun of today alone, for there were myriads of suns, suns of all days and all ages—the eternal sun which shines through the eons. That sun was shining now, and in its timeless purity Dr. Jackson again read the inscription. Then he realized what he had been fighting against throughout life. There was his rival's deed, chiseled in stone. Day after day, henceforward, the sun would rise over Boston, and its rays would fall on the inscription as long as Boston existed. Through all coming time, as generation followed generation, those fatal words would enjoy the light of day: "W. T. G. Morton, inventor and revealer of anæsthetic inhalation."

Of what use were his rectifications in periodicals, his materials, his new pamphlet? How could they fight against the sun?

As Jackson became fully aware of this, it was as if the sun, which set evening after evening behind the trees of Mount Auburn, had become a falling star rushing down into the night. With it fell all the suns, the suns of all time fell into the gloom of night— an eternal night out of which no more sun would ever arise.

Jackson began to scream, to thrash with his arms, fighting shadows, as if to summon help to deliver him from this overwhelming darkness. But no, he could not summon help, nor bring help with his gesticulations. The more he became aware of his impotence, the louder did he scream, and the more hopelessly did he fling his arms about and trample the earth, striving to escape from this horrible and overwhelming darkness.

The other visitors to the cemetery, most of them praying beside the graves of the dead, were startled by these bestial cries. Hurrying to the spot, they found a raging maniac in front of the Morton memorial. Jackson's face no longer looked human, and the cries he uttered were unlike human cries; nay, his convulsed body scarcely seemed a human form.

The creature that cried and thrashed with its limbs in Mount Auburn Cemetery was unchained madness. It was the madness which, year after year, had worn the semblance of the chemist and physicist Charles Thomas Jackson; the madness which had given birth to his intrigues, rectifications and pamphlets; and had at length grown weary of this human shape. Now this madness had broken loose from the enveloping shell, casting the shell aside with a mighty gesture, to stand before the Morton monument in its crude, naked, elemental energy.

With the aid of a few strong men, the custodian of the cemetery was able to bind the maniac and hold him fast until the police appeared on the scene.

These attacks of frenzy recurred again and again, and often lasted for days without intermission. Dr. Charles Thomas Jackson had to be placed under restraint in the McLean Asylum, in Somerville upon its seven hills. There he survived for a number of years, until death at length brought him release on August 28, 1880, when he was seventy-five.

Wells, in despair, took his own life in a prison cell. Long was an embittered old man when death struck him down as he was about to administer ether. Morton perished from a stroke induced by the excitement of reading Jackson's article. Jackson's unceasing hate brought him to a lunatic asylum. We are almost forced to believe that a mysterious doom, like that of a Greek tragedy, rested upon those whose lives were devoted to the Conquest of Pain. All of them, without exception, paid for their quest in health, happiness, repose or reason.

When they were dead, three towns competed for the honor of having been the birthplace of the discoverer of anesthesia. Connecticut erected a memorial to Wells, bearing his profile in Bushell Park, Hartford; and on December 11, 1937, a carved pew-end as a tribute to Horace Wells was unveiled in the chapel of Trinity College there. Georgia put up a statute to Long in the National Capitol. Massachusetts added Morton's name as second in the list of its fifty-two greatest sons. McLean Asylum, Somerville, Middlesex County, was the mausoleum of Charles Thomas Jackson.

CHAPTER EIGHTEEN

Not in Sorrow Shalt Thou Bear

WHILE ALL those who were primarily connected with the discovery of anesthesia were thus intertwined in a tragic doom, the discovery itself, unperturbed by the fate of the discoverers, marched steadily forward to increasing perfection.

As operation succeeded operation, the technique was continually improved, the methods of producing insensibility became more reliable, obstacles were smoothed out of the path, and dangers attending the procedure were diminished. Thus, with the discovery and adoption of anesthesia, the skill of man—who had long ere this been bold enough to employ the "healing knife" that he might cut disease out of the body—was at length able to rob the knife itself of its terrors.

A year had scarcely passed since the first painless operation under ether in Massachusetts General Hospital when a second problem was successfully solved. Having learned how to abolish the pain deliberately inflicted by the surgeon's hand, man wrought an even greater miracle by abolishing the agony of child-bearing.

This agony had been regarded as the outcome of the primal curse pronounced upon Eve after the Fall. "Unto the woman he said, I will greatly multiply thy sorrow and thy conception; in sorrow thou shalt bring forth children." Again and again, in the Old Testament, there are references to this heritage of pain. Thus, in Isaiah, 26, 17: "Like as a woman with child, that draweth near the time of her delivery, is in pain, and crieth out in her pangs."

Again, in the thirty-fifth chapter of the Book of Genesis: "And there was but a little way to come to Ephrath: and Rachel travailed, and she had hard labour. And it came to pass, as her soul was in departing (for she died) that she called his name Ben-oni: but his father called him Benjamin."

The Hellenes, likewise, regarded the pains of labor as a punishment for sin. This is illustrated by the myth of the goddess Selene, who was so much horrified when told of the pains her mother Theia had endured in giving birth to her, that she begged of Zeus the boon of perpetual virginity. Then, in one of her nightly wanderings, she caught sight of the ever-beautiful Endymion. Forgetting her vow of chastity, she loved him. Thereupon she was doomed to bear fifty children, to endure fifty times over the pangs from which her mother had suffered. That her punishment might be the greater, all these children were girls, who had inherited and would transmit the same curse of birth-pangs.

Thus, when Eve gave birth to her first child, she cried aloud in her agony; and ever since woman had had to endure the same unspeakable pangs in giving birth to a child—and not a few died in labor.

In the sixteenth century midwifery forceps were invented, and with the aid of these, when the expulsive power of the womb was deficient or when there was a disproportion between the size of the head and that of the outlet through which it had to pass, the labor could be artificially shortened and therewith the time of agony reduced.

But as if the pains inflicted on woman by a vengeful god had been insufficient, they were intensified, even after this great discovery, by the cruelty, the hard-heartedness, of man.

In the year 1569, William Chamberlen came to England as a Huguenot refugee. He had four sons, Peter I, Peter II, Simon and John. These four became the founders of a dynasty almost unparalleled in remorseless avarice. It was one of the evil pranks which fate is so fond of playing upon man that the idea of the midwifery forceps should have originated in the heads of such men as the Chamberlens.

Peter I and Peter II were professional accoucheurs, who had

seen many a woman writhing in the pangs of labor, had seen many a Rachel perish during parturition, and knew from direct experience how mothers suffered in the heavy hour. But with forceps, in cases of protracted labor, a woman could be delivered "in less than half or a quarter of an hour."

But the leading thought of these ingenious men was, not to relieve women's pain, not to save women's lives, but to make money out of the exploitation of suffering. A woman who writhed in protracted labor, a woman who was like to die as Rachel died in giving birth to Benjamin, was, for Peter I and Peter II, merely a business opportunity. If they kept the construction of their forceps secret, they might hope to make vast sums of money.

The Chamberlens were thick as thieves. After Simon and John had been initiated into the use of the forceps, the mystery was preserved as a family secret. The four covetous brethren put their heads together and established a tariff upon this via dolorosa. The pain was great, and the toll was correspondingly high—so high that few could afford the price. However, husbands who lacked cash gave promissory notes or pledged their possessions that their wives might benefit by the use of the forceps. But the wives of those who had neither money nor credit, the wives of those who had nothing to pawn, must suffer and die unaided. The Chamberlens turned deaf ears to the wailing of the poor, and paid no heed to those who implored help at a reduced fee. They guarded a family treasure, and showed the poverty-stricken to the door.

This policy was profitable, extremely profitable, so that coin of the realm and notes of hand were heaped up in the Chamberlens' strongbox.

Peter II begat Peter III. Peter III begat Hugh I. Hugh I begat three sons: Hugh II, Paul and John. Peter III, Hugh I, Hugh II, Paul, John and the sons of these, continued to guard the secret of the forceps. It was passed on from generation to generation like a family heirloom. Nor, in successive generations, would any of the Chamberlens abate their price, so wealth continued to roll in.

Toward the close of the seventeenth century, in the days of the Hughs, the Chamberlens were tempted to depart from the family tradition. The knowledge of the existence of this carefully guarded secret awakened in other avaricious minds a longing to make money out of women's recurrent needs. One day, therefore, a Dutchman named Rogier van Roonhuyse offered Hugh II a sum sufficient to induce the latter to part with the secret.

Roonhuyse, who was a vigorous trader, instead of applying it to his own use sold it at an enhanced price to Jan van Bruin. Shortly afterward Bruin died, and his daughters sold their treasure to two surgeons named Vischer and Poll. Thus at length, after frequent changes of ownership, the forceps passed into the possession of the medical faculty of Amsterdam.

Unless a malicious imp had been at work, one might have supposed that the midwifery forceps could now have been used for the general advantage of all women suffering from protracted labor. But the medical faculty of Amsterdam wanted to drive a bargain in its turn, and insisted on being paid a good round fee by any private practitioners who wanted to use the instrument.

Now it transpired that what had been passed on from hand to hand—that for which Roonhuyse had paid over hard money to Hugh II, Bruin the same to Roonhuyse, Vischer and Poll to Bruin's daughters, the medical faculty of Amsterdam to Vischer and Poll, and at length, in sound guilders, private practitioners to the Amsterdam medical faculty—was a worthless model, forceps with only one blade which cunning Hugh had palmed off on Roonhuyse, and the latter, a cheated cheat, had palmed off on Bruin, and so in turn.

The really efficient pair of midwifery forceps was, and remained, a family possession of the Chamberlens. Not until long, long afterward, in the year 1813, was there discovered in the county of Essex, in a house which the Chamberlens had once occupied, the original pair of midwifery forceps the value of which had been so ruthlessly exploited for wellnigh two centuries by an avaricious dynasty.

It was through a certain John Palfyn, a barber-surgeon in Ghent, that the midwifery forceps at length became generally applicable in obstetrics. As in every town of those days, so in Ghent there were many women who, for lack of forceps, had to suffer needlessly prolonged labor and risk to life. John Palfyn began to cudgel his brains as to what could have been the mysterious instrument with which the Chamberlens, when sufficiently feed, had been wont to abbreviate the duration of labor.

As if fate had relented, John Palfyn, the poor barber-surgeon of Ghent, was able to recapitulate the Chamberlens' discovery and to devise an effective pair of midwifery forceps.

Paris, he decided, was the place where he could best make his invention known to the world, and therefore, on foot, he made his way to the French capital, and laid his instrument before the Paris Academy. His task was now fulfilled, so, again on foot, he returned to Ghent to live and die there, poor and forgotten. At length, however, in token of gratitude, posterity erected over his tomb in the St. Jacques Cemetery the statue of a weeping woman.

The technique of midwifery improved concomitantly with the advance of scientific medicine. Many new instruments and methods were discovered for mitigating the pain of labor, but the final relief of woman from the primal curse was reserved for the nineteenth century and for the Scottish physician James Young Simpson. When no more than a boy, Simpson, the son of a baker, was told that his mother, in giving birth to him, had nearly died, and in her pain had screamed so loudly that the neighbors came to ask what was the matter. Although he had never heard the cries nor seen his mother writhing in agony, what he had been told was graphically figured in his imagination, to remain with him throughout life. He could never free himself from this picture of suffering.

His mother had screamed with pain when bringing him into the world. No mother ought to suffer in this way. Could he do anything to prevent it? The thought conceived by a half-grown boy, and ripening as the boy grew to manhood, was to determine his actions throughout life.

With indomitable ambition and iron industry, the baker's boy, self-taught at first, was able to push his way out of the narrow circle in which he had been born and to secure opportunities for regular studies. Having qualified as a doctor, he speedily became chief assistant in the lying-in wards of Edinburgh Infirmary.

Sir James Young Simpson fought the Biblical curse of painful childbirth by
using chloroform to ease the pangs of labor.

Sculpture by Dr. R. Tait Mackenzie.

Pain.

Now the pains he had hitherto known only in fancy were vividly present to his senses. By day and by night, women with tortured faces surrounded him, and from each bed there seemed to stare at him the face of his anguished mother. Early and late, from hundreds of throats, came the screams of pain which his mother had uttered when bringing him into the world. Was pain, then, the inevitable price of every new human life?

No mother ought to suffer, no mother should suffer, such pain. James Young Simpson, chief obstetric assistant at Edinburgh Infirmary, could not keep faith with the boy he had been unless he fulfilled that vow.

Many experiments had to be made with various substances, many disappointments had to be endured, and there was much vexation on account of the impotence of science, before Simpson reached his goal. He spent years in search of what he wanted. The narcotics known at that date proved unsuitable or dangerous, and mesmerism was ineffective. But, making light of discouragements, Simpson continued his search. Then, in December, 1846, came news from London that Liston had performed a painless operation on a patient under the influence of ether.

As to all doctors who were then busied with the problem of conquering pain, to Simpson these tidings of the discovery of ether narcosis seemed those of a miracle. "It is a glorious thought; I can think of naught else!" he said, and hastened to London. There he was able to convince himself with his own eyes that Liston's patients slept quietly throughout the operation, and did not exhibit a sign of pain. Well and good: he need merely put a woman in labor under the influence of ether, and he would be able to save her all pain.

Greatly excited and bubbling over with happiness, Simpson returned to Edinburgh. But his attempts to allay the pangs of labor with ether were disappointing. True, the inhalation of the vapor produced unconsciousness; but women in that condition were exceptionally sensitive, so that the penetrating odor of the substance to be inhaled aroused giddiness, nausea and vomiting. No, ether was not the substance of which he was in search, but obviously inhalation was the correct method. It was necessary to find something which would allay pain as successfully as ether without arousing unpleasant symptoms. Simpson set to work with the eagerness of a man who knows he is nearing the goal.

It was half a century or more since Priestley, Lavoisier, Cavendish and Davy had discovered the invisible world of gases, and nearly as long since Sertürner, with the extraction of morphine from crude opium, had made so signal an advance in medical chemistry. Since then synthetic chemistry had been progressing with giant strides. The artificial world created by the human intelligence had become a wondrous realm full of previously unknown substances, crystals, gases, vapors, powders, liquids and multifarious chemical combinations. Simpson, a rising professional man in his middle thirties, who for five years now had been professor of medicine at Edinburgh University, had access to the best chemical laboratories, and every noted experimental investigator was eager and willing to help him in the search for an anesthetic agent which would have all the advantages and none of the drawbacks of ether. Various new substances were recommended to him as likely to be suitable.

His work in the lying-in wards left him little free time, but what time there was he devoted to the task. His assistants James Mathews Duncan and George Keith were equally zealous. Evening after evening the three men foregathered in Professor Simpson's house, to experiment with one substance after another, trying the inhalation on themselves. Dr. Simpson's friend and near neighbor, Professor Miller, who knew what was going on, was so keenly interested and also so anxious that he used to look in every morning before breakfast to make sure that the courageous experimenters were still alive.

There was good reason for anxiety, seeing that Simpson, carried away by his eagerness, was unquestionably rash. On one occasion Lyon Playfair, an experimental chemist, said something to Simpson about bromide of ethyl as a volatile fluid; Simpson immediately proposed to try it on himself, and Playfair found it hard to dissuade him.

"No, no, my dear Simpson, we shall do better to try it first on some rabbits before you risk your valuable life. In fact I will

myself try it this evening on a couple." When, next day, Simpson asked Playfair what had happened to the rabbits, a footman was sent to the laboratory to see how the beasts fared. He returned in a minute or two carrying the rabbits by the ears. Both had died.

This was not the only disappointment, since many other substances proved unsuitable, but nothing could shake Simpson's conviction that he was on the right track. In the end, his perseverance was rewarded. One substance was at length found to fulfill his expectations—chloroform.

This substance had been discovered about sixteen years before Simpson tried it by inhalation. As in the case of so many scientific discoveries, there had been disputes about priority. It seems clear, however, that Samuel Guthrie, of Brimfield, Massachusetts, an American army surgeon, produced $CHCl_3$, tri-chlor-methane, in the year 1831, by the distillation of alcohol treated with chloride of lime. It was a heavy, sweet-smelling fluid. Almost at the same date Soubeiran, a French chemist, hit upon the same substance, which he prepared from the same ingredients, and believed himself to have been the first in the field. Then Liebig, the famous German chemist, came forward to declare that he had produced it earlier still by treating chloral with caustic potash. But it was certainly the French chemist Dumas who, in 1834, first worked out the correct chemical formula and gave the substance its definitive name of chloroform.

When Waldie, a Liverpool pharmaceutical chemist, drew Simpson's attention to chloroform, its vapor had already been used by various doctors as a remedy for respiratory troubles. Waldie told Simpson that the doctors of Liverpool valued chloroform because its use appeared to be devoid of risk while it had an agreeable smell and taste which made it preferable to any other substance hitherto used by inhalation. Jacob Bell and Flourens, the founders of the Pharmaceutical Society, had already noticed, in experiments on animals, that chloroform produced an intoxication somewhat akin to that of ether. Still, very little attention had been paid to this observation, and no surgeons had hitherto thought of trying chloroform as an anesthetic.

Dr. Simpson determined to make immediate trial of this fluid, and asked Duncan and Keith to supper on November 4, 1847. There were also present on this occasion Mrs. Simpson, her niece Miss Petrie, and a naval officer who was a friend of the family. At table, of course, there was talk of the proposed experiment with chloroform, the three nonprofessional members of the party—the two ladies and the naval officer—being equally keen on inhaling the vapor. "I have always wanted to join in one of these experiments," said Mrs. Simpson to her husband. Miss Petrie and the young naval man chimed in, and the professor agreed that they should all try it. Thus, when the meal was over, the dinner party was transformed into a chloroform party.

Each of the participants was handed a tumbler containing a modicum of chloroform in the bottom. "Are you ready?" asked Simpson. "One, two, three." He clapped his hands, and at the same instant they all began to draw long, deep breaths of chloroform vapor.

The effect was first noticeable in Miss Petrie. Usually a retiring young woman, she displayed ecstasy and excitement: "I'm beginning to fly!" she shouted. "I'm an angel, oh, I'm an angel!" Hardly had she spoken these words when her head dropped forward and she was fast asleep.

At the same moment Dr. Keith burst out laughing. Was it Miss Petrie's ecstatic words which had amused him? No one could tell, but his laughter proved infectious. Dr. Duncan, Mrs. Simpson, the professor himself, all began to laugh. They felt very happy, became extremely loquacious, shouted loudly and roared with laughter. Only the naval officer sat looking on, puzzled and aloof. He stared at the others' strange antics. "What are you all so excited about?" he was on the point of saying, but hardly had he begun to speak, in a deep bass, when his voice broke into falsetto. Then he began to crow like a cock, which made the others more hilarious than ever.

Next, as the joyful mood reached a climax, Dr. Simpson leaped up from his chair and stood on his head in the middle of the room, waving his feet in the air. Mrs. Simpson tried to get him out of this undignified posture, but before she could reach him he fell with a crash onto the floor, where he began to snore loudly. Mrs. Simpson, too, was soon overpowered with sleep.

On awaking, Simpson's first perception was mental. "This is far stronger and better than ether," said he to himself. His second was to note that he was prostrate on the floor. Hearing a noise, he turned round and saw Dr. Duncan beneath a chair—his jaw dropped, his eyes staring, his head bent under him; quite unconscious, and snoring in the most determined manner. Dr. Keith was waving feet and legs in an attempt to overturn the supper table. The naval officer, Miss Petrie and Mrs. Simpson were lying about on the floor in the strangest attitudes, and a chorus of snores filled the air.

They came to themselves one after another. When they were soberly seated round the table once more, they began to relate the dreams and visions they had had during the intoxication with chloroform. When at length Dr. Simpson's turn came, he blinked and said with profound gratification: "This, my dear friends, will give my poor women at the hospital the alleviation they need. A rather larger dose will produce profound narcotic slumber."

Indeed this scene, which might have been taken from a slapstick comedy, was to be the prelude to a new epoch. For the next scene belongs to the most tremendous moments in the history of suffering mankind. It discloses the first mother to be freed from the primal curse, the first mother to bring a child painlessly into the world.

Here is Dr. Simpson's own report:

"The lady to whom it was first exhibited during parturition, had been previously delivered in this country by perforation of the head of the infant, after a labour of three days' duration. In this, her second confinement, pains supervened a fortnight before the full time. Three hours and a half after they commenced, and ere the first stage of the labour was completed, I placed her under the influence of the chloroform. The child was expelled in about twenty-five minutes after the inhalation was begun. The squalling of the child did not, as is usual, rouse her; and some minutes elapsed after the child was removed by the nurse to another room, before the patient awoke. She then turned round and observed to me that she had enjoyed a very comfortable sleep, and would now be more able for the work before her. In a little while she remarked that she was afraid her sleep had stopped the pains. Shortly afterwards her infant was brought in by the nurse from the adjoining room, and it was a matter of no small difficulty to convince the astonished mother that the labour was entirely over, and that the child presented to her was really her own living baby."

Having made so signal a success of the first painless delivery, Simpson went on to try chloroform again a second, a third, a tenth time, and on each occasion the miracle was repeated. Morning, noon and night he had to attend women in childbirth. Indefatigably he gave them the sweet, heavy vapor to inhale, that they might enjoy protective slumber, and bring their children into the world in a painless dream. He had become a miracle-worker under the spell of his own miracle. It was as if he had determined to compensate for the pain his own mother had suffered by making the labor of all other women painless henceforth. It was on November 4, 1847, that he first used chloroform in a confinement, and only six days later, in an address made to the Edinburgh Medico-Chirurgical Society, he reported upon more than thirty painless deliveries. Thus promptly did he make his discovery known to the public, and thenceforward no woman need suffer the pangs of labor.

There happened to be a foreigner among this Edinburgh audience, Jean Baptiste Dumas, the French chemist, to whom the world was indebted for the formula and the name of chloroform. He was delighted to learn that a blessing had been bestowed upon suffering humanity, and all his fellow auditors shared his conviction that Simpson's discovery marked a turning-point in the story of pain. The primal curse, "in sorrow thou shalt bring forth children," had been annulled.

Thus from Edinburgh came the man who delivered child-bearing women from the horrible pains imposed by malignant nature. Other pains were accidental or were due to people's own actions. But the pangs of childbirth were attached, cruelly attached, to this essential phase in the reproduction of the species. The most unjust of all pains could henceforward be allayed.

What a victory of science, a triumph of human intelligence, and a glory to Edinburgh!

But such was by no means the universal opinion.

"What a Satanic invention! What a disaster! What a shame upon Edinburgh!" screamed the Scottish Calvinists who were devotees of a God who deliberately visited affliction upon His creatures.

Did not the Almighty pronounce this primal curse? Pain during childbirth was God's will. Now one of God's creatures, impiously rebelling against the divine command, had dared to frustrate God's will!

"Who is this shameless heretic? To what city of wrath does he belong?"

"Nay, but he is a son of the pious town of Edinburgh."

"What a scandal, what a disaster!"

Once before in the venerable city of Edinburgh, as far back as the year 1591, an attempt had been made to defeat the primal curse. A gentlewoman named Euphanie Macalyane, misled by Satan, had secretly applied to a midwife named Agnes Samson, begging for a remedy which would relieve her from the pangs of labor. At that time James VI (afterward James I of England), son of Mary Stuart, ruled over Scotland. Wise in his own conceit, he believed himself empowered to enforce the divine commandment. When the King learned of Dame Euphanie Macalyane's impiety, he took the strictest measures: a pyre was erected on the Castle Hill, and there the lady was burned alive as a warning to all women who might endeavor to evade the curse of Eve.

That was how, in former days, the pious city of Edinburgh had justified the ways of God to man; but now one of Edinburgh's sons was shameless enough to announce a discovery which in future was to free woman from the God-ordained pangs of labor. Human art, forsooth, was to triumph over the will of God.

The capital of Scotland was a place where the godly, the religious-minded, had always kept a sharp eye upon the proceedings of men of science, and had ever been ready to smell out heresy. Nothing could seem to them more outrageous than this attempt to defy the decrees of Providence.

No doubt a great deal had happened beside the Forth since the glorious reign of King James VI, but the Word of God was still held in high honor.

Although, in the secularized nineteenth century, death by fire had been abolished, the Church still had ways and means of bringing the impious to book.

"The doctor who promises to save you from the pangs of labor is a blasphemer, a heretic, who utters words which Satan has put into his mouth," announced the preachers to women with child, warning them that if they should allow Dr. Simpson to administer chloroform their children would be refused the sacrament of baptism.

"Many of my lady patients," declared Simpson at this time to a friend, "have strong religious scruples against anesthesia. Most of them consult their ministers." Among the faithful in Edinburgh there still prevailed the dread of a celestial King James who, when the day of judgment came, would hold an assize upon the mothers who had given birth painlessly and upon the children born to such mothers, and would sentence both mothers and children to eternal damnation.

Indeed, the doctors of Edinburgh, no less than the faithful, were affected with religious scruples. The clergy sent a circular to the physicians of the town, containing these words: "To all seeming, Satan wishes to help suffering women, but the upshot will be the collapse of society, for the fear of the Lord which depends upon the petitions of the afflicted will be destroyed."

The doctors in general, wishing to avoid falling into sin, or believing that the dictates of their faith would absolve them from accepting the dictates of humanity, were, for the most part, influenced by the considerations which the clergy adduced.

"Since God Almighty, in His wisdom, thought fit to impose suffering upon women, it would be impious to run counter to the will of the Lord," they declared, and quoted, in confirmation of the correctness of the clerical view, the scientific theory that pain was a biological necessity.

"For tens of thousands of years, births have taken place without any means for allaying pain. Has not nature disclosed the wisdom of God in her conduct of the processes of birth? Assuredly it is most presumptuous for man to have recourse to such innovations in the belief that he can improve upon the Creator's handiwork." The chorus of condemnation of the "chloroform doctor" was joined by the citizens who were alarmed for public morality. "The pangs of childbirth," they said, "are a moral guarantee of maternal affection, which is one of the sacred foundations of society. We can feel sure that a mother will show self-sacrificing love only for a child to whom she has given birth in pain. Moreover, it is incompatible with the sanctity of the act of birth that so holy a place as the lying-in chamber shall become a stage where mothers are made drunk with chloroform, for it is impossible that children born in so immoral an atmosphere shall ever grow up into pious men and women."

All Edinburgh rose in revolt against the innovator. "Impious heretic!" exclaimed the priests; "irresponsible charlatan!" said the doctors; "man of sin!" declared the laymen.

The doctor who had wished to allay the pangs of childbirth was shunned. He had always been a pious Christian, and now his brethren in the faith turned away from him. He had always acted up to the highest professional traditions, and now his colleagues were against him. He had always been a well-behaved citizen, and now his fellow citizens charged him with immorality.

But Simpson, whom diligence had raised from the position of a baker's son to become chief accoucheur in Edinburgh Infirmary—Simpson who when verging on middle age had realized the ideal he had formed in early youth—was not the man to be intimidated by this clamor.

He was animated by a conviction which armed him against every assault, the conviction that he was doing right and was acting in conformity with the divine will when he announced to women: "Not in sorrow shalt thou bear children."

It was impossible that a good God could desire His creatures to suffer; and it could not have been God's will that Simpson's pious mother should have suffered in giving birth to him, and that millions of innocent women should suffer in the act of bringing new life into the world. Whatever the ministers of religion might proclaim, Simpson was sure that God could not be a vindictive God, and that an everlasting curse could not be God's will. God had bestowed on man the gift of science, that therewith man might complete the work of the Redeemer; and humanizing progress must be a fulfillment of the divine will.

Simpson, therefore, was certain that God Himself had implanted his youthful horror at the thought of the agony his mother had suffered; that God Himself had kept the unheard cries of the mother that bore him ringing forever in his ears. God had led him to the bedside of hundreds upon hundreds of women in labor that his memory of this suffering should remain ever vivid. God had brought these things to pass that he, Simpson, might never cease from striving to free women from the pangs of labor. His discovery was God's will.

Thus, though cold-shouldered by his brethren in the faith, by his colleagues and by his fellow citizens, Simpson stood his ground undaunted. His invincible certainty gave him power.

He had been most piously brought up, and he was assured that the words of Holy Writ were the last court of appeal in all matters both of faith and of science. But it seemed inconceivable to him that the innermost convictions of his heart could conflict with the utterances of Scripture. The sincere human heart could not inspire him to heresy. His compassion with the sufferings of mothers must be in conformity with the innermost meaning of the Bible. The two truths could not possibly conflict, but must both be the truths that issued from the mind of the All-Good.

Simpson was sure that the ministers of religion in the Scottish capital must have misunderstood the words of Holy Writ.

He had very little free time. Nevertheless, the leisure hours he had formerly devoted to the search for a means of alleviating the pangs of labor, he would henceforward devote to showing that his discovery was in harmony with God's word.

Night after night he sat up studying the Book of Genesis, the teachings of the prophets, the Gospels, carefully considering the sacred text word after word, comparing the Hebrew of the Old Testament, the Greek of the New, with the English Authorized Version; turning to read what the masters of exegesis had to say about the matter, and then going back to the originals once more, until he had confirmed his assurance that the message of his own heart was in conformity with the Word of God. Yes, he was sure of it, he was right. Scientific medicine, the healing art that brought solace to suffering mortals, was the nineteenth-century exposition of the doctrine of Jesus Christ. It was plain that God had not willed the suffering of mothers, for God had sent physicians to relieve pain. Such was the assurance that came to Simpson as a result of his nocturnal studies of the Bible. When, therefore, this ostracized doctor took up the cudgels against his co-religionists, his professional colleagues and his fellow citizens, it was as one to whom God had granted a special knowledge of His Word.

Turning against his accusers who from the pulpit pointed to Genesis 3, 16, and read: "In sorrow thou shalt bring forth children," Simpson rejoined by referring to Genesis 2, 21: "And the Lord God caused a deep sleep to fall upon Adam, and he slept: and he took one of his ribs, and closed up the flesh instead thereof." —"What God Himself did," said Simpson triumphantly, "cannot be sinful."

Of course the preachers had an answer ready. "The creation of Eve out of the sleeping Adam," they objected, "took place before the Fall. The curse pronounced upon Eve and her daughters was not uttered until after our parents had been driven forth from Paradise."

But Simpson, the exegete, was ready for them. "The Creator, when He uttered those words, did not mean what you think. The word used in the Hebrew, and translated by 'sorrow' in the 16th verse, is the same word also translated 'sorrow' in the 17th and subsequent verses when Adam's punishment is decreed. 'In the sweat of thy face shalt thou eat bread; in sorrow shalt thou eat of it all the days of thy life.' In neither case does the word mean 'physical pain' but it means 'toil, labor and trouble.' In the sacred text, other words are used to denote 'bodily pain.' When uttering the doom imposed upon Adam and Eve, the Almighty spoke of labor and trouble, and this applied to Eve's bearing of children as well as to Adam's tilling of the soil."

This was less easy to answer, and while the ministers were at a loss Simpson was able to turn their silence to account, quoting Paul's First Epistle to Timothy, 4, 4: "For every creature of God is good, and nothing to be refused, if it be received with thanksgiving." Again: "Therefore to him that knoweth to do good and doeth it not, to him it is sin." (James 4, 17).—"Can you really believe," went on Simpson, "that if pain during the act of birth were God's will, any human will could have counteracted the will of the Almighty? Have you not all read: 'Dust thou art, and unto dust shalt thou return?' But if it be permitted to the physician that he works in apparent conflict with this text, by seeking to prolong life, then likewise it is permitted to the accoucheur to mitigate the pangs of labor which, to your way of thinking, are imposed by divine decree."

The preachers were puzzled. Text could be ranged against text, and each of the opposing texts was God's own word.

Then Simpson turned to the hesitant mothers and said: "You need have no fear of being wholly relieved from pain and trouble, for, even if you bring your children into the world without pain, you will have plenty of trouble in bringing them up."

To his colleagues he said: "It seems to me that a twofold mission awaits us as doctors, namely, to reduce human suffering and to prolong human life."

Then he went on to quote the statistics of their own lying-in hospitals, which showed that many deaths in childbirth were caused by unrelieved pain—deaths which chloroform narcosis might have prevented.

The struggle against the prejudices of the ministers of religion, fellow-citizens, and colleagues was an arduous one; but this impassioned champion was often able to dispel the prejudices of those who took their stand upon Holy Writ, those of good citizens, and those of doctors with a keen sense of responsibility.

"Do you not remember how the Church reproached Edward Jenner on the ground that vaccination was contrary to religion?"

he asked. "Did not Jenner's colleagues laugh him to scorn? Did not laymen regard him with suspicion? But now, when half a century has elapsed, everyone knows that in England and Wales alone Jenner's discovery has saved more lives than those of the whole population of Wales; and that in Europe it has saved more lives than those of the whole population of Great Britain."

By degrees, Simpson's tenacity was rewarded. The most fanatical of the preachers were horrified to find that more and more of the faithful were snared "in the toils of Satan." Worthy fathers of families had to accept the fact that their wives' lying-in rooms were transformed into places of intoxication; and with consternation Simpson's colleagues noted that more and more of their women patients were deserting them to be delivered by the "chloroform doctor."

For six years, nevertheless, the conflict raged as to whether painless child-bearing could be acceptable to God Almighty, or was necessarily sinful. Then loyalty to the throne was invoked on the side of chloroform. This turned the scale, and the decision was given against the primal curse and in favor of painless child-bearing.

When, three centuries before, Dame Euphanie had sought relief from the pangs of labor, she had been answered, by the King's will, by the even greater pangs of the stake. Now a woman sat on the throne, and when, during one of her later confinements, in April, 1853, she was in labor, she suffered from the pains which Dame Euphanie had so greatly dreaded. The accoucheur, James Clark, recommended the use of Simpson's discovery. Queen Victoria accepted the boon, and brought her seventh child, Prince Leopold, painlessly into the world. Simpson, had long ere this been appointed one of Her Majesty's physicians in Scotland; later, in 1866, he was made a baronet, the first Scottish physician to be granted this distinction. By the time of Queen Victoria's next confinement, the power of the opposition had been broken, and multitudes of less distinguished women had unhesitatingly followed the Queen's example.

For the general view in loyal and devout England of those Victorian days was that what Her Majesty did could not possibly conflict with the word of God, so the only thing left for the godly was to accept the Scottish accoucheur's exegesis, to give the word "sorrow" in the famous text of Genesis a new interpretation, and to pay more heed to Simpson's quotations from the Epistles of Timothy and James. The objections of the moralists were stilled; and the doctors, who had hitherto declared pain to be a biological necessity, were now careful to keep a bottle of chloroform in the midwifery bag, for otherwise they would assuredly lose their patients to some more accommodating rival.

Sir James Young Simpson, therefore, was not required to endure a martyr's lot. He had had, indeed, to work diligently and to struggle hard, having been born in a humble station, until through perseverance he fought his way into the foremost ranks of the profession; but in the end he was richly rewarded. At four-and-twenty, very early for such an honor, he was elected president of the Royal Medical Society of Edinburgh; and four years later, in the year 1839, he became professor of midwifery in Edinburgh University. In 1847, the Queen appointed him her Physician-in-Ordinary of Scotland. Thus at the time when Simpson made his wonderful discovery he was not an inconspicuous country practitioner like Long, nor a mere dentist like Wells or Morton, but a man whose reputation had already spread far beyond the confines of Edinburgh.

Also he was a man whose personality exerted a considerable charm. He was of imposing aspect, with a mighty, domed forehead. Everyone who came in contact with him was fascinated by the sight of his long, thick hair, his firmly set mouth, his penetrating eyes and his resolute but benevolent glance. "His lectures, adorned with irony and wit," wrote the *Lancet*, "illumined the dark days of the Edinburgh winter." Indeed, whatever Simpson had to say or to write in his frequent polemics was couched in a style so pithy and forceful that his opponents were carried out of themselves.

As soon as he had made his mark with the discovery of chloroform anesthesia, and had induced the public to accept it, honors were showered upon him. Over and above the insignia of rank and honor, the highest scientific distinctions fell to his lot. Honorary degrees were accorded him by the Universities of Oxford and Dublin, and he was made an honorary fellow of the King's and Queen's College of Physicians of Ireland. The foreign world, too, was eager to honor the "liberator of motherhood." In the year 1856, the Institute of France bestowed on him the Montyon Prize of 2000 francs; and when the French Academy of Medicine appointed him, by an overwhelming majority, one of their foreign members, all present rose and acclaimed the event with typical Latin enthusiasm. The King of Sweden bestowed on him the Order of St. Olaf. So high was he in favor at all the courts of Europe that when, on one occasion, a Scotsman sought audience of the King of Denmark, and His Majesty heard that the applicant came from Edinburgh, he was instantly admitted, the King saying: "If this gentleman comes from Edinburgh, I shall be glad to see him, for any compatriot of Sir James Simpson will be most welcome to me."

Simpson's fame brought patients to Edinburgh from all parts of the world, but, although his method of painless child-bearing speedily became established throughout the Continent of Europe, pregnant women traveled far to Edinburgh that they might enjoy the advantage of having the great Professor Simpson as their accoucheur, and have chloroform administered by his own hands.

Thus this Scottish discoverer enjoyed the recognition, fame and wealth for which Long, Wells, Jackson and Morton had vainly striven. When returning thanks on the occasion of his being presented with the freedom of the city of Edinburgh, he said, with proper pride: "I came to settle down and fight among you a hard and uphill battle of life for bread and name and fame, and the fact that I stand before you this day testifies that in the arduous struggle I have—won."

Nevertheless the unhappy dispute for priority in the discovery of anesthesia which raged on the other side of the Atlantic among two American dentists, a rural general practitioner and a professor smitten with madness, was, with its baleful might, to entangle the life even of Sir James Simpson, wealthy, accredited and honored though he was.

When, shortly after the discovery of ether anesthesia, the dispute broke out between Morton and Jackson, Simpson wrote to Morton acknowledging the latter's claims to priority. But when chloroform, its use spreading from the lying-in chamber to the operating theater, overshadowed for a time, especially on the European side of the Atlantic, the importance of ether, Simpson was misled by success into claiming more than its due for his own anesthetic. He declared that the use of ether for anesthetic purposes had been no more than a preliminary stage to the introduction of chloroform anesthesia, and when he was asked to write the article on Anesthesia for the eighth edition of the *Encyclopædia Britannica,* he unhesitatingly put forward the claim to having been the sole discoverer of anesthesia.

On the other side of the Atlantic, when the Boston surgeon Henry Jacob Bigelow read Simpson's allegations, he was outraged. Bigelow had attended the first painless operations at the Massachusetts General Hospital, was Morton's close friend and wellwisher, and always rushed into the breach when anyone made light of Morton's claim to priority. Now he penned a furious onslaught on the "Scottish usurper," describing Simpson as a man who wished to pose as a hero at Morton's cost.

Across oceans and continents there raged a struggle between these two inexorable campaigners—a struggle which was not to come to its unusual close until Simpson lay upon his deathbed.

James Young Simpson, whom his church had once accused of heresy and defiance of God's commandments, ended his days as devout a man as his forefathers had been. When opiates, ether and chloroform could not alleviate the agony of the angina pectoris from which he suffered, he recognized that his hour had come. Being a fervent Christian, as death approached, he was earnestly repentant for any wrongs he might have done. Obviously much which had seemed appropriate in the ardor of struggle must now appear unchristian and sinful to the dying man's calmer spirit. Afflicted with pangs of conscience, he did not wish to appear before his Maker until he had righted the wrong. Having, therefore, called for pen, ink and paper, on his deathbed he penned letters to all his adversaries in which he asked their pardon for such wrongs as he had committed.

One of these letters was addressed to Dr. Bigelow, to whom Simpson felt it needful to make a twofold atonement. Not only, being now face to face with death, did he solemnly declare that he continued to believe chloroform to be a better anesthetic than ether, but he went on to admit frankly that Morton, by his discovery and its application, had initiated "a *new era* in anæsthetics and surgery." This letter was published as a pamphlet at Edinburgh under date of April, 1870.

On May 6, 1870, two years after Morton's unhappy and inglorious end, died Simpson, favorite of fortune, whose life had only been transiently affected, as by a passing cloud, through the unhappy dispute about priority.

There was a general wish that, as one of the nation's mighty dead, Simpson should be given a public funeral and be buried in Westminster Abbey, but in accordance with the desire of his family he was interred at the site chosen by himself long before in Warriston Cemetery, Edinburgh. In St. Andrews Chapel, Westminster, close to the Davy memorial, there is a marble statue of Simpson, with the inscription:

> To whose genius and benevolence
> the world owes the blessings derived
> from the use of chloroform for
> the relief of suffering
> LAUS DEO

CHAPTER NINETEEN

Curse and Blessing

For years upon years after ether and chloroform had, throughout the world, become indispensable aids in modern surgery and midwifery, itinerant orators traveled from place to place, pitching their tents in public squares, hiring a room in an inn or a meeting-hall where for the amusement of the company they gave demonstrations of the effects of laughing gas. Yet a long, long time elapsed after Wells's conspicuous failure without any dentists' venturing to administer laughing gas for the painless extraction of teeth, and no one cared to try this gas, which had proved ineffective in small doses, as an anesthetic in the responsible province of major surgery. Nevertheless, throughout the United States, both in towns and villages, demonstrations of the intoxicating effects of laughing gas remained a lucrative source of income to strolling entertainers.

An extremely successful demonstrator belonging to this company was Gardner Q. Colton whose public performance at Hartford had led the dentist Horace Wells to make his first essays with laughing gas. Colton was actually present on the occasion when Wells had one of his own teeth painlessly extracted by Dr. Riggs, and when Wells went on to use the method successfully upon a patient. Colton never forgot these experiences. He was confident that laughing gas could allay pain; and this confidence persisted though Wells himself lost courage after the failure of

346

his public demonstration, and although the plea of Wells's heirs was rejected by Congress. But this faith of Colton's held a sting, for he ceased to hope that laughing gas would ever make headway against the competition of ether and chloroform. Yet he felt sure that if only the medical and surgical and dental professions realized the true importance of laughing gas it would no longer be a mere means of amusement but would become one of the most beneficent instruments of the healing art. Colton always felt it would be a pity that mankind should miss the chance of turning this useful remedy to account.

As things were, however, Colton failed to gain a hearing from the scientific world and had to proclaim his faith to ignorant audiences of pleasure-seeking provincials who giggled as they watched his demonstrations. No doubt, from time to time, physicians and dentists attended his performances, but they were too much under the spell of the tradition that ether and chloroform were the only useful anesthetics to pay heed to the possibilities of laughing gas.

Undeterred by this neglect, Colton wound up every demonstration with a reminder that in the year 1844 a Hartford dentist had painlessly extracted teeth from patients who had inhaled laughing gas. But for seventeen years he went on repeating this statement without obvious effect.

In the year 1863 his wanderings brought him back to Connecticut—not to Hartford, this time, but to New Haven. As usual, he ended his demonstration with the words: "In the year 1844 a Connecticut dentist"—and he went on to relate the story of Horace Wells. He concluded his harangue with the words: "But since the man who did this was a Connecticut dentist, it seems to me that a citizen of this state was justly entitled to the honor of being recognized as the first person in the world who successfully induced anesthesia by inhalation."

The perseverance of seventeen years was at length to be rewarded. Dr. J. H. Smith, a New Haven dentist, was among the audience, and marked Colton's words. New Haven is less than forty miles from Hartford. Local patriotism was awakened, and

Smith determined to repeat the experiment of his deceased Hartford colleague, in the hope that this might redound to the credit of Connecticut.

One of Smith's patients, an elderly lady, needed the extraction of seven teeth. "Would you rather bear the tortures of extraction in the ordinary way," asked Smith, "or have them pulled without a trace of pain so that you can laugh the while?"—"I would much rather be able to laugh," answered the patient. During all these years of demonstration, Colton had acquired considerable skill in administering gas, while Mr. Smith was well able to keep watch upon the patient's pulse and take any other requisite precautions. The extractions were painlessly effected. The old lady of New Haven was seized with the same propagandist zeal which long before had affected the Boston music master Eben Frost. She wanted to tell everyone about it, so she came that evening to Colton's demonstration and related the marvelous way in which seven teeth had been pulled out without any pain. She did the same thing next evening, and when Colton moved on to another town she accompanied him, to become an indispensable exhibit at the laughing-gas demonstrations; and thenceforward she was an invaluable constituent of the painless-extraction clinic of Colton and Smith. For the world had not long to wait now before the extraction of seven teeth from this enthusiastic old lady had developed into a great commercial undertaking.

Smith and Colton were quick to grasp the magic of numbers. They had begun with the extraction of seven teeth, but twenty-three days later, having taken to themselves J. Allen as third associate, they could already boast the painless extraction of three thousand nine hundred and twenty-nine teeth.

A year later, over a New York office hung the display board of the Colton-Smith Dental Association, which in 1867 could vaunt the extraction of seventeen thousand, six hundred and one teeth and six months later recorded the amazing total of twenty thousand painless extractions.

Throughout America, teeth were now being painlessly extracted under laughing gas, and while Smith and Allen continued to nurse the thriving business in New York, Colton crossed the

Atlantic to acquaint European dentists with the blessings of laughing gas.

Now that laughing gas, ceasing to be a mere means of amusement, had firmly advanced into dental parlors, it was in a position to rival the achievements of ether and chloroform and to invade the province of major surgery. The first painless surgical operation under laughing gas took place in the year 1868, at about the time of Morton's death.

The only disadvantage of laughing gas, as far as major surgery was concerned, was that its effect was so transient. But this disadvantage could be remedied. A Chicago surgeon named Edward Willys Andrew suggested the admixture of ten per cent of oxygen with the laughing gas, thus providing, with what came to be known as "interval narcosis," a method of prolonging the sleep under laughing gas, since asphyxia need no longer be feared.

By a strange chance it happened that coincidentally with the date of the death of Simpson, the discoverer of chloroform anesthesia, laughing gas was to prove a formidable rival of chloroform in midwifery. James Fox reported successful painless deliveries under laughing gas. In 1880, Fox's method was successfully adopted by Klikovich, a famous St. Petersburg accoucheur. Henceforward for a time, laughing gas, thus administered, almost replaced ether and chloroform in the practice of midwifery.

Thus it came to pass that, thanks to the perseverance of an itinerant entertainer and the courage of a New Haven dentist, Davy's, Hickman's and Wells's labors came to full fruition, laughing gas being intensively used in surgery and midwifery.

In the history of anesthesia, chance has been hardly less important than discovery. It was chance which revealed to Davy and Wells the pain-allaying powers of laughing gas, and to Long the similar working of ether. Chance was likewise to contribute to the discovery of one of the most recent anesthetics, ethylene.

In the nineteen-twenties a Chicago gardener grew remarkably fine carnations in his hothouse, and disposed of them through retailers. One day, however, his carnations became affected by a strange disorder. He entered the hothouse to cut some flowers, and found that his carnations had withered and died. Day after day the same inexplicable malady carried them off, and he did not know what on earth to do.

No one could discover why the flowers perished directly the buds opened. At length, one day, the gardener noticed a peculiar smell in the hothouse. Searching for the cause, he found a leaky gas pipe. This put him on the track; here must be the root of the mischief. To test the hypothesis, he took a freshly bloomed carnation and pressed the flower on the spot whence the gas was issuing. Sure enough, the blossom promptly closed, as if it were "going to sleep." The gardener took the "sleeping" carnation out into the open air, where it promptly recovered and "awakened." The second flower, which he held for a longer time close to the leak, passed into a sleep from which there was no awakening. He had the aperture plugged, and henceforward his flowers throve as usual.

But this seemingly petty incident in a Chicago hothouse was to have effects farther reaching than those which concerned the success or failure of a nurseryman's enterprise, and were to prove significant in the conquest of pain. The chance observation that illuminating gas issuing from a leaky gas pipe could "put carnations to sleep" was made in the year 1924. By this date, however, chance itself had been robbed of its romantic possibilities. Investigators had come to realize that "chances" of this sort were always worthy of scientific study. A great company of investigators was always on the lookout for such possibilities, and now came forward to rob the chance of its mystery.

Dr. Knight and Dr. Crocker, two botanists of the University of Chicago, heard of these carnations which had been put to sleep in a hothouse, promptly repeated what had been a chance experiment, and got their microscopes to work. The plants were elaborately studied in accordance with the rules of exact science, and the somniferous influence of illuminating gas upon living vegetable matter was elaborately investigated. Zo-ologists, too, got wind of the matter, and soon Arno B. Luckhardt and Carter found that animals reacted to this illuminating gas just as carnations did.

Experiments went on for months, with ever-renewed trials and the most elaborate notes. Luckhardt and Carter diluted coal-gas with oxygen in various proportions; they went on trying to determine which ingredient of this complicated mixture of gases had the soporific effect; they produced what they wanted synthetically, at length discovering "ethylene" which could cause sleep and anesthesia like those due to ether, but without any of the disagreeable accompaniments of anesthesia by that volatile fluid. Thus Luckhardt and Carter secured a new anesthetic which proved of great value in practical surgery. So useful was it that within a few years no less than fifty thousand painless operations were performed under ethylene anesthesia.

Pharmaceutical research had made enormous advances since Morton first administered ether in 1846. More than thirty thousand synthetic drugs have now been tried in medicine, all of them being tested as to their possibilities for the relief of pain. One of the greatest and most important industries of modern times has developed out of chemistry, and in this field a huge army of investigators, physicians, physiologists and chemists are continually on the lookout for new and valuable analgesic and anesthetic remedies. Systematic research has led to a continued output of new pain-allaying gases, vapors and mixtures of gases.

While, among these anesthetic gases and vapors, laughing gas, ether, chloroform and ethylene remain the chief, there are numerous others, such as chemically pure acetylene, discovered by the German chemists Gauss and Wieland, the so-called narcylene, also propylene and cyclopropane. Specially useful for the initiation of anesthesia are chlorethyl, bromethyl and solaesthin.

In the year 1866, Ellis recommended a new method of combining the use of various anesthetics. In the 'eighties of the last century Billroth introduced a forerunner of the ACE mixture (consisting of one part of alcohol, two parts of chloroform and three parts of ether); then came Schering and Picet's method which, perfected by the drop-after-drop procedure of Léon Labbé, ultimately found its way into general surgical practice.

Meanwhile, of course, the administration of both the older and the newer substances had been extraordinarily developed. The glass globe with two apertures made by the Bostonian instrument-maker Chamberlain in accordance with Morton's instructions had undergone various transformations until the far more imposing inhalers in use by modern anesthetists were introduced. Nowadays a rubber mask, fitting tightly over mouth and nostrils, is connected with a gas bag into which oxygen, ether, etc. are admitted in varying quantities while the patient breathes into and from the gas bag. Anesthetists also use a fairly recent instrument enabling them to keep watch upon the patient's blood pressure.

Dr. John Snow, to whom anesthetic medicine owed the first modern ether inhaler, also constructed an improved chloroform inhaler. Another anesthetist who greatly improved the technique of gas administration was Dr. Roth-Draeger. A further advance came from the application of Gal's re-breathing principle; McKesson constructed a re-breathing inhaler with an automatically controlled mixing chamber. J. T. Gwathmey invented a flask for improved dosage; von Foregger constructed the metric bottle; and others introduced special manometers for the regulation of the supply of gas.

In the opening decades of the twentieth century, especially in America, there has been a great development of highly specialized inhalers, making the dosage of various anesthetic substances an extremely precise affair.

In the early days of anesthesia, it was the discoverers themselves who administered gas or various vapors; but since the eighteen-eighties in many countries the administration of anesthetics has become a specialty. In 1893, there was formed in England the Society of British Anesthetists, one of whose rules it is that only special anesthetists ought to administer these agents. Various other countries have followed this example.

Prior to the introduction of anesthesia by inhalation, the only channel open to medicine for the production of artificial sleep was that of the mouth, the gullet and the stomach. The discovery that volatile substances could be administered by inhalation through the lungs opened an entirely new path for remedial medicine. It became plain that through inhalation a pain-allaying sleep could be more speedily induced, with less risk and with more capacity for regulation than by any other method.

Simultaneously with this advance in pneumatology, there was a steady improvement in synthetic chemistry and in the technique of narcosis for the prevention of pain by the induction of artificial sleep. Pitha and J. T. Gwathmey were the first modern anesthetists to revive the method of administering narcotics per rectum, which had been known in the Middle Ages to the School of Salerno. Recognizing that absorption takes place rapidly from the intestines, they pressed this part of the alimentary track into the service of narcosis. Pitha gave belladonna enemata; and Gwathmey produced artificial sleep by introducing into the rectum a mixture of oil and ether, the sleep being subsequently rendered more profound by giving ether or chloroform by inhalation.

This combined method did not come to full fruition until, in 1917, Eichholz discovered avertin, a substance resembling alcohol, but one which produces anesthetic sleep without a transitional period of excitement and intoxication. It is very easily administered in the form of an enema as a "basal narcotic." It is given to the patient while in bed in his own room or ward. Sleep ensues; then the patient is transferred to the operating theater, is there put under ether or chloroform, is operated upon, and taken back to bed without ever awakening, and without having been alarmed or excited by entering the theater in the conscious state.

The path by which pain-allaying substances made their way to the sleep centers was considerably shortened by the pneumatic method and by rectal administration, as contrasted with the traditional route of administration by way of the stomach. But the lungs and the lower bowel, like the stomach, are merely receptacles and transformers in which narcotics must be or may be elaborated before they make their way into the circulation. Then only can the blood carry them to the centers where their chemical physiological influence induces a pain-allaying sleep.

In the year 1853 the Edinburgh physician Alexander Wood invented the hollow needle for subcutaneous injection (though it had really been invented long before by venomous serpents, insects, scorpions, etc.), thus providing a technical instrument by which sleep-producing, pain-allaying chemicals could be introduced directly into the circulation without having to pass through the devious channels of the stomach, the bowel or the lungs. A short cut to the sleep centers had been discovered.

At first Wood's subcutaneous or hypodermic needle was used only for the administration of remedies to relieve neuralgic pains, but ere long it was also turned to account for the new and highly important anesthetic procedure—anesthesia by injection.

Wood made his discovery public in the year 1855; a year later it was introduced into the United States by Fordyce Barker, whereupon there ensued the inevitable disputes about priority, two physicians from Philadelphia and Washington, respectively, declaring that they had used a hollow needle as early as the year 1839.

But the immense popularity later attained by the hypodermic method of administration was due to the application of the hollow needle to a specially constructed syringe, often called on the Continent the Pravaz syringe, but in England and the United States always spoken of as the hypodermic syringe.

Its discoverer, a Frenchman named Charles Gabriel Pravaz, was born in the year 1791 in a little Savoyard village. In youth he served as an engineer officer, but after the Allies entered Paris in the spring of 1814 and Napoleon abdicated at Fontainebleau he severed his connection with the army. He became principal of a home for the aged, where he had ample opportunity of watching the miseries that result from the maladies of advanced life. What was to be done for the relief of this suffering, for the alleviation of these miseries? Morphine was the most effective remedy, but this alkaloid, which the German pharmacist Sertürner of Einbeck had discovered, was not well tolerated by the enfeebled stomachs of elderly persons. It had been found generally that morphine administered by mouth was by no means an ideal anodyne, so that at that period it was comparatively little used in general practice.

The French physician, Pravaz, was to turn to full advantage the discovery of the noted German chemist. Having left the home for the aged, he established himself as a practitioner in Lyons, specializing mainly in orthopedics. At the same time he was continually pondering the question which had begun to worry him when he was in charge of the home for the aged and had found the stomachs of the inmates intolerant of Sertürner's morphine. Yet morphine was a most valuable product the dosage of which could be regulated accurately. How was it to be introduced *directly* into the blood stream, instead of by way of the mouth and stomach.

In 1853, just before his death, he solved the problem, this year marking a progress in the alleviation of pain no less signal than that marked by the discovery of the chief of the opium alkaloids. Pravaz invented the hypodermic syringe. Only now did the most powerful of narcotics, morphine, come into its own.

"I should not like to be a doctor without morphine at my disposal," declared a famous German physician at the beginning of the nineteenth century. But the full advantages of the drug could not be secured without the aid of the hollow needle and of the Pravaz syringe.

Physicians had good reason to prize the hypodermic syringe, by use of which, injecting morphine beneath the skin, they could relieve the most intense colic within a few minutes, and throw the patient into a peaceful, refreshing slumber. Poets have sung its praises. To begin with it was used only to relieve "the thousand natural shocks that flesh is heir to," to allay the pain attendant upon all sorts of illness or accident. But in 1869, sixteen years after Pravaz' discovery, another French physician, Claude Bernard, pointed out that the hypodermic syringe might find a useful place in the art of anesthesia. He was the first to give a hypodermic injection of morphine as a basal narcotic before administering ether or chloroform by inhalation; and Pitha, Nussbaum and Crombil developed the method in such a way that the soporific influence of the anesthetic could be maintained and pain averted after operations for as long as twelve hours.

Thus the invention of the hypodermic syringe facilitated the combination of the two greatest anesthetic discoveries, alkaloidal chemistry and pneumatic therapeutics, to make of them a unified weapon against pain.

The nineteenth century was the century of the triumph of science over nature. There was scarcely a year in which the investigatory spirit of man failed to discover new forces or to liberate them from their natural bonds. One of the most important advances of the time was the discovery of electricity. Doctors, in their search for means to relieve pain, soon turned this new and wonderful force to account.

In the year 1902 the French physician Stephane Leduc tried to induce artificial sleep by means of the electric current. He put one electrode on the patient's forehead and the other beneath the back, passing a current interrupted one hundred times per second. He found that patients thus treated became semiconscious, were unable to speak or move and ceased to feel pain. When the current was switched off, normal consciousness promptly returned.

No investigator can see into the dark pit of profound narcotic sleep, where pain ceases. Nothing but a descent into its abysses by way of the dream, which is illumined by a glimmer from the world of conscious life, can give us an inkling of the mystery which underlies artificial sleep.

The same thing happens almost always in narcosis. At the threshold of artificial sleep, the patient begins to dream. As he enters the dream world, his expression changes. He begins to utter strange words, and dreams himself away from this world of pain to enter the painless world of narcosis. Doctors, nurses and the administrators of anesthetics and other narcotics who can watch this process, are always fascinated by the enigma of the narcotic dream.

The researches of those who have made a special study of the processes of sleep and dreams—such investigators as Elmer Jones, Monsle Wold, Stout, Jastrow and Klages, have unraveled much of the mystery of the disappearance of pain in the dream. We know, now, that the dream experience is always one of insensibility to pain, so that we never dream of suffering bodily pain.

From the dream a road leads back into consciousness, the road known as memory. Memory tells us that the dream is a world in which pain no longer exists. In a dream we are drilled with bullets, pierced with daggers, without feeling the least trace of pain—for in the dream, as Klages contends, we experience without sense organs, and therefore without any painful sensations.

This enables us to understand the way in which, during narcosis by inhalation, dreams and painlessness are intertwined. Dreaming draws a veil in front of our consciousness; a dream is the cap of invisibility which makes the patient unseen by pain and therefore immune to its attack.

The work of these investigators of dream life also has shown that all forms of intoxication are "variants of the dream consciousness," variants of that phase of consciousness which knows nothing of painful sensations. This disclosure of the psychical kinship between intoxication and the dream explains, finally, the pain-allaying effect of all those narcotics which, like laughing gas, can make pain impossible by inducing states of intoxication.

Besides performing the pain-allaying miracles that result from an artificial dream-sleep and from intoxication, narcotics perform an additional miracle, that of making the patient "forget pain."

Like the "plant of artificial sleep," the "plant of forgetfulness of pain" does its wonderful work in the great laboratory of nature. Hidden away in the vegetable organism of the nightshade and the henbane, a drowsy "numbness" grew out of Mother Earth—but scientific chemistry was needed before the "juice of oblivion" became accessible to the practitioners of the healing art.

Chemistry was able to extract from the nightshade and the henbane their alkaloidal products, but was also able to produce a synthetic scopolamin substantially identical with the natural alkaloid. Since this happened after the discovery of the hollow needle and the hypodermic syringe, nothing more was needed than a subcutaneous (or, of late, an intravenous) injection to instil forgetfulness directly into the blood and to expunge pain from the memory. Thus, by a strange trick of consciousness, could be achieved the "forgetting of pain," even as pain is forgotten during states of intoxication, or as it is forgotten in the dream, and in sleep. By such an injection, the consciousness is chemically modified so that the memory of pain vanishes. Pain becomes like a dream which has been dreamed and then forgotten. That which occurs without leaving any memory of its occurrence may have been lived but it has not been effectively experienced. For only that which forms part of the continuity of consciousness, that which is veritably remembered, has been "experienced" and "suffered." We are not entitled to call anything "pain" if it does not penetrate into consciousness. Scopolamin, by blocking the path which leads into consciousness, excludes, so long as its action persists, the normal workings of an ego that is gifted with memory and therefore capable of feeling pain.

Thus the patient who has had a hypodermic injection of scopolamin and then has an operation performed, continues to give signs of pain during the operation, but directly the operation ceases he falls into a deep sleep from which he awakens free from all memory of pain. The condition is one analogous to somnambulism. The objective manifestations of pain persist, but the personality which is capable of noting and realizing pain has temporarily ceased to exist.

The first experiments with this state of semi-narcosis known to anesthetists as "twilight sleep" were made in the year 1899. Composite injections of scopolamin and morphine or of scopolamin and narcophin were given. Dr. Korff used these injections as a substitute for ether or chloroform narcosis.

But their effective introduction into practice did not occur till later when the Freiburg doctors Steinbüchel, Bernhard Krönig and Karl Gauss used twilight sleep in midwifery instead of administering chloroform. Within the next few years Dr. Gauss delivered more than three thousand women under twilight sleep, and the remarkable phenomenon of forgetfulness of pain has been noticed, with very few exceptions, in his practice and in that of other accoucheurs.

To Dr. H. Fuchs, a Danzig physician, we are indebted for a precise description of twilight sleep (of late, with an improved technique, rechristened "obstetric analgesia"): "As soon as a labor pain comes on, a woman under twilight sleep cries or screams just like an unanesthetized woman. If you ask her whether she feels the pain, she answers in the affirmative, but in the intervals between the pains she falls asleep. After delivery, when the effects of the hypodermic injection have passed off, she will be found to have completely lost memory of the pains. When the method is fully successful, the patient has no remembrance whatever of the labor process."

Synthetic chemistry has by no means reached its climax. We can foresee no limit to the number of possible chemical combinations; the zeal and courage of the investigators is unbounded, and the chemico-therapeutical industry goes on developing without pause. The performances of the past and the promise for the future seem to justify a hope that the scope of drug treatment will perpetually widen and that the dominion of "chemical medicine" will be progressively strengthened.

In past millennia, mental therapeutics, "healing by the powers of the mind," was predominant over chemical medication, but has, of late, been forced more and more into the background by the enormous and incontestable advance of drug treatment. But the apostles of psychotherapy have been by no means willing to accept defeat, many of them continuing to claim that their art must take precedence of all others. Despite the chemists, the laboratory workers and other advocates of physical remedies, the mental therapeutists have gone on cultivating their priceless heritage of "healing by the mind and by magic."

During the nineteenth century, the "century of chemistry," at the very time when anesthesia was celebrating such triumphant advances, there was inaugurated in the United States the doctrine of Christian Science whose adherents, numbered by millions, insist that spiritual healing is the only sound therapeutic method.

While doctors were using the hypodermic syringe to relieve pains of every kind, while operators gave their patients ether or chloroform to obviate the agonies which would otherwise have been caused by the healing knife, Christian Scientists unceasingly proclaimed that in God's world neither pain nor illness could exist.

According to the doctrine of Christian Science, pain is a mere illusion which can plague suffering man only so long as he continues to believe in its existence. Let him rid himself of his mental image of pain, and the pain will vanish. "Correct thought," based upon Holy Writ, is, say the Christian Scientists, enormously superior for the relief of pain to any physical narcotics. With the aid of spiritual anesthesia, a Christian Scientist can bear a child painlessly, and can be saved from the smart of any operation.

Mary Baker Eddy, the foundress of Christian Science, promulgated her doctrine in the year 1866. It was not until toward the turn of the century that Émile Coué began to spread his doctrine of autosuggestion and to insist that he could "talk away" pain. The great Coué boom did not come until after the War, but before and after the War there were everywhere to be found "saints" and "healers," with innumerable disciples, declaring and believing drug treatment to be a mistake, and insisting that pain could be abolished by purely spiritual methods.

All these faith-healers, these modern magicians, coming to the front in a scientific age, worked outside the domain of what is usually considered science and were more akin to the old-time miracle-workers; but mesmerism, having assumed a new dress and a new name as hypnotism, persistently claimed the title of a science.

This transformation of mesmerism into a science was effected by James Braid (1795–1860), an able Scottish physician who practiced in Manchester.

In a Manchester lying-in hospital, Lafontaine was trying to allay the pangs of labor by the use of "animal magnetism" in accordance with the recipes of Mesmer, the eighteenth-century wonder-worker. James Braid was one of those doctors who regard the fight against pain as their chief mission. Everything which might contribute to this task seemed to him worthy of attention. Though a convinced rationalist, he did not despise mesmerism, being sure that unprejudiced observation was the first duty of the enlightened man of science. Why should he not watch Lafontaine trying this mesmeric hocus-pocus? There might be something in it which would be of use to scientific medicine. For many weeks he studied Lafontaine at work on the attempt to make delivery painless by means of "animal magnetism." The rationalist could not be easy until he had discovered the nature of the physiological processes which led to insensibility under the influence of "mesmeric passes." He perceived that Lafontaine's patients had a spasm of the eyelids which made it impossible for them to open their eyes.

Thus there occurred what so often happens as a prelude to an important discovery. Braid noticed a phenomenon of frequent occurrence which had previously been ignored. He drew inferences from it, tested these inferences by renewed experiments, found them confirmed—and thus made his discovery.

James Braid, the physician, inferred from his observation of the spasmodically closed eyes that the mesmeric sleep must be due to an act of concentration, the outcome of a restriction of consciousness involving the entire nervous system and the optic nerve. Then, following the enigmatic laws of a discoverer's brain, Braid came to the conclusion that this restriction of consciousness could be induced by a concentration of vision. But, if that were so, the concentration could be brought about at will, sensations, feelings and thoughts being deliberately extruded from the narrowed consciousness. Thus Braid became enabled, by ordering the patient to concentrate, to induce a condition which he called neurohypnotism (the term being subsequently shortened to hypnotism), in which pain could be annulled voluntarily.

Braid's first experiments were performed upon his own wife. He took a shining tin box, held it before her eyes and told her to fix her gaze on it. She looked firmly at the object, and suddenly went to sleep. Then Braid ordered her to do this, that and the other—many of them the most unreasonable things. She obeyed every command without protest, as if under stress of an irresistible inner impulse. Pricking her arm with a pin, he said commandingly: "You feel no pain"—"I feel no pain," answered his wife from the depths of her trance. In her narrowed consciousness, every word uttered to her became a reality.

"Now you are awake once more," he said, to conclude; and promptly his wife awoke.

That evening a friend called on Braid. The doctor told him to be seated and said authoritatively: "Look firmly at my eyes." His friend obeyed and, after looking for a second or two, was unable to turn away his eyes. Then he fell asleep and, at the word of command, did whatever Braid told him, until awakened—once more by order.

The experiments made upon his wife and upon his friend

were repeated by Braid on numerous patients. Hypnotism had been discovered. A year later, in 1843, Braid published his book *Neurypnology, or the Rationale of Nervous Sleep*. In this work he freed the phenomena of mesmeric sleep from their mystery, disclosing the physiological substratum and giving a precise account of the technique of hypnotism. He said that the hypnotist used no transcendental or supernatural powers, and that the method was applicable by every intelligent practitioner.

This discovery of the hypnotic method of allaying or preventing pain was made in that wonderful fifth decade of the nineteenth century when all the fundamental methods of modern anesthesia were revealed. James Braid discovered hypnotism in 1842, the very year in which Long, at Athens, Georgia, performed a painless operation on Venable who had been put to sleep by the inhalation of ether.

But James Braid was less fortunate with his mental or spiritual anesthesia than were the discoverers of chemical anesthesia. His neurohypnotism was not taken seriously by his professional colleagues, the medical faculty being outraged that a qualified physician should fool about with what they stigmatized as "quackery." Moreover, the pious of England, who insisted that nothing must be done to free woman from the "primal curse," frowned upon the idea of spiritual anesthesia even as, a few years later, the Scotch frowned upon the "chloroform doctor" in Edinburgh.

It was outrageous, they declared, both for the operator and for the patient, that anyone should, for a time, surrender his will to another and allow the other to order him about. It was greatly to be deplored that any such thing should occur in a Christian land. God's displeasure would undoubtedly be visited on the offenders. The law and the Church should promptly take order about the matter.

At length Braid, though himself a religious man, was believed to be in league with the Devil, and it was really all the better for him that ere long hypnotism and its discoverer were forgotten, for thus only did this notable pioneer escape contumely. It was not until about forty years later that the method was rescued from oblivion by a French doctor, A. A. Liébeault of Nancy.

It was left for this country practitioner to force hypnotism into its rightful place in scientific medicine. To begin with, in his practice, he was able to appeal to the thrifty instincts of the French peasants, who grudged every centime they had to disburse upon the payment of medical fees.

"If you like," said Liébeault, "I can treat you in the ordinary way, with powders, pills and compresses. But these things cost a lot of money. Should you prefer it, I will hypnotize you, and cure you without fee or reward."

Naturally this argument made a strong appeal. The peasants thronged Liébeault's consulting room, looked fixedly at his eyes, in accordance with his directions, relaxed and "thought of nothing at all," as he ordered them.

"Your eyes are growing tired, your limbs are heavy, you feel sleepier and sleepier," said Liébeault, in a monotonous voice to these patients who paid him no more than a sou apiece. So great was the afflux of patients that "Père Liébeault," as the patients came to call him, found it difficult to cope with them. After more than three decades of practice, he could proudly say: "I continue to defend the system of hypnosis, armed by the experience of thirty-four years, during which I have treated more than twelve thousand patients."

For Liébeault had to wait thirty-four years before his system was generally accepted. At first he was regarded as a lunatic, and was universally mocked. No more than a very few copies of his first book on hypnotism were sold. Owing to a lucky chance, Liébeault at length secured recognition.

Bernheim, a Parisian professor and an able physician, was unable to cure one of his patients. The patient went to Nancy, and Liébeault cured him by hypnotism. Then, in the year 1882, he received the unexpected honor of a visit from a distinguished Parisian colleague. Bernheim came all the way from the metropolis to congratulate Liébeault upon curing an illness which had resisted the ordinary resources of the medical art. Liébeault made the most of his opportunities, and was so well able to convince Bernheim of the value of his method that in 1864 Bernheim arranged for the publication of the first part of Liébeault's book *De la suggestion,* and in 1866 of the second part, under the title *La thérapie sugges-*

tive. Bernheim's doughty support broke down the medical faculty's resistance. The leaders of psychological medicine in the France of that day were Charcot and Babinsky, men with open minds, ready to try new methods at the Salpêtrière. Having thus secured acceptance in France, the theory and methods of hypnotism made the round of the world, and both major and minor operations, even amputations, were soon being performed under hypnotic anesthesia.

The enthusiastic advocates of this mental or spiritual anesthesia declared their method preferable to chemical anesthesia because, without drug-induced disturbance of the general nervous system, they were able, by purely psychological methods, to exclude pain from consciousness, while leaving the other workings of the mind intact.

But various drawbacks soon became apparent. Although it could be statistically proved that ninety-four per cent of all persons were hypnotizable, it appeared that hypnotic anesthesia for surgical purposes could be achieved in no more than ten per cent. In 1890 Ochorowicz constructed his hypnoscope, as an instrument for ascertaining the degree of hypnotizability. However, the researches made with this instrument showed that hypnosis could not be compared with chemical anesthesia as a means for allaying pain.

Of late, nevertheless, there have been doctors eager to study the interrelations between the mental and the bodily in human beings, and extending their researches into the realm of narcosis. Combining psychical with chemical methods, they hypnotize their patients and reinforce hypnotic anesthesia by the use of various chemical narcotics, such as opium, morphine, cannabis indica and ether. They also aim at prolonging the state of painlessness by post-hypnotic anesthesia and thus prevent pain subsequent to the operation.

But the long and the short of the matter is that hypnosis has not proved a trustworthy means for allaying pain. For this we must still look to modern chemo-therapeutics.

Reason will not countenance the mythological views of those who hold bodily pain, of whatever kind, to be a punishment for original sin. In the nineteenth century such a view was regarded as superstitious by the enlightened. The discoverer of morphine, the founders of anesthesia by inhalation, the famous investigators who have perfected new and ever new means of allaying pain, can point proudly to the way in which they have been able to dissipate many of the woes of the flesh, and to show that the general effect of these methods has beyond question been enormously advantageous. Thanks to them, mankind has been largely relieved from the curse of suffering. Alkaloidal chemistry and anesthesia by inhalation already can look back to a century of achievement and to the records of millions upon millions of cases in which suffering has been abolished. Still, the "curse imposed by a vengeful God" has not been wholly banned. We have conquered pain, but have done so at a great price. The conquest of pain brings dangers. The victorious history of anesthesia is also the history of a thousand perils, many of which medical skill has enabled us to overcome, but many of which seem unavoidable. Blessing and curse, the conquest of pain and the spread of suffering, seem to march hand in hand. The pages of the history of victorious anesthesia are also pages shot with disaster.

Death treads on the heels of pain-allaying substance, and if the doctor wants to relieve pain he must come to terms with death. A narcotic works only by throwing the patient into an artificial sleep which is death's own brother; only by carefully devised means can the doctor save from death those whom he has rendered insensitive to pain. Every doctor who relieves pain must measure his strength and skill with death.

This risk of death was already entailed in the use of the preventives of pain that were known before the days of modern scientific medicine. In nature's great workshop, where artificial sleep is manufactured in roots, leaves and flowers, the juices contain the means of death as well as those which can induce artificial sleep. The popular imagination wove around the pain-allaying mandragora a strange legend in which this sinister association is alluded to. The belief was that when mandragora was pulled up by the roots the plant uttered dreadful cries which infallibly killed those who heard them.

The death that was supposed to lurk in all naturally given narcotics was the main reason why they fell into disrepute, with the result that analgesic remedies were shunned, and in the eighteenth century the most horrible agony was thought preferable to the risk of using drugs to assuage it.

The danger of the natural narcotics was due not solely to their impurity but also to the method of their administration. Since they were given by mouth, it was impossible to regulate their poisonous effects.

With the rise of modern chemistry, science made an important step in the way of reducing the deadly peril attendant upon the alleviation of pain. Alkaloidal chemistry rendered possible the isolation of the active principles contained in plants. They were thus freed from harmful accessories, and their dosage could be carefully graded. Then, with pneumatic anesthesia, the doctor gained control of pain-allaying remedies which were administered through the lungs, so that the number of vapor-laden breaths could be accurately determined.

But, even so, the victory was no more than partial, and death did not give up the game. Its power still persisted where alkaloids, gases or the vapors of volatile fluids were concerned. For modern anesthesia, if pain is to be completely prevented, must induce a state of absolute insensibility. This condition is closely akin to death. If the administrator should cease for a moment or two to mind his step, death can snatch away the patient as well as the patient's pain.

Laughing gas and ether were first used for the relief of asthma, but, as was explained in an earlier chapter, before Davy's experiments with laughing gas Lantham Mitchell uttered a grave warning against the use of this "dangerous gas" which might carry "contagion" and bring death. Similar warnings were uttered when anesthetization with ether began. We find plenty of them in the medical press of that day, as, for instance, in the *Journal of Science*, the *Midland Medical and Surgical Journal*, and the *London Dispensatory*—all of which strongly advised physicians against the perils of administering by inhalation so dangerous a stupefacient as sulphuric ether.

Davy and Wells, when they began their experiments on themselves with laughing gas, did so fully aware that they were risking their lives. When Wells, after the failure of his public demonstration at Boston, losing patience and discretion, gave his next patient an excessive dose of laughing gas, he nearly killed the man to whom he had promised the advantages of painless extraction.

The student Wilhite and his lively friends, amusing themselves with an ether party at Athens, Georgia, ran the risk of prison when they heedlessly etherized a Negro boy, and, but for speedy medical aid, might well have killed the lad. Morton understood the dangers he ran when he boldly continued experimenting on himself; and if Bigelow, at the time of the third operation under anesthesia at the Massachusetts General Hospital, had not been shrewd enough to impress caution on Dr. Dix, there might have occurred an untimely death which would have imperiled the application of Morton's wonderful discovery.

Over and above this risk to life, etherization was attended by a number of inconveniences. Ether vapor is irritating. It may cause so much coughing and excitement during the initial stages of its administration that many hesitated to give it, and anesthetization was often marked by a violent struggle between doctor and patient. Vomiting and a prolonged flow of ether-impregnated saliva often followed the narcosis, so that the doctor had relieved his patient of pain during the operation only at the cost of a prolonged period of nausea and vomiting.

When Simpson tried ether on women during childbirth he found that parturients were strongly inclined to suffer excessively from the noxious effects of ether. That was why he was so eager to discover a substitute, and believed himself to have found in chloroform the ideal anesthetic. From the lying-in chamber, Simpson's chosen remedy speedily made its way into the operating theater, to be used within a few months in most of the hospitals of Europe, until its victory seemed decisive. In America, likewise, its use made much headway; at the time of the Civil War we learn from official reports that when anesthetics were given to the wounded, chloroform was used in sixty per cent of the cases, ether in thirty per cent, and mixed anesthesia in the remaining ten per cent. Certainly in Europe during the first years after Simpson's discovery, "to give an anesthetic" was practically synonymous with "to give chloroform."

Shortly after Simpson's death, the Rotunda, the great lying-in hospital of Dublin, published the results of deliveries under chloroform in cases of tedious or obstructed labor. The tabular statements were tantamount to a tribute to the lifework of the great Edinburgh physician and accoucheur. Whereas, in pre-anesthetic days, in the case of primiparae the average duration of labor was eighteen hours and the death rate among the mothers was one in eleven, after the use of chloroform the duration of labor fell to two hours on the average, while the mortality was reduced to one in three hundred and twenty.

Similar statistics could be compiled on all hands. Twelve months after Simpson's death it was possible to draft medical reports concerning the Franco-Prussian War, from which it appeared that, in the contending armies, no less than 1800 pounds of chloroform had been used on wounded soldiers for the alleviation of pain.

Had the danger of fatality been dispelled by the introduction of chloroform into anesthetic practice? Had the grip of death's bony hand been removed from the bottle which held the narcotic? By no means. All that happened was that the danger was for a time overlooked. In the imposing array of figures from Dublin, in the world statistics from Europe and America, little heed was paid to this matter. The statisticians, accustomed to think in almost astronomical figures, paid little attention to small numbers, even when they were the numbers of those who had been prematurely snatched away to the realm of mighty death. This was notably true in considering the benefits of chloroform enjoyed by American soldiers during the Civil War.

Nevertheless, as early as 1847, an Edinburgh physician named Snow reported a death under chloroform anesthesia; and two years later Disray announced another. Gradually the numbers on record increased, and by 1853, when Queen Victoria made chloroform during confinements fashionable, Behrend compiled a list of fifty-three fatalities, and Dr. Hayward, of the Massachusetts General Hospital, could record as many as sixty deaths under chloroform;

while ten years later, in Sabart's records, the deaths were announced to have been one hundred and ten.

In the year 1864 there came into existence in England a Chloroform Committee to study Snow's data and to investigate the toxicity of chloroform. When a second committee followed this up by studying the accounts of 26,000 administrations of chloroform, it was found that there had been a considerable percentage of deaths under anesthesia. By the 'eighties the toll of deaths under chloroform was so great that the figures of the number of pounds of chloroform used during the Franco-Prussian War seemed less imposing. The disasters of death under chloroform had to be seriously weighed against the blessings of relief from pain.

By this time the world had become aware that death, as well as the anesthetist, handled the chloroform drop-bottle which brought the boon of painless slumber, and that unless the anesthetist was a past master of his craft, death might easily win the victory.

In 1888 the Nizam of Hyderabad, reputed to be the wealthiest man in the world, appointed a commission under the presidency of Dr. Lawrie to make experiments upon the lethal influence of chloroform. One hundred and sixty-seven dogs were chloroformed for experimental purposes.

The main question before the Chloroform Commissions was, when death occurred under chloroform, was it because the heart stopped beating or because the breathing ceased? The Hyderabad Commission, Dr. Syme and the Edinburgh school considered the failure of breathing to be the main danger; but the *Lancet*, Dr. Erichsen and the London school held that heart failure was responsible for death under chloroform; the Glasgow Committee and the Chloroform Committee of the British Medico-Chirurgical Society espoused the latter view.

On the whole, during the later years of the period in which the administration of pure chloroform as an anesthetic was still common, the attention of anesthetists was predominantly directed to the risk of respiratory failure; but as I write this chapter Dr. Eden Paul, drawing upon personal experience as an anesthetist, calls my attention to an important and comparatively recent ad-

vance in our knowledge of this matter. He writes in a private
letter:

> "Overlooked for a long time was the danger of heart-fail-
> ure, not during, but after prolonged administration. This is
> one of the forms of 'delayed chloroform poisoning,' and is akin
> to the delayed death from alcohol that may supersede upon
> ostensible recovery from large doses. Before this danger was
> recognised, operations under chloroform were unduly pro-
> longed. The patient unexpectedly died after making a good re-
> covery from both operation and anesthetic. The same thing
> occurred after the unduly free use of chloroform in labour
> cases."

In a word, the multifarious dangers of chloroform grew more
and more obvious, and in his monograph *The Mastery of Pain* Sir
Benjamin Ward Richardson rightly pointed out that it was a good
thing ether became known sooner than chloroform, for if chloroform had been the first anesthetic the frequency of death under its
use might easily have stifled anesthesia in the germ.

One of the first attempts to minimize the dangers of chloroform was the simultaneous administration of oxygen, this being
recommended in 1886 by Neudörfer, a Viennese physician. From
Vienna, too, as I have already related, came the ACE mixture,
which was also recommended by an Englishman, George Harley.
Various chloroform committees advised against the use of any kind
of mask for the administration of chloroform. They advocated
the "open" method with a very free supply of air. In 1901, after
the report of the third Chloroform Commission had been published, embodying the results of a study of the effects of varying
doses of chloroform, Harcourt constructed a special apparatus for
graduated administration. Then, only a few years ago, much light
was thrown on the subject by Rein, who experimented on the
coronary circulation (circulation of the blood in the heart muscles).

Laboratory experiments on chloroform have furnished valuable
information concerning the possibilities of death during its administration. Under certain conditions, when chloroform is freely
exposed to light and air, some of it can be transformed into
phosgene, one of the deadliest gases used in chemical warfare.

The upshot of this accumulation of evidence was that the decline of chloroform was as rapid as had been its advance. Reports that hail from the nineteenth century show that its use had diminished by fifty per cent, and that it was being very widely superseded by ether. In Massachusetts the return of ether to the leading place was especially marked. Dr. Walter Channing, a professor at Harvard, had early insisted upon the practical advantages of ether as compared with chloroform. In the eighteen-seventies, when attention began to be concentrated upon the frequency of death under chloroform, Jeffries, a Boston ophthalmologist, strongly advocated the use of ether in preference to chloroform.

Massachusetts, indeed, had remained faithful to ether even when chloroform was celebrating its greatest triumphs elsewhere. The state of Massachusetts went so far as to prohibit the use of chloroform in its hospitals. For inexplicable reasons, as far as Europe was concerned, the town of Lyons clung to ether no less firmly than did Boston. Among other early champions of ether as against chloroform were Juillard, a Genevese surgeon, and Dumont and Roux of Lausanne. Roux reported 3240 operations under ether, all without anesthetic mishap. Thus by degrees ether regained the front place.

The German Congress of Anesthetists in the year 1893 was to be decisive for the rehabilitation of ether. The German Surgical Society had organized a collective investigation upon narcosis. Reporting on this to the Congress, Dr. Gurlt announced that, whereas chloroform was undoubtedly responsible for numerous deaths, the answers to the questionnaire showed that 14,615 administrations of ether had not been attended by a single fatality.

The position of ether was further strengthened thirty years later, when, in 1923, James Taylor Gwathmey introduced the method of the rectal administration of ether, which many doctors have found most useful to allay the pain of childbirth.

But the praises of "ether redivivus" thus sung by many doctors were counterbalanced by assertions that, after all, the administration of ether could prove fatal. Kapeller was the leader of the "ether pessimists" and his gloomy assertions were confirmed by reports from the front-line hospitals during the World War.

A comparison of the results of operations performed under ether and laughing gas indicated that the mortality was three times greater among those operated upon under ether.

Then it was that laughing gas, which for so many years after its first use had been under an eclipse, came to the front once more —though not, of course, without demur. For although statistics showed that deaths under the administration of laughing gas were minimal—perhaps no more than one per million—many doctors found this anesthetic unsatisfactory. "No doubt," they said, "laughing gas is one of the least dangerous of anesthetics, but it is not absolutely trustworthy." Nussbaum reported many cases in which he had failed to bring about anesthesia by laughing gas, and had been compelled to return to the more dangerous chloroform.

But by this time medicine had had at its disposal many other anesthetic agents besides laughing gas, ether and chloroform. Could you want anything better than ethylene? Well, it appeared that death also had his hand on the ethylene bottle, for ethylene is the most poisonous ingredient of coal-gas which causes so many fatalities. Besides, it is a powerful explosive, which spreads death and destruction in wartime; it was employed by the Germans on July 20, 1917, in the Battle of Ypres. Its explosive violence could be exerted in peace, also, on the operating table. A few years ago a patient was killed at Baltimore by an ethylene explosion because the surgeon had incautiously used a thermo-cautery.

Even the newest substances used in pneumatic therapy, even the newest gases and vapors, while relieving pain, can still levy a toll of death.

"The sleep of the narcotized patient is more like death than natural sleep"—"The patient lay like one dead on the operating table, motionless and insensible as a corpse."—Such were the reports made during the early days of anesthesia. What is obvious on the face of the matter has been confirmed by modern bio-electro-chemical investigation, which has disclosed that, under the semblance of narcosis, there is hidden a condition analogous to death, which may be called "lesser death." The only difference between actual death and "lesser death" is that in the lesser death of anesthesia we can regulate the depth of unconsciousness almost at will.

Almost—but not quite, and not with absolute certainty. The

appeasement of pain during narcotic sleep is the outcome of poisoning. The gases and vapors which enter the circulation by way of the lungs replace, to a greater or less extent, the oxygen in the blood, lower the vitality of the tissues, reducing electrical tension and the vitally essential short-wave–length radiation. Thus they interfere with the chemical and electrical processes essential to normal vital activity.

Although it was at first believed that, in narcotic poisoning, nothing was impaired but the electric potency of the brain, we now know that anesthesia influences all the tissues of the body. The anesthetic influence extends to living protoplasm as a whole, diminishing, just as happens at death, the electrical tension and the short-wave radiation of every organ and every tissue. When one of the bodily organs is ailing or weak, it cannot put up an adequate resistance to the unwholesome effects of an inhaled poisonous vapor. If a patient is suffering from liver disease, for instance, the affected liver may succumb to the anesthetic poison. Then the liver dies, and therewith the patient dies. The same remark applies to the heart, the kidneys, and all other important organs. If death ensues in one of these, the other organs, and therewith the sufferer as a whole, inevitably die.

When investigators were first studying death under chloroform, the experts in the various commissions disputed at great length whether the death was a heart-death or a brain-death. Today we know that the death which is an essential potentiality of the pain-allaying substances can affect every organ, every tissue, and thus, having conquered the weakest point of the organism, may extend its empire over the whole body.

This bio-electro-chemical research ought to prove most helpful in our campaign to avert the dangers of anesthesia by inhalation. By gaining greater insight into the nature of death, into the way in which poisons kill, anesthetists will be able to reduce the risks of the remedies they use. We now know the extent to which the various tissue cells can hold their own against the deleterious effects of chloroform, ether, laughing gas and ethylene. We know that laughing gas does not reduce the electrical short-wave radiations so much as do ether and chloroform; and that in old and weakly persons, ethylene anesthesia is preferable to any other.

Twilight sleep is likewise dangerous; dangerous too are all narcotic and anesthetic methods. Attempts at the electrical induction of artificial sleep have temporarily been abandoned because a defect in the powerful apparatus employed may kill the patient. Such methods can become practically available in surgery only when we have acquired a perfected electrical technique.

In a word, unceasing caution is requisite on the part of those who are striving to achieve the conquest of pain—lest death should, in the end, prove the conqueror. One of the most successful campaigners against the risks of inhalation is the famous American anesthetist Palvel J. Flagg, who founded the Society for the Prevention of Asphyxiation, and whose *The Art of Anesthesia* is a valuable introduction to the study of the means for robbing anesthesia of its dangers.

If, in his use of a narcotic powder or the anesthetic flask, the doctor gets the better of death, then victory often will be snatched from him by the demon of addiction. For in these matters there is a vicious circle, each enemy playing into the hands of another, death into the hands of addiction and addiction into those of insanity. The physician, whose sole purpose is to relieve the patient's pain, must do so with something that may bring either bodily death or spiritual destruction. Heavy is the price paid for the alleviation of pain.

The remedial root, the juice, the gas or the vapor to which the doctor has recourse in order to allay pain is the root, the juice, the gas or the vapor for which the addict craves. That which relieves pain creates intoxication, produces pleasurable visions which the sufferer wants to enjoy again and again till habit has him in its grip. But a drug habit may destroy body, soul and spirit, the last fate being worse than the first, worse than death, being death while the sufferer is yet alive.

According to an old Persian saying, in the means for the relief of pain there are hidden two dark forces beside those that bring solace—the forces of crime and madness. Homer warns us that these remedies may make a man forget home and family and may turn human beings into swine. Van Swieten, the famous Dutchman who was physician-in-ordinary to Empress Maria Theresa, wrote of narcotics: "Available to those who practice the healing art are remedies which can for a time make the soul unaware of pain, but their use is dangerous, for they produce a strange mental confusion."

Nations, generations, civilizations, have been enslaved by drug addictions of one sort and another. Herodotus informs us that the Scythian nomads were fond of using Indian hemp as an intoxicant. In the eleventh century Hassan ben Sabbah founded a sect of fanatics whose headquarters were on Mount Lebanon and whose chief, known to the crusaders as the Old Man of the Mountain, was wont to make them drunk with Indian hemp or hashish. Under the influence of this drug they enjoyed agreeable visions, believing themselves to be in Paradise. The Old Man of the Mountain was able to persuade his followers that if they obeyed his orders unquestioningly they would dwell forever in Paradise. Believing his words, when thus intoxicated the hashish-men robbed and murdered as the chief directed. Such was the origin of our word "assassin." The English term "assassin" is derived from the Arabic *hassassi,* a drinker of hashish.

As "bhang," the same drug, prepared for smoking, has long been a dangerous intoxicant in various parts of Asia and Africa; and of late it has attained undesirable notoriety in the United States, where, under the name of "marijuana," cigarettes containing it are peddled among the young people at American high schools and colleges. It has been estimated that about one-half of all juvenile criminals are marijuana addicts.

From of old, opium as a pain-allaying drug has been a danger because its use tended to become habitual. On Assyrian cuneiform tablets and on Egyptian papyri we read that, 1500 or 2000 years before Christ, women, lads and lasses would visit the poppy fields by night to incise the unripe poppy capsules, collecting the exuded juice, drying it and using it to prepare an intoxicating beverage.

Along the trade routes from Babylon and Nineveh, caravan after caravan bore this intoxicant culled from the poppy to Iran, Mesopotamia, Ecbatana, Teheran and Meshed, and across Egypt into Northern Africa.

According to pagan priests and magicians, the sleep that followed the administration of opium was a bridge over which the soul could reach the abode of the gods; and for the Mohammedans, to whom the Prophet had forbidden the use of alcohol, opium provided a happy substitute by means of which they could obtain a foretaste of Paradise.

Along the paths of Mohammedan conquest, opium, called "Mash-Allah" (meaning "Praised be God"), made its way from Araby to India, Persia and Turkey, putting its stamp upon the whole of Mohammedan civilization.

As the Middle Ages advanced, this product of the poppy became a leading commodity of Oriental trade, and the Great Mogul declared the export of opium to be a state monopoly.

More than any other land, however, did China have its destinies influenced by opium, for wars were waged on account of the drug. To begin with, in the Middle Kingdom, opium-smoking was a privilege of the mandarins, but soon the practice spread to the common people, and became an important political problem. In 1729 the Son of Heaven, Emperor Yung Chen, issued a decree wherein he attempted to check the immoderate use of opium by restricting its cultivation.

Shrewd Dutch and British traders tried to make profit out of a prohibition which had been decreed for the public advantage; so that after a time, the East India Company was shipping as many as 20,000 chests of opium to China every year. The Chinese rulers felt it incumbent upon them to take steps to check the destruction of their people by a vice which was thus being pushed among them by unconscientious foreigners. The Chinese government raided the English opium-depots in Canton, and destroyed the smuggled poison. Thereupon the British government sent a punitive expedition, and fought the infamous Opium War which Gladstone described as unrighteous in its origin and as a war which had covered England with shame. Nevertheless the war was fought to a successful finish, and in 1860 Emperor Kia-king had to sign the Peace Treaty of Tientsin, by which a number of specified Chinese harbors were opened for the unrestricted import of opium. By the end of the nineteenth century opium to the annual value of many millions of pounds, francs, gulden and ducats was imported into China, and, according to statistics published in the year 1906, twenty-seven per cent of all adult male Chinese were opium-smokers.

Peculiarly disastrous was the influence of the opium habit in Java and in Algiers—for under the influence of the drug the Javanese and the Malays in Java were apt to be seized by a raging madness in which they "ran amok," rushing through the streets and killing all who stood in their way. As far as Algiers was concerned, in the middle of the nineteenth century the Moors of that city were so addicted to opium that half of them ended their days in an asylum.

In the year 1898 a German chemist discovered heroin, the most dangerous of the thirty or more alkaloids contained in crude opium. In the year 1927 a Dutch firm was shipping to China 4600 pounds of heroin, this being more than double the legitimate annual medical demand for the drug throughout the world.

But if Europe made profit out of an Asiatic vice, it was not to be spared retribution. Intercourse with the East brought to the West, not only the eighty-eight wise sayings of Lao-tse, not only the political wisdom of Confucius, not only the *Arabian Nights' Entertainments* and the philosophy of Hindustan, but also the opium pipe and the age-long Asiatic experience of its use.

Opium-smoking apart, since the days of Paracelsus Europe had been familiar with laudanum, an alcoholic solution of opium. Paracelsus himself regarded opium as the "philosopher's stone" because of the power the drug had to induce visions. Since it could stimulate the artistic imagination, many famous writers became opium addicts: Thomas de Quincey, for example, author of the *Confessions of an English Opium-Eater*, who was said to have reached a dose of eight thousand drops of laudanum per diem; Coleridge and Southey, the famous poets of the Lake School; and in France the immortal Baudelaire. These masters of the written word displayed incomparable skill (and perhaps a riotous fancy) in their descriptions of the entrancing visions they owed to laudanum, and those who were carried away by their inspired words were only too ready to follow the masters along the primrose path of drug addiction.

The pain-allaying gases and vapors revealed by pneumatic chemistry had an exhilarating influence which encouraged pleasure-seekers to indulge in laughing-gas parties and ether parties. Here were new habit-forming drugs which enticed many down a slippery slope. The reader will remember how, at the first of all chloroform parties, Simpson's niece, Miss Petrie, ecstatically shouted: "I'm beginning to fly! I'm an angel, oh, I'm an angel!" Many who heedlessly inhaled chloroform, or had been given it under medical auspices, had delighted in this sense of euphoria, of well-being, and, like the drunkard in Scripture, said, "I will seek it yet again." To poor Wells, a broken man in New York, chloroform intoxication was his only joy, for which, in the end, he had to pay with suicide.

Yet to these dangerous remedies—to chloroform, ether, laughing gas, opium, heroin and Indian hemp—the doctor must have recourse if he wants to mitigate the suffering which the surgeon's knife or the pangs of childbirth otherwise inevitably entail. Now whenever pain is alleviated, there is danger that the person thus freed from suffering may become the prey of an addiction. For those who are ill and in pain the risk of acquiring a drug habit is enormously greater than it is for the healthy.

The patient on the operating table finds, nowadays, that operation has been robbed of its terrors. A gas or a vapor enters his lungs, thence finds its way into the circulation, and leads him farther and farther into the strange world of dreams. But often, having enjoyed the advantages of a painless operation, he will remember the delightful sense of intoxication he had when going to sleep, will bear in mind his dream-illumined lapse into painlessness. Thus many who have been operated upon under anesthesia will later develop a craving for the anesthetic—for laughing gas, ether, chloroform, narcylene or ethylene—for every anesthetic and every analgesic may become a source of addiction.

In the hypodermic syringe, the doctor has an incomparably effective means of allaying pain. He is called to a man or woman writhing with biliary or renal colic, to one suffering from cardialgia or neuralgia, to a woman in the throes of labor: how natural to give a prick, a hypodermic of morphine! And in many cases it is indeed the best treatment. The result is wonderful. One minute the patient is in agony, and can think of nothing but the intolerable pain. Life has no meaning but this agony. Next minute the pain has vanished, is almost forgotten, a sense of well-being pervades the tortured body, eases the racked mind, pervades every limb. Pain has disappeared, and life is now rose-tinted, a glorious intoxication.

One who has thus been uplifted from torment to ecstasy does not forget. The memory persists long, long after the relief of pain, and the mind craves a renewal of the ecstasy. There was something more than mere freedom from pain, there was positive pleasure; the humdrum of everyday life is a poor substitute for this ecstasy. The mind craves a repetition of the lost delight; seeks it yet again; until, after a few or many repetitions, the seeker has become a slave of that which he seeks, has become a drug addict.

The promptness with which pain is relieved by the hypodermic syringe, and the ecstatic sense of intoxication associated with the use of these refuges from reality, have created whole armies of drug addicts.

Habituation affects the addict's innermost being, working a veritable devastation, even modifying the next generation. Charcot reports that, at Salpêtrière, the unborn child became wildly agitated in the mother's womb if she was an opium or morphine addict and the attempt was made to withdraw the drug suddenly. Such children were almost always sickly after birth, and could be kept alive only by the administration of morphine.

Concomitantly with the marked development of individualism during the nineteenth century, self-portraiture became, among intellectuals, one of the favorite methods of expression. Modern psychology, having traced the workings of the mind into its abysmal recesses, gave fresh scope for this tendency. Consequently modern psychological medicine has at its disposal the most detailed pictures of the Dantesque inferno in which the soul of the morphinist lives, moves and has its being.

One of the greatest curses of morphinism, which drives the unresisting addict along the downward path, is the inclination toward a steady increase in the dose. At first a hypodermic dose of a sixth or a quarter of a grain will be ample to produce the desired effect. Gradually, however, the dose must be increased, until from ten times to a hundred times the amount is required.

Sleep shuns the addict, or, if he does sleep, it may only be to fall into the abysses of nightmare.

To the morphinist, his poison becomes more essential than bread, as necessary to his life as air. His thoughts and feelings are concentrated upon the need for procuring a sufficiency of the poison. What was first taken to relieve pain or to give pleasure, has become an inexorable tyrant. The drug holds its victim in its grip. The morphinist becomes a half-normal being only when he has dosed himself with a sufficiency of his poison. He will sell his body and his soul to get the drug.

He therefore will surrender everything to satisfy his craving: will sacrifice his business, his family, his ambition, his happiness and his self-respect. These things mean nothing to him in comparison with his overmastering need. At length symptoms of physical and moral decay ensue. The intelligence becomes impaired, the memory fails, the moral sense vanishes, the will grows powerless. The addict is extremely irritable, his respiration is slow and inadequate, he suffers from grave digestive disorders and is sexually impotent—such are the consequences of immoderate indulgence in opium or morphine.

But if morphinism thus becomes a curse, demorphinization, the withdrawal of the drug, is a perilous and extremely painful process. Morphine, like all habit-forming drugs, but most typically in its case, makes the body react by producing an antitoxin. This is why the customary dose ceases to be effective, and a steady increase in the quantity administered is necessary to produce the desired effect. Then, if the dose be suddenly withheld, the body of the addict goes on, for a time, producing the antitoxin, which, being no longer neutralized by the morphine, itself acts as a poison. This accounts both for the intensity of the craving and for most of the alarming, nay, agonizing, effects of sudden withdrawal.

This picture of morphinism could be painted in even darker colors as regards addiction to heroin. New drug habits are continually arising, or old ones are being revived in new forms. I have mentioned the marijuana craze which works havoc in the United States and has invaded Great Britain. The Dangerous Drugs Acts in the last-mentioned country, similar laws elsewhere, and international action through the League of Nations in Geneva, have not yet succeeded in putting an end to the trade in these intoxicants or in fully arresting the misuse of narcotics.

At Vienna, in the eighteen-eighties, a noted young physiologist who had prospects of a great scientific career became an opium addict. Sigmund Freud was his medical attendant, and tried various means of cure.

Thirty years earlier, Dr. Scherzer, returning from a journey in Chile, Bolivia and Peru, had brought back with him the leaves of a plant named Erythroxylon coca, which were chewed by the inhabitants of those countries as a means for masking the symptoms of hunger and fatigue. In the laboratory of Friedrich Wöhler, the famous chemist, Dr. Albert Niemann isolated the active principle contained in these leaves, an alkaloid to which he gave the name of cocaine. It was not long before various American doctors declared that this new-found drug, cocaine, was an effective remedy for the morphine habit.

Having tried other measures in vain, Dr. Freud gave his patient cocaine in the hope of cure. The hope was vain. And no competent physician now tries to use this drug as an aid to demorphinization, for it has been found that the remedy, instead of curing, aggravates the disease, superimposing a new and no less dangerous addiction upon the first. The attempt to relieve morphinism by the use of cocaine is an appeal to Beelzebub, the prince of the devils, to cast out devils.

The introduction of cocaine into medicine was the source of a new and disastrous addiction. Nevertheless, this alkaloid was to prove of great importance in the history of anesthesia. Before its discovery various attempts had been made at local anesthesia, as by freezing the part to be operated upon with an ether spray; but now, by the use of cocaine, local anesthesia was placed upon a sure foundation.

The discovery began, strangely enough, during the experiments that were being made by Dr. Sigmund Freud in his vain attempt to cure morphine addiction by the use of cocaine.

Concerning this episode, Freud reports: "In 1884 an important matter, though one which lay outside my main interests, led me to send to Merck for a supply of the still little-known alkaloid cocaine that I might study its physiological effects." Freud enlisted the services of his friend Carl Koller, then house surgeon at the Vienna

General Hospital. The two made a joint study of the alkaloid. They were able to confirm what Friedrich Wöhler had already noticed, that "cocaine was a substance which had a somewhat bitter taste and exerted a numbing influence upon the gustatory nerves, so that they became almost completely insensitive."

Following up this pointer along the paths of self-experimentation, Freud found that cocaine, locally applied, was able to paralyze the nerves of local sensation without having any marked effect upon the central nervous system. It seemed to him, therefore, that it must be possible, by the local use of cocaine, to paralyze temporarily the sensibility of certain areas. Thus, in the summer of 1884, began the development of a new and trustworthy form of local anesthesia. But private affairs sidetracked Freud from his investigation. "While I was engaged on this work," he writes, "I had a chance of making a journey which would enable me to see my betrothed once more after a separation which had lasted two years."

The young physician could not forego the opportunity. He departed, leaving the continuance of the experiments to his friend Carl Koller. The latter was specializing in operations on the eye. It naturally occurred to him, therefore, to try the effect of cocaine upon the nerves of the conjunctiva and cornea.

"The experiments I had performed in collaboration with Freud," writes Koller, "showed me that cocaine was a local anesthetic. I got to work in Stricker's laboratory for the study of physiology and pathology. Having prepared a solution of cocaine, I instilled a few drops into the eye of a frog. Then I tried the same solution on a guinea pig; and subsequently on myself and on several of my colleagues. On September 15, 1884, I read a paper on the subject at Heidelberg; and on October 17, 1884, a more detailed account before the Vienna Medical Society. Soon afterwards, I recommended my colleague Jellinek, assistant in Schroetter's laryngological clinic, to try cocaine as a local anesthetic in his practice. It proved successful."

Next let me quote Freud once more: "When I got back to Vienna, I found that my friend Koller, who had been working with me upon cocaine, had made decisive advances in its use. He therefore can rightfully be considered the discoverer of local anesthesia with cocaine which has been so important in minor surgery. But I am not disposed to feel a grudge against my wife because that honor did not accrue to me."

A more notable discovery in a very different field was reserved for Sigmund Freud—that of psychoanalysis.

Hardly ever does a discovery appear, so to say, from the void. In the case of local anesthesia, initial attempts can be traced back to very early times. When Loret was making excavations in the necropolis of Saqquarah, he found on the doorposts depictions of a scene which probably dated from somewhere about the year 2500 B.C. This clearly shows that the ancient Egyptians used compression of the peripheral nerves as a means of producing local anesthesia.

From a study of the far more recent history of medicine we learn that, toward the close of the eighteenth century, James Moore performed amputations under local anesthesia produced by compression of the sciatic and anterior crural nerves. Everyone knows that a limb "goes to sleep" under such conditions.

I have already referred to the use of cold as a local anesthetic. Long before the discovery of cocaine, the nerve endings were numbed by the application of ice and snow. The famous Hunter used the method; and in some of Napoleon's campaigns Baron Larrey was able, during bitterly cold weather, to operate in this way painlessly upon wounded soldiers. In 1852, James Arnott applied a "freezing mixture" of ice and salt to render the region on which he was to operate insensible.

Then, with the development of the chemistry of gases and vapors, the cooling effect of volatilization was turned to account for anesthetic purposes. The first attempts were made by Ozanam in 1858 with liquefied carbonic acid; but the most effective pioneer in the use of the evaporation of volatile fluids from the skin was Sir Benjamin Ward Richardson, who in 1867 introduced the ether-spray. Ether, applied to the skin by means of an atomizer, and evaporating rapidly, reduced sensibility to such a degree that abscesses could be opened painlessly. Later other substances were used for the spray, such as methyl ether and methylene bichloride.

But the insensibility induced by the active principle contained in coca leaves was known at a much earlier date in the country to which coca was indigenous. The shamans of Old Peru used to chew coca leaves and apply the coca-impregnated spittle to the wounds of patients they operated upon; and Dr. Scherzer who, as aforesaid, was the first to introduce coca leaves to Europe, found that this practice still prevailed among the Peruvian natives.

But the intuitive genius of a man of exceptional type was needed to put these isolated facts together and combine them into a great innovation. It was the Viennese physician Carl Koller who, taking note of the already familiar principles of local anesthesia, applying thereto Wöhler's and Freud's observations on cocaine, and turning the hypodermic syringe to account, was able to devise a new and more effectual method of producing local insensibility. He was, in fact, the first to inject a chemical substance underneath the skin in order to induce local anesthesia.

This marked a signal progress in the conquest of pain.

Hitherto narcotics and anesthetics in general had acted by causing artificial sleep. Consciousness, and therewith personality, had to be suppressed before pain could be prevented. The thinking, feeling, talking, acting and living man or woman had to be rendered unconscious, insensitive, wordless, motionless, like one of the dead, before pain could be subdued. Thus the tribute of an entry into the Valley of the Shadow of Death had to be paid by any who wished to be freed from pain. But now, through the discovery and the perfecting of local anesthesia, this masquerade of death was rendered superfluous.

Anesthesia had seemed a miracle to those who first saw a patient cast into an artificial sleep by the inhalation of a vapor, and no longer shrinking from the knife. Now came a second miracle performed under the eyes of those who watched the technique of local anesthesia. Here was a patient who retained self-awareness, who was still in touch with the outer world, who could see, hear, think, answer the surgeon's questions, perceive that sharp instruments were being thrust through the skin—but who felt no pain. He could watch the operation on himself as indifferently as if it had been performed upon another.

What had happened? Over and above the complete narcosis, whereby the whole man, body and mind, was reduced to insensibility, there had been devised a method of local numbing, thanks to which the particular region which was to be subjected to operation was rendered insensitive while the general consciousness of the person concerned, his body and his personality, remained in the normal waking state. It was no longer necessary to suppress the entire consciousness of an individual, to "knock him out," as it were, in order to achieve the conquest of pain. Local interference with the conduction of sensory impulses sufficed. Since the impulses originating in what was happening at the site of operation were not conveyed to the sensorium, pain was not felt, for though pain is primarily, in most cases, a local affair, locally produced, it is perceived in the central nervous system.

To begin with, local anesthetization by cocaine was used only in ophthalmology and laryngology. It is to Vasili Konstantinovich von Anrep that we owe the first application of local anesthesia to general surgery. But, though local anesthesia was discovered in Europe, it was on American soil that its widespread development first ensued, and the perfection of its technique occurred. One of the leading surgeons on the staff of Johns Hopkins Hospital, the late William S. Halsted, was the first to inject cocaine into a nervetrunk, thus producing anesthesia in the peripheral areas to which the branches of this nerve were distributed. Thus Halsted was able to perform major operations which had hitherto been painless only under general anesthesia.

Then, in 1885, only a year after Koller's discovery, Dr. Leonard Corning, also an American, introduced spinal anesthesia. By passing the needle of a syringe charged with a cocaine solution into the lumbar portion of the spinal cord, and injecting the contents, he was able to produce insensibility which lasted three hours in the whole of the lower part of the body and the lower limbs. This made it possible to perform painless operations upon the intestines and the ovaries while the patient remained fully conscious.

A third American doctor, Robinson by name, improved on this method. He allowed a little of the cerebro-spinal fluid to exude through the hollow needle before he injected a corresponding quantity of the cocaine solution, and thus induced complete anesthesia of the lower half of the body.

Just as, when the subject of discussion is a battle, and how it was lost and won, the accounts of what actually took place vary as between the countrymen of the contending parties, so do disputes arise concerning matters of scientific priority. The controversy between Massachusetts, Connecticut and Georgia, each state claiming to have been pioneer in the discovery of anesthesia by inhalation; the dispute among America, France and Germany concerning the discovery of chloroform—these controversies are echoed by that which has raged as to the true originator of spinal anesthesia, lumbar puncture, and all the other great advances in local anesthesia. As regards this last matter, a dispassionate observer will decide that America, Germany and France have equal merits.

For while Halsted, Corning and Robinson, in America, made very important discoveries, and were the first to perform major operations under local anesthesia, in German-speaking lands, almost at the same date, and independently of what the Americans were doing, Anton Wölfler, Billroth's chief assistant, performed painless operations under local anesthesia by cocaine.

France, too, stands in the first rank, being not only the land to which we owe the hypodermic syringe, but also that where Paul Reclus devoted himself to the development of local anesthesia from the year 1885 until his death at the time of the outbreak of the Great War. His labors enriched scientific medicine with a knowledge of regional anesthesia by infiltration, produced by the injection of normal saline solution into a nerve-trunk (*anésthésie tronculaire*), and also by that of *anésthésie splanchnique,* which proved most useful for major abdominal operations.

Turning to Germany, we find that in 1899 August Bier, a surgeon of Greifswald, without puncturing the spinal cord, introduced the method of injecting a weak solution of cocaine into the theca spinalis, having passed the needle between the third and the fourth lumbar vertebrae. In this way anesthesia of the lower half of the body could be produced, lasting for several hours. Bier first tried his method on animals, and then on himself and his assistant Hildebrandt. The method of "lumbar puncture" thus inaugurated enabled Bier to perform major operations on fully conscious patients. This plan was found peculiarly useful in operations where considerable shock otherwise might have been anticipated.

Simultaneously with Bier, but independently of him, the great Parisian surgeon Théodore Tuffier introduced spinal anesthesia, so that this method is equally ascribable to Tuffier, Bier and the Americans.

Notwithstanding the work of the Americans, the introduction of infiltration anesthesia which paralyzes the sensory nerves is usually and justly ascribed to the German physician and philosopher Carl Ludwig Schleich, and is therefore often spoken of as Schleich's method. In this way complete insensibility of the skin, the muscles, the tissues and even the body cavities can be induced, so that infiltration anesthesia has proved most valuable, especially for superficial and not unduly protracted operations.

I need hardly say that there have been combinations of general anesthesia by inhalation with local anesthesia. In various countries experiments have been made in this direction, especially with laughing gas. The patient is first anesthetized with nitrous oxide, and then the operation is performed under local or spinal anesthesia. The comparative safety of this method has made it extremely popular.

By recourse to one or other of the aforesaid methods of local anesthesia, many of the dangers and disadvantages of general anesthesia can be avoided—but not completely dispelled. The advocates of spinal anesthesia and lumbar puncture, having made numerous experiments on animals and extensive microscopical observations, declare that the action of cocaine on the spinal cord has never done any harm. But many doctors point to practical experience when they insist that the dangers of the method have been underestimated and its efficacy exaggerated.

Whereas Carl Ludwig Schleich, in a comprehensive work, lays much stress on the disadvantages and dangers of general anesthesia by inhalation, his adversaries maintain that Schleich's method has actually increased deaths among the anesthetized in consequence of cocaine poisoning.

It cannot be doubted that the introduction of cocaine into medical practice has been attended by the risk of making cocaine addicts, for cocaine, like morphine, is one of those poisons which has proved to be both a blessing and a curse. The South American natives have long been aware of the perils of cocaine—although they never learned to extract the alkaloid. Being accustomed to chew coca leaves as a stimulant and intoxicant, experience led them to speak of the coca tree as the "tree of hell," for they could not fail to note that the drug had debilitating and demoralizing effects both bodily and mentally. The introduction of cocaine into Europe was soon followed by the curse of cocainism. The alkaloid, administered by injections or sniffed as a powder up the nostrils, is apt to induce hallucinations, leading to insanity, suicide, crime and often death. Those who make a practice of taking pinches of "white snuff" form a special order among the unfortunate drug addicts, and doctors have plenty of work to do in trying to restrict, prevent or annul the evil consequences of this poison from the "tree of hell"—which the skill of modern chemists has enabled them to manufacture synthetically also.

Modern pharmaceutical chemistry has shared in all phases of the great advance of modern science. One of its most notable achievements has been the successful struggle which has been waged to overcome the injurious subsidiary effects of narcotics, replacing the harmful radicals by others so that the desired effects might be obtained without the old disadvantages. In 1892, tropacocaine was discovered; in 1897, eucaine; in 1904, stovaine; in 1905, alipin; and in the same year novocaine, the most reliable of the substitutes for cocaine. This last remedy, which has become indispensable in modern local anesthesia, was first produced by two Munich scientists, Alfred Einhorn, the chemist, and H. Braun, the clinician. Not long ago two physicians, A. S. Loevenhart and H. L. Schmitz, produced isocaine, which combines the advantages of novocaine for infiltration narcosis and those of cocaine for ophthalmology.

When the means of achieving the conquest of pain had been discovered by science, but they had been found to bring the danger of death and the risk of habituation in their train, it was necessary for the chemists to set to work and do what they could to dispel the tragedies that lurked behind the triumphs.

Even though mankind has not yet made the last step along this road, it cannot be denied that what has been effected in barely a century through the discovery of general anesthesia, local anesthesia and the unceasing advance of chemo-therapeutics marks a wonderful progress—perhaps the most wonderful ever made.

For what was operative surgery prior to the discovery of anesthesia? What was it even in the days when it was no longer practiced by barber-surgeons and quarrymen, but had become the craft of renowned professional surgeons? The famous William Cheselden could not sleep for nights when he had decided to perform a major operation, being cut to the heart by the thought of the pain he was about to inflict and by the risks to which he was exposing his patient. The surgeon, in those days, had no time to operate cautiously. He who could get through the work most speedily was accounted the best surgeon, for he saved the unfortunate patient a needless extension of torture. Operations were timed by the stop-watch. Cheselden removed a gallstone in fifty-four seconds. Langenbeck, chief surgeon of the Hanoverian army in Napoleon's day, "performed an amputation at the shoulder-joint in the time needed to take a pinch of snuff." Liston, who lived on into the time when Morton had discovered ether and Simpson chloroform, was famed for the speed of his operations, so that he could complete an amputation in thirty-two seconds.

Since the one object was to get the business over and done with, it was impossible to respect the tissues during this butcher-work as a modern surgeon is taught to respect them; and it would have been impossible to pay heed to the rules of antiseptic and aseptic surgery, had these rules been discovered. Actually, however, wound-infection continued to levy its ghastly toll until twenty years after the discovery of anesthesia. Not until Semmelweiss, Pasteur and Lister had made their discoveries were wounds safeguarded against microbial infection, but this great advance in operative surgery was rendered possible only by the preliminary discovery of anesthesia.

Today, when surgeons have at their disposal, not only the most up-to-date anesthetics, local and general, and a perfected administrative technique, but when antisepsis and asepsis have rendered wound-infection almost a thing of the past, the operator has become, in very truth, a master of nature. He can devote himself undisturbed and unhurried to applying the rules of an art which has been completely transformed by anesthesia and asepsis.

Knife in hand, Billroth, Kocher, Halsted, Tuffier, the brothers Mayo, Harvey Cushing, Sauerbruch and many another great modern surgeon have been able to perform operations which, down to the middle of the last century, would have seemed impossible. The "healing knife" can work its miracles upon the stomach, intestines, uterus, larynx, heart and even brain.

CHAPTER TWENTY

Pain, Where Is
Thy Sting?

THE PHYSICAL and psychological study of pain has furnished important weapons for use in the conquest of pain. Such study is wholly modern, for although pain is perennial, and has afflicted man from the very earliest times, its scientific investigation is a recent affair. Even when, by the methods of general and local anesthesia, surgeons were able to operate without causing pain, when physicians were able to make free use of the hypodermic syringe, and when chemo-therapeutics had a huge arsenal filled with pain-allaying remedies, medical theory still had very little to say about the processes of pain. We had no more than the vaguest descriptions of its manifestations, a recapitulation of the helpless wailing of sufferers. They used terms devoid of scientific accuracy, speaking of pain as piercing, lancinating, boring, raging, twitching, pulsating, gnawing, cutting, dragging, tearing, dull, acute, burning, radiating—and what not.

Even the descriptions which skilled physicians could add to these epithets uttered by those under the harrow were but the same vague terms translated into Greek or Latin—learned circumlocutions such as were characteristic of the medical jargon of the day. What was penned by doctors about pain concerned only its duration and intensity. They considered it quantitatively and not qualitatively. As regards the essential physiological nature of pain, the anatomical channels by which the nervous impressions producing pain are conducted to the sensorium, its psychological mechanism, its clinical and biological significance—until far on into the nineteenth century nothing more was known about it than had been known in the beginning of time.

Even when, after the discovery of anesthesia and antisepsis, there was, in the second half of the nineteenth century, so rich a blossoming of surgery, for a long time no adequate attempts were made to grapple with the problem of pain. Billroth, for instance, though he was one of the three or four most outstanding surgeons of this period, devotes no more than a couple of pages to pain in his comprehensive treatise on surgery, and sheds no enlightenment.

For thousands of years, millions upon millions of persons had suffered pain of every kind without knowing its substantial nature, the sensory energies that were involved, the inner mechanism of the most urgent of human experience. Yet during this long story of pain—a story which seemed to have neither beginning nor end—modern man could look back upon three centuries during which, in other respects, the profoundest mysteries of bodily function had been plumbed.

Why was it, then, that this particular abyss, toward which human thought and fancy have always been attracted, was not fathomed until so late?

The reason is plain enough. The most sublime forces of the human mind, religion, philosophy, sympathy, are to blame for the long continuance of our failure to understand the nature of pain. They stood in the way of its scientific explanation.

Religious sentiment obscured the boundaries between bodily and mental pain. According to the Old Testament writers, when the just were afflicted, this was because the Almighty wished to try them, to discipline them. That was why Job accepted pain as a divine sending; and with the advent of the Christian dispensation, pain came even more definitely to be regarded as a means of enlightenment. The martyrs voluntarily accepted it. The saints were so eager to participate in the sufferings of God's Son that their bodies often imitated Christ's wounds through the miracle of stigmatization.

This same acceptance, this same affirmation of bodily pain, underlay all religions, the Oriental ones no less than those of the

West. As regards the Oriental religions, the willing endurance of pain was a necessary qualification for rebirth.

But in so far as bodily pain was regarded as God's punishment for sin, or as a trial, a grace and a sacrament, it was necessarily withdrawn from scientific research.

When philosophy entered into the religious heritage, it took over, with other doctrines, this outlook on pain, so that the philosophers, no less than the saints, considered pain to be a moralizing agent. The Stoics' assertion that pain was not an evil influenced the whole of Western philosophy. In his *Anthropology*, Kant wrote: "Pain is the spur to activity, and only through pain do we feel ourselves to be fully alive. Without pain, we should be lifeless." Nietzsche, the philosopher whose motto was, "Praised be that which steels us," held that pain favored the preservation of the species.

So long as human thought was under the dominion of such religious and philosophical conceptions as these, the distinction between mental and bodily pain was obscured.

A purely metaphysical estimate of pain continued to prevail throughout the early days of psycho-physiological research. Beaunis, Mantegazza and Ribot still identified bodily and mental pain; while Dumont declared that pain had no real existence, being purely metaphysical.

With religion and philosophy, the two chief "guardians of the threshold," which frustrated an insight into the world of pain, there was associated a third guardian, sympathy. Who should dare to induce pain experimentally in order to watch its physiological reaction? Who might venture to watch through the microscope the changes that went on in pain-affected tissues? In days when there was so vigilant a campaign against vivisection, it was hard for any investigator to venture experiments upon animals.

Toward the middle of the nineteenth century, however, a new school of physiological research came into existence, the school of those who had shaken off metaphysical shackles. Of course this new discipline was not exempt from the maladies of childhood, so that there ensued a fierce controversy between two rival factions of experts. One group declared that sensibility must be a function of the peripheral nerves of general sensation, while the members of the other group insisted that, over and above the familiar sensory apparatus, there must be one endued with a specific receptivity for pain.

But this barren dispute was ended by one of the most remarkable discoveries of the nineteenth century, which resulted from a study of the skin. The cutaneous region, the outermost stratum of the sensitive organism, held the answer to the riddle of the physiological mystery of pain. Before the researches of Alfred Goldscheider, the skin had been regarded as an organ endowed with only one kind of sensation. This physiologist showed that it contains a number of different perceptive organs, being a mosaic of a complicated pattern, in which each item represents a particular kind of sensibility. Goldscheider found that there are three kinds of sensitive areas in the skin, those for pressure, warmth and cold; and he was able to prove that each localized point reacted only to the appropriate stimulus: the cold-perceiving points only to cold, the warmth-perceiving points only to warmth and the pressure-perceiving points only to pressure. The function of each point was specific.

Goldscheider's researches were carried a stage further by Max von Frey, who showed that there exists another kind of specific receptors in the skin, namely, the areas for the appreciation of pain, which are quite distinct from the others, reacting neither to temperature nor to pressure, but transmitting to the sensorium only those stimuli which arouse the sensation of pain.

It appears that these receptors are stratified. In the innermost or lowest stratum are the receptors for warmth; nearer the surface lie the receptors for cold; still nearer the surface are those for pressure; and the outermost of all are those for the appreciation of pain, there being about one hundred of such "pain-points" in every square centimeter of skin.

Moreover, there is a difference in the durability of the reaction to stimulus as between these different kinds of receptors. Whereas those for pressure and temperature react only during the persistence of the stimulus, those for pain continue to react after the stimulus has been removed.

Soon after the discovery that special receptors exist in the skin for the stimuli that induce pain, there was found to be a specific nervous apparatus for the conduction of such stimuli from the receptor organs to the spinal cord and thence to the brain, where they convey their message to the sensorium. Adrian, who believes that when pain is felt there arises a condition of electrical potential which moves centralward along the nerves, has been able to detect in isolated fibrils a centripetal movement of negative waves which, on reaching the brain, arouse the sensation of pain. Special fibers in the vegetative or sensory nervous system serve to conduct the stimuli of pain. The gray matter of the spinal cord, though itself insensitive, acts like a pain-accumulator. When the conductive powers of the gray matter are impaired by the formation of cavities in the spinal cord, as in the disease known as syringomyelia, such impressions, those of "common sensibility," are still conducted, whereas sensations of pain are arrested. But we still do not know in what part of the brain substance, or of the cerebral cortex which contains twelve thousand million ganglion cells, the sensation of pain is "localized."

The importance of the study of the skin for the elucidation of the phenomena of pain has been disclosed by the interesting researches of the British neurologist Henry Head. He has shown that the pain-receptors in the skin give important indications, not only of disturbances affecting the skin itself, but also of those going on in the deeper regions of the body. The skin, in a word, may hurt, not only because something attacks it from without, but also because something wrong is going on in an internal organ. In themselves, the intestines, the uterus, the bones and the tendons are almost insensitive, so that they can be cut without this causing any pain. Only when they are inflamed do we become aware of them, for the associated congestion and swelling exert a pressure upon the surrounding nerves which may become extremely painful. But, apart from this, affections of the internal organs, those of the pelvis for instance, may give rise to hypersensitiveness and pain in particular regions on the surface of the body when no pain whatever is felt locally. Head has been able to show that in many cases the hyperalgesic zones are very sharply delimited. Indeed, Head believes that internal affections arouse so much "sympathy" in the appropriate regions of the surface that, in such cases, a gentle stroking of the appropriate area is felt as painful. Head considers that each internal organ has its appropriate cutaneous zone which reacts in this way, and these zones are known as Head's zones.

Study of the pain receptors, the pain tracts and the pain centers has naturally increased our knowledge about the causes of pain. Our previous information about the matter was restricted to the obvious naked-eye facts. During Emperor Trajan's reign, a noted physician recorded thirteen causes of pain; Avicenna, in the beginning of the eleventh century, recognized fifteen; Hahnemann, the founder of homeopathy, seventy-five; Georget, eighty-eight; and Mantegazza, fourteen.

We know today that, however manifold the causes of pain may be—whether pressure, pricking, incisions, tension, lack of oxygen, chemical poisoning, heat, electric current, etc.—pain is almost always due to the working of some stimulus. Borelli recognized only coarse material stimuli, those of a mechanical nature. Richet and Wundt believed that pain was a function of the intensity of the stimuli. Joteyko regarded pain as the outcome of a strong stimulation akin to that of chemical poisoning. Tschirch spoke of the effects of disorganative chemical stimuli which "transform living tissue into dead tissue."

Thus in the light of modern research pain appears to depend upon the working of a particular part of the sensorium, a sort of sixth sense-organ supplementary to the familiar five senses. Even as internal contemplation is the counterpart of vision and hallucinative hearing the counterpart of audition, so is mental suffering the psychological counterpart of bodily pain.

This outlook leads to an expansion of the previously familiar series of material causes of pain, mechanical, chemical and what not. We have to recognize that science must postulate a pain-stimulus which was hitherto regarded as mysterious. The very same pain-perceiving apparatus which customarily works through the transmission of a pain-stimulus from the periphery of the body to the sensorium can, conversely, induce in the sensorium an idea of pain which is transmitted from the sensorium to the peripheral nerve-endings, to the pain receptors in the skin, there to arouse pain.

Clinical observation furnishes us with countless instances of the way in which nervously sensitive persons may suffer from intense pain which is autosuggestively produced, through the mere idea of it. A hysteric may, through memory, reproduce pain previously experienced; and war psychiatry can report many cases in which pain which used to trouble the patient objectively is reproduced as painful sensation—perhaps in an amputated limb.

Now that we know how important a part the psychological image of pain plays in the experience of bodily pain, we can discriminate more accurately between the grades of painful sensibility. The intensity of pain is quite as much dependent upon the reactions of the perceiving subject as upon the number of peripheral pain receptors that are stimulated and the duration of the stimulus. Now the condition of the sensorium in this respect is a subjective matter, depending on personal characteristics, the outcome of heredity, environment, racial and social circumstances, varying with sex, occupation, age, climate and individual temperament.

Women, upon whom nature imposes the painful and arduous task of child-bearing, can, in general, bear pain better than men. Electrical experiments have shown that women can endure exposure to an electric current ranging up to 250 volts, whereas men can rarely endure more than 30 volts. Social circumstances, too, have a great deal to do with sensibility, the countryman being, as a rule, less sensitive than the townsman, and the mental workers more sensitive than the manual workers. British and French investigators have proved that sensibility to pain diminishes with advancing years. Environment, temporal as well as physical, plays an important part in determining sensibility to pain. There have been periods, like that of the Thirty Years' War and that of the dominance of the Inquisition, when sensibility to pain was greatly blunted by the general prevalence of savagery. The sensitiveness of different races and peoples varies much. The European is at least twice as sensitive as the savage; and de Ségur, in his history of the Napoleonic campaign of 1812, reports that the Russians bore pain much better than did the French. But I need hardly say that these generalizations are often invalidated by experience of particular instances.

The qualities of consciousness differ from person to person, and for the measurement by objective methods of varying subjective sensibility to pain an instrument known as the algometer has been invented whereby cutaneous sensibility can be determined by mechanical tests.

Naturally, as part of the study of pain, the question of the usefulness of pain has been broached. I have shown that religion and philosophy consider pain to be of positive value, but the doctors no less speak of its "biological purposiveness." Greek physicians used to describe pain as "the baying watchdog of health," and down to our own time the view has prevailed in the medical profession that pain fulfills an important bodily function. Physicians are ready to declare that pain is essential to the preservation of life and health, since it is a "danger signal" to the body when danger threatens.

There can be no doubt that pain generally has been regarded as of the utmost importance to diagnosis. It was considered to guide the doctor to the actual seat of disease and inform him as to its nature. Unquestionably there are pains which give reliable pointers in these respects, but the modern view is that pain is by no means a thoroughly trustworthy danger signal or a reliable guide to the diagnostician.

A study of the paths along which pain is conducted and Head's delimitation of the aforesaid zones have certainly shaken the theory of the "biological necessity" of pain. It has become plain that intense and lasting pain rarely remains localized, having a strong tendency to "radiate." When this happens, the patient does not feel the pain in the affected part of the body, for it is "referred" to a different site. Thus inflammation of the liver is often felt as pain in the right shoulder; children with incipient hip-joint disease complain of pain in the knee; undiagnosed aneurism of the aorta may be treated as rheumatism of the shoulder; and the main trouble of a woman with uterine disease may often be sacrache or lumbago. So common are these phenomena of "irradiation" and "eccentric projection" that the diagnostician who depends upon the apparent site of the pain will often be misled. In many cases, however, one with an accurate knowledge of Head's zones will be able to avoid such errors.

The "diagnostic value of pain" is further impaired by a "fallacious intensity" which seems to mock at any idea that pain can be biologically useful. Normal and necessary vital phenomena, such as birth and growth, often may be associated with intolerable pain of a kind which can hardly be regarded as a warning. Both growth and the act of birth are phenomena essential to the preservation of the individual and the species; yet if we were to regard the pains attendant upon these processes as warnings, we should have to suppose that labor pains and "growing pains" were designed by nature to warn human beings against reproduction and growth.

Sometimes pain seems to rage for its own sake, like a tale told by an idiot, signifying nothing. Take many kinds of neuralgia, for instance, in which there are no demonstrable changes in the tissues, so that the pain seems to occur altogether independently of any organic processes. Such agonies, so far as we can see, have no purpose whatever. Besides, while pain may thus shout its "warnings" when there is apparently no cause, in other cases these warnings seem a mere mockery, as in the death-agony, when the sufferer's condition is beyond relief and the fatal issue is inevitable.

Apart from the enigma of false and futile danger signals, pain, being a malicious demon, may vex us by its absence when a warning would be useful. Just as it "cries wolf" when there is no wolf, just as it racks and twists the sufferer when the organic processes (to all seeming) are going on normally, just as it shouts causeless warnings, so, on the other hand, will it often fail to give any warning at all when the danger is very great, when some grave morbid process is going on, and when, if we had a timely warning, we could do something to arrest it. In such grave and widespread disorders as general paralysis of the insane, in arteriosclerosis which leads to softening of the brain, in acute and chronic nephritis, or when the lungs are being eaten away by tubercle, there may be no pain whatever. If we still know so little about one of the most terrible of diseases, cancer, this is largely due to the uncertainty of pain as a diagnostic sign. For in cancer of the bowel pain will be absent in the early stages when, were we informed of its ravages, the surgeon's knife could still be used to good effect; whereas later, when the case has become inoperable, and when X-rays and radium treatment are no longer of any avail, the victim of intestinal cancer will be martyrized by useless "danger signals."

According to modern medical views, moreover, the notion of the utility of pain is contradicted by the disastrous effects it can have upon the patient's bodily organs and upon his mental state. Alfred Goldscheider has been able to show that pain, when it becomes intense, can have the most injurious and destructive action upon the tissues. Pain makes the heart irregular, changes the rhythm of respiration, slows or arrests the secretions of many of the glands.

Even so, though we are compelled to revise the traditional view that pain is biologically useful and necessary, this does not mean that a definitive opinion as to the biological function of pain has yet become possible. In the future, perhaps, when we have completely shaken off the conventional notions as to the value of pain, we may be able to study it without bias and to unravel the peculiar laws of this phenomenon.

In any case modern medicine, recognizing how often pain is a deceiver, has accepted the sublime task of relieving pain whenever possible. As an outcome of this wholehearted attempt to achieve the conquest of pain have arisen both the perfecting of anesthetic methods in surgery and midwifery and the pharmacological researches which have produced so many synthetic remedies useful for the relief or prevention of pain. Pain is tracked to its lair and attacked wherever it shows itself as an accompaniment of illness, where it burns in a wound, where it arises from the assault of a hostile environment, where it is caused by the use of the "healing knife." Always and everywhere doctors do their best to allay pain.

In its determination to drive pain out of all lurking-places, modern medicine has, of late, given much attention to a possibility so bold that in earlier centuries the mere proposal aroused condemnation—that of euthanasia. Therewith our Promethean minds declare war against the most cruel, because the most purposeless, of all pain, that which afflicts those who are beyond hope of rescue.

Among the Hellenes, already, euthanasia was a conceivable expedient—euthanasia, the "good death" or "easy death." But Hippocrates, the most famous of Greek physicians, named the Father of

Medicine, was opposed to it, making his pupils swear: "Nor will I, even though requested to do so, administer any lethal dose, or advise its administration."

To Christian devotees in the Middle Ages the idea of compassionate killing was repugnant, for they held that pain as well as life came from God, and must be accepted in accordance with God's will. "Thou shalt not kill" was regarded as the most important of the Ten Commandments and man must not infringe it, however great a sufferer's torment might be. The Catholic Church clings to this conviction today. When in Italy Nobel proposed to found Euthanasia Institutes in Rome and Milan, places where persons whose agonies were intolerable might have their passing shortened and alleviated by asphyxiating gases, the *Osservatore Romano* protested in the strongest terms against any attempt to legalize euthanasia, which was "pseudo-philanthropic" and "pseudo-scientific."

Philosophers and imaginative writers were the first to recommend euthanasia in the western world. Thomas More was a devout Catholic, but in his *Utopia,* published in the year 1516, he wrote: "Those who suffer from incurable disease must be treated and cared for, but those whose illness is not only incurable but likewise terribly painful ought to be granted the boon of death by the magistracy and the priests."

Francis Bacon, too, in the *Novum Organum* also advocated euthanasia, writing: "It seems to me that the function of the physician is to give health and to mitigate the tortures of pain. But this he should do, not only when the relief of pain can lead to healing, but also when it can lead to a quiet and easy death." This great modern thinker reproached the physicians of his time for not paying attention to the study of euthanasia. It was, he said, quite as much the duty of the doctor to comfort the dead or the dying and to ease departure from life, as to heal illness and restore health.

Montaigne and Buffon were also of opinion that in cases of incurable and painful disease, we are entitled to mitigate the agonies of death. Theophile Gautier, who watched the slow and agonizing death of Heinrich Heine, wrote: "Only a mother or a wife can endure to witness such continuous torture without shuddering at the dreadful spectacle." Berlioz, whose sister was dying of cancer of the breast, furiously exclaimed: "But is there no doctor in the world willing to put an end to this martyrdom?"

Among the most enthusiastic advocates of euthanasia is Maurice Maeterlinck, who in his book *La mort* recommends that in incurable maladies the doctor should intervene with "active sympathy." H. G. Wells writes somewhere of a future society in which euthanasia will be practiced for the good of all; and Robert Hugh Benson, in his novel *The Lord of the World*, refers to "the executors of euthanasia who carry about with them apparatus wherewith they can cut short the death-agony, and open a sweet way into the everlasting peace of the kingdom of heaven for those suffering from incurable disease."

Hitherto doctors have held divided views about euthanasia. Most practitioners are still faithful to the spirit of the Hippocratic oath. They share the opinion of Baron Desgenettes who, when asked by Napoleon why he did not kill the plague-stricken in Jaffa, replied: "My duty is to keep them alive." When the question of euthanasia was being discussed in Italy, the famous Italian physician Luigi Ferrannini insisted that no one, neither relatives nor the state, was entitled to use the resources of science in order to destroy life, which was man's most valuable and inalienable gift.

The contemporary medical opponents of euthanasia often insist upon the possibility of errors in diagnosis and of advance in medical science. One of the most decisive of opponents of euthanasia is Professor Forgue, who declares that doctors must reckon, not merely with the possibility of mistakes in diagnoses, but also with advances in medicine and especially in surgery, which can make that curable tomorrow which is incurable today.

At one time the French papers were fond of referring to the case of a doctor who grew desperate while watching his son in the throes of suffocation from diphtheria. When the little boy was in agony, his father ended the horrible struggle by administering a fatal dose of morphine. Next day Roux announced his discovery of anti-diphtheritic serum.

This case would almost seem to justify the old saw: "While there is life there is hope." Professor Forgue writes: "We doctors must be the nurses and not the executioners of human suffering, and it is our duty to maintain hope to the last." Many doctors, I need hardly say, hold other views, and strongly advocate euthanasia. Lawyers, also, take sides on this matter, which has come before the courts, and has been variously decided by judges and juries. The permissibility of euthanasia is recognized in some countries but denied in others.

In the year 1906 Miss Anna S. Hall of Cincinnati applied to the Ohio legislature for permission to end the miseries of her mother, who was suffering from an incurable disease, by the administration of chloroform. The permission was granted. Six years later the United States Congress rejected a proposed law to authorize euthanasia. In France, at about the same date, J. Regnault moved that euthanasia should be authorized under state regulation. In Germany a bill was brought before the Reichstag to empower the law courts to grant a permit for euthanasia in all cases of incurable disease. In Italy, Crispi, being then premier, strongly opposed a similar proposal.

Since 1918, in Switzerland, the criminal code has accorded extenuating circumstances in the case of murder committed for sympathetic reasons; Norway has followed this example. Since 1922, in the criminal code of the Soviet Union killing for compassion has been exempt from punishment.

Of late there has been much discussion of the problem in Britain, where attempts have been made to modify the law in favor of allowing euthanasia on compassionate grounds. At the instance of Lord Ponsonby, there has been founded The Voluntary Euthanasia Legislative Society, of which Lord Moynihan, an eminent English surgeon, is chairman.

The scientific study of pain has riddled the ancient theory of its biological purposiveness, rejuvenating the old problem of the legitimacy of euthanasia, and setting the matter in a new light. But there are, doubtless, many difficulties in the way of deciding an issue so complicated, involving as it does religion, humanitarianism and legislation, as well as purely medical principles.

Vesalius, an early zealot for the study of anatomy, could get material only by stealing bodies from the gallows. For though, before the rise of Christianity, under the Ptolemies some of the Egyptian doctors had examined the corpses of executed criminals, throughout the Middle Ages dissection was regarded as utterly irreligious as well as illegal and immoral, and many distinguished doctors among Vesalius' contemporaries were still strongly opposed to it. More recent innovations, such as vivisection, vaccination and the use of chloroform, were strenuously opposed by the faculty, and Semmelweiss' discovery that puerperal fever is an infective disorder was angrily repudiated both by doctors and by midwives. In the end, however, medical science marches on, enforcing recognition from religious fanatics, traditional moralists, the law and antagonistic experts. The question at stake as regards euthanasia is whether the doctor, who is in general the guardian of life, is entitled to use his knowledge (which includes a knowledge that the suffering of the death struggle is purposeless) to pass a sentence of death in order to save the dying from needless pain. We must leave it to the future to decide whether euthanasia, like other venturesome advances in science, has enough intrinsic truth to overwhelm the arguments against it.

What will remain as an undisputed achievement of the conquest of pain is anesthesia. I refer, of course, to perfected anesthesia, guided by the latest advances in technique, with its foundations firmly established upon modern knowledge of the processes of pain. For it is only a thoroughly scientific study of the problem of pain which has secured for anesthesia its definitive standing.

No doubt anesthesia came into being empirically, largely by chance. The discoverers did what they did without knowing the physiological nature of narcosis, or in what way laughing gas, ether and chloroform really produced insensibility. But even though the practical acceptance of anesthesia was brought about by the persistent use of a chance discovery, the gain for the healing art was undeniable. Still, the full efficiency of the new method in the fight against pain was realizable only through a systematic and scientific study of the processes of pain. Only thenceforward could a hearty "Amen" be uttered confirming the value of this momentous medical discovery.

Physiological research, which has traced the processes of pain into their innermost chemistry and into the electrical changes that occur in the cells, also has been able to elucidate the way in which the mechanism of pain-perception can be put out of action. Nevertheless, a painless operation still has the aspect of a miracle. The first operation under anesthesia seemed a wonder to those who witnessed it, for they were totally ignorant of the intimate physiological causes of what was going on before their eyes; but despite the extent of modern knowledge, narcosis is scarcely less wonderful today.

The physician who now conquers pain by narcosis looks beyond the obvious phenomenon that his patient's pain has been annulled by the induction of sleep. Phase by phase he recognizes what goes on. To begin with there is analgesia, the condition in which, while the rest of the nervous system continues at work, the peripheral sensation of pain is abolished. Then comes true anesthesia, when, in serial order, the suppression of pain is followed by the disappearance of tactile sensation, the power of vision and then that of hearing. The skilled onlooker knows that, as the effects of the anesthetic or narcotic pass off, the elements of consciousness will return in the inverse order: first hearing, then vision, then sensibility to pressure, and last of all sensibility to pain. He is familiar with the bodily reaction to anesthetic gases and vapors, to morphine, to local anesthetics; he knows the laws of their working when they effect the suppression of pain. His knowledge enables him to choose the method of anesthesia best adapted to the particular case, so that risk to life can be minimized or wholly excluded.

Theoretical knowledge is never sterile, and least of all in medicine. The inconspicuous researches of those investigators who have studied the physiology of pain and the detailed effects of anesthetic and analgesic remedies upon the organism have been invaluable in assisting the strenuous campaign waged by modern medicine against the cruelty of nature which is so ready to use the bludgeon of pain.

Nothing but scientific study could have brought anesthesia to full fruition. In return, our increasing knowledge of anesthesia has enriched other branches of science. Much of our recent and more thorough acquaintance with Man the Unknown (as Alexis Carrel calls him) has been gained since and because of the discovery of anesthesia.

Anatomy, of course, gave us our first glimpses into the interior of the human body—but it was a dead body which was revealed by the anatomist's scalpel. A knowledge of the living interior, of the functional mechanism of the living organs, was obtainable solely from a study of the living body, which could be invaded only at the cost of provoking screams of pain. The intolerable sufferings caused by the use of the knife forced speed upon the surgeon, and owing to the haste with which he worked he had little opportunity for studying the functional activities of the living organism. Not until the boon of anesthesia rendered the suppression of pain possible could investigators begin the undisturbed contemplation of what goes on in the living body. Thus the important work of Vesalius, the arch-dissector, could be supplemented after the discovery of anesthesia. Had it not been for anesthesia, physiology and biology would have remained amateurish and speculative, since a study of living organs at work—and undisturbed by pain—was essential to their progress.

Many of the most important and valuable acquirements of cellular pathology, of bacteriological, biochemical and pharmacological research, have resulted from experiments on animals. Chemical poisons were first tried upon the animal body before being used for remedial purposes in human beings. Millions of victims— unhappy rabbits, mice, fowls and guinea pigs—were inoculated with horrible diseases that man might learn how to protect himself. From their artificially tainted blood, chemo-therapeutics was able to extract antitoxic sera. But as far as operative experiments were concerned, their full benefit for man could not be secured until the animals could be anesthetized. It is true that prior to the middle of the nineteenth century there were many bold and hard-hearted investigators who, experimenting on animals, obtained important physiological and pathological knowledge; but this was in defiance of a steadily growing conviction that the benefits were being gained

Bibliography

Académie des sciences. Compte rendu. Tom. 24. 1847.
Académie des sciences. Compte rendu des séances de l'académie des sciences.
I. *semestre,* 1850.
Académie Royale de Médecine, Bulletin XII., *année* II., 1846–47. (Paris.)
pp. 418–19.
Adams, James Truslow: *Der Aufstieg Amerikas.* (Seidel, Vienna, 1933.)
———: *The March of Democracy.* (Charles Scribner's Sons, New York,
1932.)
Æsculap: Opium, 1914, No. 4. S. 8 and 25; Mandragora, 1923, S. 222.
Albert: *Geschichte der Narkose.* (Vienna, 1876.)
Allcott, A., and Bolton, H. S.: *Chemistry Today.* (Oxford University Press,
1936.)
Allen, Thomas, H.: Medicine, Mythological Pain, *Science History of the Uni-
verse,* VII.
Alrutz, S. G.: *Ueber Schmerz und Schmerznerven.*
American Medical Association: The morphine habit. *Journal of the American
Medical Association,* Jan. 15, 1916.
Anæstasy, E.: *L'Origin biologique du sommeil et de l'hypnose. Archiv. de
Psych.,* Paris, 1908, VIII., pp. 63–76.
Anæsthetic and Analgesia: A visit to the birthplace of William Morton.
(1932, No. 3. p. 45.)
Annals of Medical History, 1925, VII., pp. 267–296.
Annals of Medical History, Nov. 3, 1931.
Archives Générales de Médecine, XVIII. 1. Series, p. 453. (Paris.)
Armitage, F. P.: *A History of Chemistry.* (Longmans, Green & Company,
New York, 1921.)
Aveling, J.: The Chamberlens and the midwifery forceps. (London, 1882.)

Bacon: *De dignitate et augmentis scientiarum libri* IX.
Baeumler, Christian: *Der Sogenannte Animalische Magnetismus oder Hyp-
notismus.* (Vogel, Leipzig, 1881.)
Ball, Benjamin: *La Morphinomanie.* (Asselin & Honzeau, Paris, 1885.)

Barkers, S. W.: An interview with William Morton. *Harper's Magazine*, 1865, No. 31, p. 453.

Baskerville, Charles, and Hamor, W. A.: *The Chemistry of Anæsthetics.* (Easton, Pennsylvania, 1911.)

Beard, G. M.: *Stimulants and Narcotics.* (G. P. Putnam & Sons, New York, 1871.)

Behan, Richard J.: *Pain.* (D. Appleton Company, New York, 1922.)

Bekhterev, Vladimir Mikhaylovich: *Die Leitungsbahnen.* (E. Besold, Leipzig, 1894.)

Bennet, J. H.: *The Mesmeric Mania of 1851.* (Edinburgh, 1851.)

Bergson, Henri: *Dreams.* (B. W. Huebsch, New York, 1914.)

Bernard, Claude: *Leçons sur les anæsthetiques et sur l'Asphyxie.* (J. B. Baillière et fils, Paris, 1875.)

Bernheim: Hypnotic Anæsthesia. *Practitioner*, 1896.

Bigelow, Dr. Henry Jacob: *Surgical Anæsthesia.* (Little, Brown & Company, Boston, 1900.)

Bigelow, John: *The Mystery of Sleep.* (Harper & Brothers, New York, 1877.)

Binz: *Der Aether gegen den Schmerz.* (Bonn.)

Birnbaum, K.: *Psychopathologische Dokumente.* (J. Springer, Berlin, 1920.)

Birt, E.: *Schmerz, Narkose, Anæsthesie.* (1931.)

Bishop, E. S.: *The Narcotic Drug Problem.* (The Macmillan Company, New York, 1928.)

Blount, J. G.: Anæsthesia. *North Carolina Medical Journal*, July 20, 1896.

Bolton, S. K.: *Sir Humphry Davy.*

Boston Daily Advertiser, March, 19, 1870.

Boston Medical and Surgical Journal: Articles about the introduction of ether anæsthesia. November 18 and December 9, 1846.

Boston Medical Library: Full Exposure of the conduct of Charles Thomas Jackson, leading to his discharge from the Government service.

Bowditch, N. I.: *A History of the Massachusetts General Hospital.* (John Wilson & Son, Boston, 1851.)

———: *The Ether Controversy.* (J. Wilson, Boston, 1848.)

Bowlby, A.: *Pain, Its Importance in Diagnosis and Its Tendency to Mislead.*

Bramwell, J. Milne: *Hypnotism.* (J. B. Lippincott, Philadelphia, 1903.)

Branch, Douglas: *The Sentimental Years* (1836–1860). (D. Appleton-Century, New York, 1934.)

Brauchle, E.: *Hypnose.* (Reclam, Leipzig.)

Braun, Adolf: *Krankheit und Tod im Schicksal bedeutender Menschen.* (Enke, Stuttgart, 1934.)

———: *Medizinisches aus der Weltliteratur.* (Enke, Stuttgart, 1937.)

Braun, Heinrich: *Die Lokalanästhesie, ihre wissenschaftlichen Grundlagen und praktische, anwendung.* (J. A. Barth, Leipzig, 1905.)

British Medical Journal, Hickman, I., p. 843, 1912; Hypnotism as an Anæsthetic, April 5, 1890.

Brooks, Van Wyck: *The Flowering of New England.* (Dutton, New York, 1936.)

Brophy, T. W.: *The Position that Dental and Oral Surgery Is Destined to Occupy in America.* (Tucker, Newell & Company, Chicago, 1891.)

Brower: Insanity from Cocaine, *Journal of the American Medical Association,* January 1886.

Brunn: *Geschichtliche Einfuehrung in die Chirurgie.* (Berlin-Vienna, 1924.)

Budin, P.: Les Chamberlens. *Bulletin general de therap.* Paris, 1885.

Buehler, Charlotte: *Der menschliche Lebenslauf.* (S. Hirtel, Leipzig, 1933.)

Bugge, Dr. Guenther: *Das Buch der grossen Chemiker,* 2 Bd. (Chemie GMBH, Berlin, 1929.)

Bullard, C. A.: *History of Anæsthesia.*

Castex, G.: *La douleur physique.* (Thèse, Paris, 1905.)

Champeau, Daniel: *Un Novateur, Charles-Gabriel Pravaz.* (Thèse, Paris, 1931.)

Claparède, E.: *La fonction du sommeil.* Riv. d. sci. Bologna, 8, 1907, II., p. 143.

Clendening, Logan: *Behind the Doctor.* (A. A. Knopf, Inc., New York, 1933.)

———: *The Human Body.* (Garden City Publishing House, New York, 1930.)

Clevenger: *Pain and Its Therapeusis.* (American Medical Association Press, Chicago, 1897.)

Cohn, Alfred E.: *Medicine, Science and Art.* (Chicago University Press, 1931.)

Collas, Georg F.: *Der Flagellantismus in Altertum.* (G. Vigand, Leipzig, 1919.)

Collyer, R. H.: History of the Anæsthetic Discovery. *Lancet,* 1817.

Colton, G. Q.: *A True History of the Discovery of Anæsthesia.* (A. G. Sherwood & Company, New York, 1896.)

———: *Anæsthesia, Who Made and Developed This Great Discovery.* (A. G. Sherwood & Company, New York, 1886.)

Comba, Erneste: *Il problem della soffrenza.*

Conklin, E. G.: *Heredity and Environment.* (Princeton University Press, 1922.)

Coleman, W. M.: The Cause of Sleep. *Journal of Abnormal Psychology,* Boston, 1912. 8, VI, 329–67.

Cottler, J.: *Heroes of Science.*

Crawford, M. C.: *Old Boston Days and Ways.* (Little, Brown & Company, Boston, 1924.)

———: *Romantic Days in the Early Republic.* (Little, Brown & Company, Boston, 1912.)

Crommenick: *Thèse sur la douleur.* (1846.)

Crothers, T. D.: *Morphinism and Narcomanias from other Drugs.* (W. B. Saunders & Company, Philadelphia, 1902.)

Crowther, J. G.: British Science. (*See Science Today*, edited by above. Eyre & Spottiswoode, London, 1934.)

——: *Men of Science, 1936.* (W. W. Norton & Company, New York, 1936.)

Cyril, V.: *La coco.*

Darigues: *La douleur en chirurgie.* (Paris, 1927.)

Darrow, Floyd Lavern: *Makers of Science and Invention.* (Harcourt, Brace & Company, New York, 1923.)

Darwin, Charles R.: *Expression of Emotions in Man and Animals.* (J. Murray, London, 1872.)

Davy, Humphry: *Researches, Chiefly Concerning Nitrous Oxide.* (J. Johnson, London, 1800.)

Deffarge, A.: *Histoire critique des anesthésiques anciens.* (J. Bière, Bordeaux, 1928.)

Defried, A.: *Pioneers of Science.* (George Routledge, London, 1928.)

Delboeuf et Fraipont: *Accouchement dans l'hypnotisme.*

Der Schlaftrunk eine Kulturhist. Studie. (Unsere Zeit. 1872.)

Deutsch: *Morphinismus.* (Enke, Stuttgart, 1901.)

DeWitt, Th. F.: Fifty Years of Surgery under Anæsthesia. *Northwestern Lancet*, 1896.

Diaz, A. M.: Quelques faits d' anæsthesie chirurgicale sous l' influence de la suggestion. *Revue de l'Hypnotisme.* VI.

Dictionaire des sciences médicales. (Paris, 1812–22.)

Discovery by the Late Dr. Horace Wells. (Hartford case, 1850.)

Dr. Wells, the Discoverer of Anæsthesia. (J. A. Gray, New York, 1860.)

Dieffenbach, F.: *Der Aether gegen den Schmerz.* (1847.)

Dudley, O. T.: *The Shadow of the Earth.*

Dupuy, A.: *Essay sur la douleur.* (Paris, 1901.)

Durand: *Charles Gabriele Pravaz.* (Paris medicale, 25 octobre, 1924.)

Dwinelle, W. H.: The Cascet and the Ribbon. The Honor of Ether. (J. W. Woods, Baltimore, 1849.)

Eastnab, W. E.: The Chemistry of Sleep. *Atlantic Monthly.* Boston, 1911. 8. v. 108. pp. 52–62.

Ebstein, Erich: *Tuberkulose als Schicksal.* (Enke, Stuttgart, 1932.)

Edgar, J. G.: *Davy.*

Edinger: *Zur Lehre vom Schmerz.*

Elliotson: *Surgical Operations Without Pain.* (H. Baillière, London, 1843.)

Ellis, Havelock: *The World of Dreams.* (Constable & Company, London, 1926.)

Ellsworth, P. M.: *An Inquiry into the Origin of Modern Anæsthesia.*

BIBLIOGRAPHY 413

Emerson, Edward Waldo: *A History of the Gift of Painless Surgery.* (Houghton, Mifflin & Company, Boston, 1896.)

Engel, Eduard: *Geschichte der englischen Literatur.* (F. Brandstetter, Leipzig, 1929.)

Engelmann, G.: *Die Geburt bei den Urvoelkern.* (Vienna, 1884.)

Erving, Henry Wood: *The Discoverer of Anæsthesia.* (New Haven, 1933: Repr. *Yale Journal of Biology and Medicine,* V. No. 5, May, 1933.)

Esdaile, Dr. James: *Mesmerism in India, and Its Practical Application in Surgery and Medicine.* (London, 1846.)

Everett, A. L.: *The Privilege of Pain.*

Fasbender, Heinrich: *Geschichte der Geburtshülfe.* (G. Fischer, Jena, 1906.)

Federal Cases, Book 17, Morton's patent trial, December, 1862.

Feklin, R. W.: *Hypnotism or Psycho-Therapeutics.*

Finkler, Walter: Das Geheimnis des Schlafes. *Umschau,* 1933, 57, pp. 353–356.

Finney, J. M.: *The Significance and Effect of Pain.* (Boston, Ether Day Address, 1914.)

Fish, Carl Russell: *The Rise of the Common Man, 1830–1850.* (The Macmillan Company, New York, 1937.)

Fishbein, Morris: *The Medical Follies.* (Boni and Liveright, New York, 1925.)

Flagg, J. F. B.: *Ether and Chloroform, Their Employment in Surgery, Dentistry and Midwifery, 1851.* (Lindsay & Blakiston, Philadelphia, 1851.)

Flagg, P. J.: *The Art of Anæsthesia.* (J. B. Lippincott Company, Philadelphia, 1922.)

Fletcher, L. J.: The habit of morphia taking. *Lancet,* October, 1885.

Flexner, James Thomas: *Doctors on Horseback.* (Viking Press, New York, 1937.)

Foerster, Otfried: *Die Leitungsbahnen des Schmerzgefuehls.* (Urban & Schwarzenberg, Berlin and Vienna, 1927.)

———: *Die Schmerzbahnen.*

———: *Der Schmerz und seine operative Behandlung.*

Fogarazzo: *Il dolore nel Arte.*

Foster, William: *Romance of Chemistry.* (The Century Company, New York, 1927.)

Fox, F. W.: Chemistry and Medicine. *Journal of South African Chemical Institute,* Johannesburg, May, 1933.

Foy, G.: *Anæsthetics, Ancient and Modern.* (Baillière, Tindall and Cox, London, 1889.)

Franqueville, Comte de: *Le premier sciècle de l'Institut de France (1795–1895.)* (Rothschild, Paris, 1895.)

Frey, M. von: *Beitraege zur Physiologie des Schmerzsinnes.*

———: *Ueber den Schmerz in physiologischer und klinischer Hinsicht.*

Fuller, Henry C.: *The Story of Drugs.* (The Century Company, New York, 1922.)

Garrett, T. L.: Origins of Hypnotism. *Psychology Digest,* July, 1937.

Gay, M.: *Statement of the Claims of Dr. Charles T. Jackson.* (D. Clapp, Boston, 1847.)

Georgia University: special series addresses, 1927, I, No. 14, pp. 1–12.

Gibson, Ch. R.: *Heroes of Science.* (Seeley Service & Company, London, 1913.)

Goldscheider, A.: *Gesammelte Abhandlungen Band* I. *Physiologie der Hautsinnesnerven.* (J. A. Barth, Leipzig, 1898.)

Goldscheider, Alfred: *Das Schmerzproblem.* (1920.)

———: *Neue Beobachtungen ueber Hautsinnesnerven.*

———: *Ueber den Schmerz in physiologischer und klinischer Hinsicht.*

Goldsmith, Margaret: *Franz Anton Mesmer.* (Arthur Barker, Ltd., London, 1934.)

Goodrich, S. G.: *Lives of Benefactors.* (J. E. Hickman, Boston.)

Gordon, H. L.: Sir James Young Simpson and Chloroform. In *Masters of Medicine.* (Longmans, Green & Company, New York, 1898.)

Graham-Mulhall, S.: *Opium, the Demon Flower.* (Montrose Publishing Company, New York, 1928.)

Grangee: *Pravaz und die Nadel.*

Grandy, Luther B.: *A Contribution to the History of the Discovery of Modern Surgical Anæsthesia.* (Richmond, 1893.)

———: The Discovery of Anæsthesia. *New York Medical Journal,* July 20, 1896.

Green, P.: *Pain.*

Gregory, Joshua C.: *The Scientific Achievements of Sir Humphry Davy.* (Oxford University Press, 1930.)

Greve, Christian: *Aphorismen zur Kulturgeschichte der Zahnheilkunde.* (Georg Thieme, Leipzig, 1930.)

Groeber, Arthur: *Ueber totale allgemeine Anæsthesie.* (Thèse, Leipzig, 1901–3.)

Grzywa: *Narkosenhandgriffe und Bemerkungen zur Avertin—und Evipan-Natriumnarkose in den Tropen. Zentralblatt f. Chirurgie,* No. 29, 1934.

Gumpert, Martin: *Das Leben fuer die Idee.* (S. Fischer, Berlin.)

Gwathmey, James T.: *Anæsthesia.* (D. Appleton & Co., New York, 1914.)

Haggard, Howard W.: *Devils, Drugs, and Doctors.* (Blue Ribbon Books, New York, 1929.)

———: *Mystery, Magic and Medicine.* (Doubleday, Doran & Company, Garden City, N. Y., 1933.)

———: *The Lame, the Halt, and the Blind.* (Blue Ribbon Books, New York, 1932.)

Hale, W. J.: *Chemistry Triumphant.*

Harding, Thomas Swann: *Fads, Frauds, and Physicians.* (L. MacVeagh, New York, 1930.)

Hardy, Thomas J.: *The Gospel of Pain.*

Hart, Ivor B.: *Makers of Science.* (Oxford University Press, London, 1923.)

Harte, Richard: *Hypnotism and the Doctors.* 2 vols. (L. N. Fowler, London, 1903.)

Hartzog, H. S.: *Triumphs of Medicine.* (Doubleday, Page & Company, New York, 1927.)

Hayden, W. R.: History of Anæsthesia, or Painless Surgery. *International Journal of Surgery*, New York, 1896.

Hayward, G.: *Some Account of the First Use of Sulphuric Ether by Inhalation in Surgical Practice.* (Boston, 1847.)

Hecker, Dr. Ewald: *Hypnose und Suggestion im Dienste der Heilkunde.* (Wiesbaden, 1893.)

Hellpach, Willy: *Heilkraft und Schoepfung.* (Carl Reissner, Dresden, 1934.)

Herrick, Clarence L.: *The Somatic Equilibrium and the Nerve Endings in the Skin.*

Herzog, R.: *Die Wunderheilungen von Epidauros.* (Dietrich'sche Verlbh, Leipzig, 1931.)

Hesse, Lendle, Schoen: *Allgemeinnarkose und oertliche Betaeubung.* (J. A. Barth, Leipzig, 1934.)

Hilton, James: *The Mystery of Pain.* (Boston, 1886.)

Hirschberg, J.: *Ueber die geschichtichen Anfaenge der wundaerztlichen Betaeubung. Deutsch. med. Wochenschrift*, 1892, No. I.

Hoche, A.: *Schlaf und Traum.* (Ullstein, Berlin, 1928.)

——: *Vom Sinn des Schmerzes.* (Lehmann, Muenchen, 1936.)

Hodges, Richard Manning: *A Narrative of Events Connected with the Introduction of Sulphuric Ether into Surgical Use.* (Little, Brown & Company, Boston, 1891.)

Hollaender, Eugen: *Anekdoten aus der mediznischen Weltgeschichte.* (Ferdinand Enke, Stuttgart, 1925.)

Holmes, Harry N.: *Out of the Test Tube.* (Emerson Books, Inc., New York, 1935.)

Holmes, Oliver W.: Anæsthesia. *Century Magazine*, 1893.

Holmyard, E. J.: *The Great Chemists.* (Methuen & Company, Ltd., London, 1928.)

Honigmann, Georg: *Das Wesen der Heilkunde.* (F. Meiner, Leipzig, 1924.)

Hosie, A.: *On the Trail of the Opium Poppy.*

Hovorka, O. V.: *Geist der Medizin.* (Braumueller, Vienna, 1915.)

Hovorka and Kronfeld: *Vergleichende Volksmedizin.* (Strecker & Schröder, Stuttgart, 1908.)

Hrdlicka, A.: *The Most Ancient Skeletal Remains of Man.* (Government Printing Office, Washington, 1916.)

Humbert, E.: *La douleur.* (Lausanne Bridel.)

Humphrey, John: *Drugs in Commerce.* (Pitman, London.)

Husemann, Theodore: *Die Schlafschwaemme und andere Methoden der allgem. und oertl. Anæsthesis in Mittelalter. Deutsche Zeitschrift fuer Chirurgie,* XLII.

Huxley, Thomas H.: *Science and Education.* (D. Appleton & Co., New York, 1899.)

Ingerslev: *Die Geburtszange.* (Stuttgart, 1891.)

Institut de France. Académie des sciences. Rapports de prix. Programme des concours. 1841-1855.

Isensee, Emil: *Geschichte der Medizin,* 3 Bd. (Liebmann, Berlin, 1842.)

Jacobs, J.: *Dr. Crawford W. Long.* (Atlanta, 1919.)

Japp, A. H.: *Famous Men.*

Jaquet, A.: *Ein halbes Jahrhundert Medizin.* (Benno Schwabe, Basel, 1929.)

Johnson, Charles B.: Lest we forget or Dr. Crawford Long, the first anæsthetist. *Illinois Medical Journal,* August, 1917.

Joire: *De l'emploi de l'analgesie hypnotique dans les accouchements. Revue de l'Hypnotisme,* XIII.

Jones, Bence: *Life and Letters of Faraday.* (Longmans, Green & Company, London, 1870.)

Jones, Elmer: The Waning of Consciousness under Chloroform. *Psychological Review,* January, 1909.

———: *Journal of Art and Science,* IV, No. 7, p. 158. 1818.

Joteyko and Stefanowska: *Psycho-Physiologie de la douleur.*

Jottkowitz, Benno: *Die Narkose in der Chirurgie.* (Thèse, Berlin, 1890.)

Juenger, Ernst: *Blaetter und Steine.* (Hamburg, 1934.)

Kane, H. H.: *Drugs That Enslave.* (P. Blakiston, Philadelphia, 1881.)

Keen, W. W.: *Selected Papers and Addresses.* (T. W. Jacobs & Company, Philadelphia, 1923.)

Keith, A.: *Ancient Types of Man.* (New York, 1911.)

Kemble, James: *Idols and Invalids.* (Fountain Library, London, 1935.)

Kern, J. H.: *Miracles of Morpheus.*

Killian, Dr. H.: *Narkose.* (Julius Springer, Berlin, 1934.)

Klebs: *Ueber natuerliche Krankheitsfamilien. Zueitschrift fuer Heilkunde,* 1880, I.

Kleinwächter, L.: *Die Gynaekologie des Altertums.*

———: *Geburtshilfe in Centralafrika.* (Rohlfs Archiv.)

Knopf, A. S.: William T. G. Morton. *Medical Record,* January, 1921.

Koch: *Rede bei der Einweihung der Sertuerner Gedenktafel.*

Koller, Carl: Historical Notes on the Beginning of Local Anæsthesis. *Journal of the American Medical Association,* May 26, 1928.

Kraus, Fr.: *Allgemeine und spezielle Pathologie der Person.* (Leipzig, 1926.)
Kroemke, Franz: *Friedrich Wilhelm Sertuerner, der Entdecker des Morphiums.*

Laboulbène: *Histoire de l'anæsthesie.* (Paris, 1885.)
Laewen, A.: *Der Schmerz und neuere Wege seiner chirurgischen Bekaempfung.*
Laignet-Lavastine: *Histoire de la médecine.* (Albin Michel, Paris, 1936.)
Lammert, H.: *Zur Geschichte der Narkose.* (Muenchen, 1868.)
La Motte, Ellen N.: *The Opium Monopoly.* (The Macmillan Company, New York, 1920.)
Lancet, April 5, 1930, p. 758; Hickman, a forgotten pioneer.
Leake, Chauncey D.: Historical Development of Surgical Anæsthesia. *Scientific Monthly,* Lancaster, 1925.
————: Valerius Cordus and the Discovery of Ether. *Isis,* No. 21, VII, 1. 1925. Bruxelles.
Leonard, J. N.: *Crusaders of Chemistry.*
Leube, O. W.: *Ueber die Bedeutung der Chemie in der Medizin.* (Berlin, 1884.)
Levinstein, Edward: *Die Morphiumsucht.* (A. Hirschwald, Berlin, 1877.)
Lewin, Louis: *Phantastica; narcotics, and stimulant drugs.* (K. Paul, Trench, Trubuer & Company, London, 1931.)
————: *Die Gifte in der Weltgeschichte.* (J. Springer, Berlin, 1920.)
Libby, Walter: *History of Medicine in Its Salient Features.* (Houghton Mifflin Company, Boston, 1922.)
————: *Introduction to the History of Science.*
Liebeault, A. A.: *Le sommeil provoqué et les etats analogues.* (Paris, 1889.)
Liebig: *Annalen der Chemie.* (Leipzig-Heidelberg, 1872.)
Lilly, W. S.: The mystery of sleep. *Nineteenth Century and After.* London, 1913, 8 v. 74 pp. 1266–83.
Lindsay, Mrs. Lillian: *A Short History of Dentistry.* (J. Bale Sons & Danielson, Ltd., London, 1933.)
Lockemann, Georg: Sertuerner.
————: John Priestley (In Bugge: *Das Buch der grossen Chemiker,* Chemie, Berlin, 1929.)
Loebel, Josef: *Medizin.* (Rowolt, Berlin, 1933.)
London People Journal: Article about the introduction of ether in the surgical practice. (January 9, 1847.)
Lord, Joseph L.: A defence of Jackson's claims to the discovery of etherization. *Littell's Living Age.* (Boston, 1848.)
————: *Memorial addressed to the trustees of the Massachusetts General Hospital, in behalf of Charles T. Jackson, M. D.* (Thurston, Torry & Company, Boston, 1849.)
Lucas—Championnière: *La douleur au point de vue chirurgical.*

Luckhardt, Prof. A. B.: *Historical Highlights and Shadows in the Discovery of General Anæsthesia.* (Reprint, No. 1930.)

Lyman, H. M.: *The Discovery of Anæsthesia.* (1886.)

Mace, Paul: *Morphine, morphimanie morphimanes.* (Thèse, Paris, 1903–1904.)

Macfie, R. C.: *Romance of Medicine.* (Cassell & Company, London, 1907.)

Mackenzie, J.: Pain. *Brain,* XXV, 1902, 368.

McCarthy, K. C.: *Gaseous Anæsthetics.* (Rad-mar Press, Inc., 1933.)

McCormick, C. O.: Rectal Ether Analgesie in Labor. *Journal of American Medicine,* April, 1933.

MacLaurin, C.: *Post Mortem.* (George H. Doran, New York, 1922.)

————: *Mere Mortals.* (George H. Doran, New York, 1925.)

McManus, James: *Notes on the History of Anæsthesia.* (Clark & Smith, Hartford, 1894.)

————: *The Wells Memorial Celebration, Notes on the History of Anæsthesia.* (Clark & Smith, Hartford, 1901.)

Maindron, Ernest: *Les fondations de prix a l'académie des science.* (Gauthier Villars, Paris, 1881.)

Major, Ralph H.: *The Doctor Explains.* (A. A. Knopf, Inc., New York, 1931.)

Manaceine, M. de: *Sleep.*

Mantegazza, Paolo: *Fisiologia del Dolore.*

Marot, Dr.: *Morphinomanie et suggestion. Revue de l'Hypnotisme,* Vol. VII.

Marshall, H. R.: *Pain, pleasure, and anæsthetics.*

————: *Physical Pain.* (1855.)

Massachusetts General Hospital, Boston. *Bylaws, Annual Report,* 1846–1847.

Maupassant: *L'endormeuse.*

May, Percy: *The Chemistry of Synthetic Drugs.* (Longmans, Green & Company, New York.)

Mayhew, H.: *The Wonders of Science.*

Medical Record, XVI, 1879: *Ueber die Entdeckung der Anæsthesie.*

Meine, H.: *L'Hysterie dans l'art antique.*

Merk, Ludwig: *Experimentelles zur Biologie der Haut.*

Merwin, S.: *Opium trade.*

Mesnet: *Un accouchement dans le somnabulisme provoque. Revue de l'Hypnotisme.* Vol. VII.

Meyer, H., Gottlieb, R.: *Die experimentelle Pharmaologie.* (Urban und Schwarzenberg, Berlin, Vienna, 1936.)

Miller, Albert H.: *Thomas Beddoes, Pioneer in Inhalation Therapy.* (Reprint, New York, October, 1932.)

————: Two notable controversies: over the invention of the electric telegraph and the discovery of surgical anæsthesia. *Annals of Medical History,* New York, March, 1934.

Mitchell, S. W.: "The Birth and Death of Pain," in *Collected Poems of S. Weir Mitchell*, The Century Company, New York.

Moll, Dr. Albert: *Hypnotism.* (London, 1897.)

Moore, Harry H.: *American Medicine.* (D. Appleton & Co., New York, 1927.)

Morgere, Francesco: *I doveri del medico di fronti al dolori.*

Morris, Charles: *Heroes of Progress in America.*

Morton, Elizabeth: The Discovery of Anæsthesia. *McClure's Magazine,* September, 1896.

Morton, William James: *Memorandum Relating to the Discovery of Surgical Anæsthesia.* (New York, 1855.)

Morton, W. T. G.: *Appeal to the Patrons of Science.*

————: *Pain and Anæsthesia.* (Washington, 1863.)

————: *Proceedings in Behalf of the Morton Testimonial.* (Rand & Avery, Boston, 1861.)

————: *Statements.* (Washington, 1853.)

————: *The Use of Ether as an Anæsthetic at the Battles of the Civil War.* (Press of American Medical Association, Chicago, 1904.)

Mott, Valentine: *Pain and Anæsthesia.* (Washington, McGill, 1863.)

Moyer, W.: *The Witchery of Sleep.*

Moyon, B.: *Sulla Utilita di dolore.*

Mueller, Benno: *Narkologie.* (Leipzig, 1903.)

Mueller, Franz Carl: *Geschichte der organischen Naturwissenschaften im neunzehnten Jahrhundert.* (Georg Bondi, Berlin, 1902.)

Mueller, Dr. Vilmos: *Csodatevoek.* (Singer und Wolfner, Budapest.)

Mumford, James Gregory: *A Narrative of Medicine in America.* (J. B. Lippincott, New York, 1903.)

Munaret, Le Dr.: *Eloge Historique de Charles Pravaz.* (Thèse, Lyon, 1854.)

Murray, Robert Henry.: *Science and Scientists in the Nineteenth Century.* (Sheldon Press, London, 1925.)

Nevius, L. W.: *The Discovery of Modern Anæsthetia.* (Cooper Institute, New York, 1894.)

Newman, Sir George: *Interpreters of Nature.* (Oxford University Press, New York, 1927.)

New York Evening Post, Articles about Morton. May 26, May 29, June 30, 1873.

Nichols, H.: *Des experiences sur la douleur.*

Nicoletti, L.: *Il problema del dolore.*

Nosworthy, M. D.: *The Theory and Practice of Anæsthesia. Hutchinson Scientific,* London, 1935.

Nutting & Dock: *History of Nursing.* (G. P. Putnam's Sons, New York, 1922.)

Oettinger, W. F. V.: The earliest suggestion of the use of cocaine for local anæsthesia. *Annals of Medical History*, 1933. N. s. v. 5, p. 275–278.

Oppenheimer, Z.: Zur Physiologie des Schlafes (Archiv fuer Anatomie und Psychologie, 1902, pp. 68–102.)

Osborn, H. F.: *Men of the Old Stone Age*. (Charles Scribner's Sons, New York, 1925.)

Osler, Sir William: *History of Medicine*.

———: *Evolution of Modern Medicine*. (Yale University Press, New Haven, 1922.)

Osten, Gert: *Schmerzensmann.*

Ostwald, Wilhelm: Sir Humphry Davy (in Bugge: *Das Buch der grossen Chemiker*, Berlin, 1929).

———: *Grosse Maenner*. (Akademische Verlagsanstalt, Leipzig, 1919.)

———: Michael Faraday (in Bugge: *Das Buch der grossen Chemiker*, Berlin, 1929).

———: *Psychographische Studien*.

Otis, Sidney: Letter from Mrs. Edward Whitman about the marriage of her daughter with Dr. Morton.

Packard, F. R.: *The History of Medicine in the United States*. (J. B. Lippincott & Company, Philadelphia, London, 1901.)

Panofsky, Ernst: *Beitrag zur Typengeschichte des Schmerzensmannes*.

Paris, John Ayrton: *The Life of Sir Humphry Davy*. (H. Colburn & R. Bentley, London, 1831.)

Parker, George: The discovery of the anæsthetic powers of nitrous oxyd. *Lancet*, January 7, 1928.

Parrington, Vernon Louis: *The Romantic Revolution in America, 1800–1860*. (Harcourt, Brace & Co., New York, 1927.)

Pattan, J. M.: *Anæsthesia and Anæsthetics*. (New York.)

Payne, Enoch George: *The Menace of Narcotic Drugs*. (Prepared by the Department of Education. Prentice-Hall, Inc., New York, 1931.)

Ploss, H. H.: *Ueber die Lage und Stellung der Frau waehren der Geburt bei verschiedenen Völkern*. (Leipzig.)

Pool, E. H.: *Medicine and Mankind*. (D. Appleton-Century Co., New York, 1936.)

Poulin, Jean: *L'anæsthesie avant l'emploi du chlorforme et de l'ether*. (Thèse, Libraire le François, Paris, 1931.)

Preyer, Dr. W.: *Die Entdeckung des Hypnotismus*. (Berlin, 1881.)

Raeder, O. M.: *America in the Forties*. (University of Minnesota Press, 1929.)

Reclus, P.: *La cocaine en chirurgie*.

Rice, Nathan P.: *Trials of a Public Benefactor*. (Pudney & Russell, New York, 1859.)

Richards, Lysander S.: *Analysis and Cause of Unconsciousness and Sleep*. (Rapide Service Press, 1920, New York.)

Richet, Charles: *Étude biologique sur la douleur.*
——: Douleur, in *Dictionaire de Physiologie.*
Roberts, E.: *Famous Chemists.* (G. Allen & Company, London, 1911.)
Rood, F. S.: *Anæsthesia and Anæsthetics.* (W. Wood & Co., New York, 1930.)
Rothe und Binz: *Der Aether gegen den Schmerz.* (Stuttgart, 1896.)
Rowbotham, F. J.: *Story-lives of Great Scientists.* (Wells Gardner, Darton & Company, London, 1918.)

Salmonski, A.: *Zur Geschichte der Sauerstofftherapie.* (Leipzig, 1902.)
Salomon, Dr. Felix: *Englische Geschichte.* (Koehler, Leipzig, 1923.)
Sauerbruch, F. and Wenke, H.: *Wesen und Bedeutung des Schmerzes.* (Junker & Duennhaupt, Berlin, 1936.)
Schelenz: *Sertuerner.* (Bericht der pharmaceutischen Gesellschaft, 1913.)
Scheler, Max: *Vom Sinn des Leides.*
Scheuber: Ueber die Geburtshilfe der Japaner. *Centralblatt fuer Gynaekologie*, 1883.
Schleich, Ludwig: *Schmerzlose Operationen.* (J. Springer, Berlin, 1906.)
Schmeltz: *Opération chirurgicale faites pendante le sommeil hypnotique. Revue de l'Hypnotisme*, IX.
Schrenck-Notzing: *Ueber Hypnotismus und Suggestion.* (Muenchen, 1889.)
——: *Die Bedeutung narkotischer Mittel fuer den Hypnotismus.* (Leipzig, 1891.)
Schulz, Kurt: *Der heutige Stand der Narkose, Charlottenburg, 1930.* (Thesis, Berlin.)
Seelig, M. G.: *Medicine: a Historical Outline.* (William and Wilkins, Baltimore, 1931.)
Shaw, S. P.: *Who Discovered Anæsthesia?* (Palmer & Howe, Manchester, 1868.)
Siebold, E. J. von: *Ueber die Anwendung des Schwefelaethers in der Geburtshilfe.*
Sigerist, Henry E.: *Amerika und die Medizin.* (G. Thieme, Leipzig, 1933.)
Simpson, Sir James: History of Modern Anæsthetics. *Boston Medical and Surgical Journal*, 1879.
——: *Landmarks in the Struggle between Science and Religion.*
——: Letter to Bigelow. *Boston Gynaecological Journal*, May, 1870.
Sims, J. Marion: History of the Discovery of Anæsthesia. *Virginia Monthly*, May, 1877.
Smith, A. J.: *Documentary Evidence for Long.* (Philadelphia, 1915.)
Smith, Truman: *An Examination of the Question of Anæsthesia.* (J. A. Gray, New York, 1858.)
——: *An Inquiry into the Origin of Modern Anæsthesia.* (Brown & Gross, Hartford, 1867.)
——: *Wells.*

Stanley, E.: *Report on the Ether Discovery.* (U. S. Congress, House of Representatives, 1852.)

Stearns, F. P.: *Cambridge Sketches.*

Stefan, Zweig: *Die Heilung durch den Geist.* (Insel, Leipzig, 1931.)

Sticker, G.: *Historische Studien und Skizzen zu Natur—und Heilwissenschaft.* (J. Springer, Berlin, 1930.)

———: *Zur Vorgeschichte der Schmerzebehandlung. Zeitschrift*: Schmerz Narkose, Anæsthesie, VIII. 2.

Stieglitz, Julius: *Chemistry in Medicine.* (The Chemical Foundation, Inc., New York, 1928.)

———: *Chemistry and Her Effect upon the Progress in Medicine.* (Johns Hopkins University, 1926.)

Stock, John E.: *Memoirs of the Life of Thomas Beddoes, M.D.* (John Murray, London, 1811.)

Straus, E.: *Vom Sinn der Sinne.* (Berlin, 1935.)

Stroemgren, Hedvig L.: *Die Zahnheilkunde in 18 Jahrh.* (Levin & Munksgaard, Kopenhagen, 1935.)

Strong, C. A.: Physical Pain and Pain Nerves. *Psychological Review,* 1896, III, 64.

———: *The Psychology of Pain.*

Struempell, A.: *Ueber die Schmerzempfindung.*

Suepfle: *Schlaftrunk in franz. Quellen des 16. Jahrh.* (Alemannia, XIII, 1886.)

Talmeyr, Maurice: *Les possedés de la morphine.*

Taylor: Amputations. *American Journal of Surgery,* 1833, pp. 364–370.

Taylor, Frances Long: *Crawford W. Long.* (Paul B. Hoeber, New York, 1927.)

The Federal Cases: Annulment of Morton's patent. (West Publishing Co., St. Paul, 1895.)

The Semi-Centennial of Anæsthesia, Boston, 1897. (Massachusetts General Hospital.)

Thorpe, Lee Burton: *History of Dental Surgery.* (Nat. Art. Publishing, Ft. Wayne, Ind., 1910.)

Thorpe, T. E.: *Humphry Davy,* 1896.

Tilden, Sir William A.: *Famous Chemists.* (G. Routledge, Ltd., London, 1921.)

Tillmann: *Hundert Jahre Chirurgie.* (Leipzig, 1898.)

Todd, C. L.: *Easier Motherhood.* (John Day Company, New York, 1931.)

Tschirsch, A.: *Ausfuehrliche Geschichte des Opiums und Morphiums.*

———: *Allgemeine Pharmakologie.* (Tauchnitz, Leipzig, 1933.)

———: Der Schmerz. *Zeitschrift fuer Psychologie,* 1901, XXVI, p. 14.

Tucker, W. G.: Michael Faraday. *Albany Medical Annals,* July-August, 1910.

Turner, W. A.: Extractions Under Hypnotism. *Journal of the British Dental Association*, March 15, 1890.

Tyndall, John: *Faraday as a Discoverer.* (Longmans, Green & Company, London, 1868.)

United States Congress: *Report on the Ether Discovery*, 1852; *Minority Reports on Dr. Morton; Statement Supported by Evidence of W. T. G. Morton.* (Washington, 1853.)

United States House of Representatives: two reports in 1852.

United States Senate: reports in 1853 and 1863. Petition for Dr. Morton, 1863.

Urbantschitsch, R. V.: *Praktische Lebenskunde.* (Amalthea, Vienna, 1931.)

Urdang, G.: Sertuerner. *Pharmaceutische Zeitung*, 1928, No. 14.

Vierordt, Dr. Hermann: *Medizinisches aus der Geschichte.* (Tuebingen der Lauppp'schen Buchhandlung, 1910.)

Virchow: *Krankheitswesen und Krankheitsursachen.* (Virchows Archiv, 1880 Bd. 79.)

Voisin, Auguste: *Morphinomanie guerie par suggestion hypnotique. Revue de l'Hypnotisme, I.*

Voivenel, Paul: *Il Medico davanti al Dolore e davanti alle Morte.* (Corvaccio, Milano, 1938.)

Waldie: Chloroform. *Lancet*, July 26, 1870.

Wall, Charles H. La: *Four Thousand Years of Pharmacy* (Lippincott, Philadelphia, 1927.)

Walsh, James Joseph: *Modern Progress and History of Dentistry.* (Fordham University Press, New York, 1912.)

———: *The History of Nursing.* (P. J. Kenedy & Sons, 1929.)

Warren, Edward: *Some Account of the Letheon.* (Dutton and Wentworth, Boston, 1847.)

Warren, J. Collins: *The Influence of Anæsthesia on the Surgery of the Nineteenth Century.* (American Surgical Association, Boston, 1897.)

Warren. J. M.: *The History of Anæsthesia from an American Point of View.*

Watson, Irving: *Physicians and Surgeons in America.* (Republic Press Association, 1896.)

Welch, William H.: *A Consideration of the Introduction of Surgical Anæsthesia.* (Lecture. October 16, 1908, Massachusetts General Hospital.)

Wellcome, Henry S.: *Henry Hill Hickman.* (Wellcome Foundation, London, 1930.)

Wetterstrand, Dr. Otto: *Ueber den kuenstlich verlaengerten Schlaf, besonders bei der Behandlung von Hysterie.* (Muenchen, 1896.)

Williams, Henry Smith: *Drugs against Men.* (Robert M. McBride & Company, New York, 1935.)

———: *Twilight Sleep.* (Harper & Brothers, New York, 1914.)

Winkel, Franz von: *Zur Geschichte der Betaeubungsmittel fuer schmerzlose Operation.* Rektoratsrede, Muenchen, 1902.)

Winslow, Charles Edward Amory: *Evolution and Significance of the Modern Public Health Campaign.* (Yale University Press, New Haven, 1923.)

Witkowsky: *Accoucheurs et sages femmes célèbres.* (Paris, 1893.)

———: *Anecdotes et curiosites historiques sur les accouchements.*

———: *Histoire des accouchements chez tous les peuples.* (Paris.)

Witting: *Nekrolog auf Sertuerner.*

Wolzendorff: Der Aber—und Wunderglaube in der Chirurgie. (*Klinische Wochenschrift,* Berlin, 1877.)

Wong, K. C., Wu Lien Teh: *History of Chinese Medicine.* (Shanghai, 1936.)

Wood. E.: *Operation chirurgicale pratiquee dans l'état d'hypnotisme.. Revue de l'Hypnotisme,* IV

Wundt, W.: *Hypnose und Suggestion.*

Young, Hugh H.: *Long, the Discoverer of Anæsthesia.*

Zumbusch, Leo V.: *Ueber den Schmerz.* (Universitaetsrede, Muenchen, 1933.)

Chronological Table

XIII. Cent.	Raymondus Lullius discovers "sweet vitriol."
XVI. Cent. (first half)	Theophrastus Bombastus Paracelsus von Hohenheim, experimenting on fowls, finds that "sweet vitriol" has a soporific effect, and recommends the use of this "white water" in painful diseases. He also prepares laudanum from crude opium.
1542	The strolling apothecary, Valerius Cordus, in a pharmacopœia printed at Nuremberg, describes the method of preparing "sweet vitriol."
XVII. Cent.	Sir Isaac Newton and the chemists Godfrey and Boyle allude to the medical effects of "sweet vitriol," which had been forgotten since Cordus' day.
XVIII. Cent.	James Moore recommends compression of certain nerve-trunks to produce temporary local anesthesia.
1772	Joseph Priestley, an English noncomformist divine, working at Calne on Lord Shelburn's estate, discovers nitrous oxide.
1792	Frobenius, a German chemist, gives "sweet vitriol" its present name of "ether."
1798	Humphry Davy, assistant to the Penzance surgeon Borlase, experimenting with the gas discovered by Priestley, inhales it, detects its analgesic and exhilarating effects, and because of the latter calls it "laughing gas."
1799	At Dr. Beddoes' Pneumatic Institute, Clifton, near Bristol, Davy introduces laughing gas into medical practice.
1800	Davy publishes an account of his work, and lectures on laughing gas at the Royal Institution.
1806	Friedrich A. W. Sertürner, of Paderborn, extracts, from crude opium, morphine, the first known alkaloid.
1818	In the *Journal of Science and Art,* Michael Faraday, Davy's sometime laboratory assistant and body-servant, publishes an account of the pain-allaying effects of ether, which he compares to those of laughing gas.

1824   Henry Hill Hickman, a young English general practitioner, experiments on animals concerning the analgesic effects of carbonic acid and laughing gas.

1828   Hickman applies to Charles X, King of France, for authorization and support in the extension of the foregoing experiments to man.

1831–2   S. Guthrie, an American, Soubeiran, a Frenchman, and J. Liebig, a German, independently discover chloroform.

1834   Dumas, a French chemist, works out the chemical formula of chloroform and gives the substance its present name.

1840   At about this date, in England, John Elliotson proposes to use for surgical operative purposes the analgesia that can be induced by animal magnetism. A little later, in India, James Esdaile painlessly removes large tumors from natives whom he has put to sleep by "magnetic passes."

1842   An American country practitioner, Dr. Crawford W. Long of Jefferson, Georgia, performs the first painless operation under ether.

1842   James Braid, a Manchester physician, discovers hypnosis, and, the same year, publishes his *Neurypnology,* in which the foundations of practical hypnotism are laid.

1844   A. A. Liébeault, French country practitioner, begins hypnotic treatment at Nancy.

1844   Horace Wells, an American dentist, makes the first experiments on himself with laughing gas inhaled to produce analgesia, at Hartford, Connecticut, and unsuccessfully attempts in Boston to demonstrate the method before the medical faculty of Harvard University.

1846   Dr. Charles Thomas Jackson of Boston, chemist, physiologist and geologist, recommends his sometime pupil, the dentist W. T. G. Morton, to try rectified sulphuric ether in order to allay pain.

1846   On October 16th, at the Massachusetts General Hospital in Boston, the first publicly performed painless operation under ether takes place. Morton administers it and Dr. John C. Warren, chief surgeon, operates.

1846   On October 17th, Bigelow, in an operation under ether narcosis, ascertains the importance of watching the pulse during administration.

1846   On November 1st, at the Massachusetts General Hospital, the first painless major amputation is performed. Morton gives the ether. On November 3rd, Bigelow officially announces Morton's discovery to the Academy of the Arts and Sciences.

On November 21st Oliver Wendell Holmes, poet, novelist and physician, gives the method the name of "anesthesia."

1846 On December 21st, the first operation under ether anesthesia to be performed in England is carried out at University College Hospital, London, by Robert Liston.

1847 In January, both in France and Germany, painless operations are performed under ether anesthesia. Within a few months the practice spreads over the world.

1847 Jacob Bell and M. J. P. Flourens, having experimented on animals, announce that chloroform has an anesthetic effect.

1847 James Young Simpson, an Edinburgh obstetrician, introduces chloroform by inhalation for the relief of the pangs of childbirth. Its use as anesthetic for surgical operations speedily follows, in England for the most part replacing ether.

1852 James Arnott introduces local anesthesia by cold, numbing the site of operation by applying an ice-and-salt freezing mixture. (Baron Larrey, one of Napoleon's army surgeons, had used cold as a local anesthetic at the battle of Eylau.)

1853 Alexander Wood invents the hollow needle.

1854 From a South American journey Dr. Scherzer brings back to Europe some coca leaves, having learned that they are chewed by the natives as a stimulant. In the days of the Incas the shamans had applied the chewed leaves to allay pain.

1855 Gaedicke, a German chemist, extracts an alkaloid from coca leaves.

1858 John Snow, an Edinburgh physician, constructs chloroform and ether inhalers.

1860 In Wöhler's laboratory, Albert Niemann isolates cocaine.

1864 In conjunction with Dr. J. A. Smith and Dr. Allen, the American itinerant lecturer Gardner Quincey Colton founds the New York Dental Association for the painless extraction of teeth under laughing gas.

1864 First Chloroform Commission for the study of deaths under chloroform.

1866 Allis recommends the use of mixed anesthetic vapors.

1867 Sir Benjamin Ward Richardson signalizes the local anesthetic effect of the rapid evaporation of volatile substances, and introduces the ether spray.

1868 First major operation under laughing gas.

1880 Klikovich, a Russian professor, introduces laughing gas into midwifery practice. It had already been recommended by Fox.

1880   The Chloroform Committee of the British Medical Association declares itself opposed to the use of chloroform as an anesthetic.

1880   Billroth improves the "combined method" by introducing an anesthetic mixture ("Billroth's anesthetic") consisting of alcohol 3 parts, ether 3 parts and chloroform 10 parts. Subsequently Schering, Piet and Léon Labbé recommend the drop-method of administration.

1881   In Calcutta, Alexander Crombil adopts the practice of giving a hypodermic of morphine as a preliminary to anesthesia by inhalation. In 1869, this was recommended by Claude Bernard; and after Crombil the method was elaborated by Pitha and Nussbaum.

1884   In Vienna, during the spring, Sigmund Freud, in conjunction with his friend Dr. Carl Koller, studies the local anesthetic effect of cocaine.

1884   In the summer, at the ophthalmic clinic of the Viennese General Hospital, Dr. Carl Koller experiments with cocaine, first on animals, then on himself. On September 15th, at the Ophthalmological Congress in Heidelberg, he announces his discovery of local anesthesia by this method.

1884   A. A. Liébeault publishes his book *De la suggestion*.

1885   William Halsted, an American surgeon, works at Johns Hopkins Hospital upon local anesthesia.

1885   James Leonard Corning, an American neurologist, discovers spinal anesthesia, later improved by Dr. Robinson.

1885   In this and subsequent years, Paul Reclus, a French physician, discovers *"anésthésie tronculaire"* and *anésthésie splanchnique.*

1883–1887   Alfred Goldscheider, by the use of hot and cold cylinder tests, discovers heat and cold spots in the skin, thus amplifying our conception of the skin as a sense organ.

1886   Publication of A. A. Liébeault's *La thérapie suggestive.*

1893   Anesthesia becomes a formal specialty in England.

1893   By the German Congress of Anesthetists ether is recommended as preferable to chloroform.

1893–1898   Henry Head discovers the cutaneous zones known as "Head's zones."

1894   The German physician and philosopher Carl Ludwig Schleich discovers the method of infiltration anesthesia which bears his name.

1894–1897   Max von Frey discovers the "pain spots" in the skin.

1899   August Bier, a Greifswald surgeon, introduces "Bier's lumbar anesthesia." At about the same date Théodore Tuffier, a

French surgeon, following a similar line of investigation, introduces rhachianesthesia.

1899   Dr. Korff recommends combined scopolamine and morphine or scopolamine and narcophine narcosis, a method subsequently developed by von Steinbüchell, Bernhard Kronig, and Karl Gauss into the method known as "twilight sleep," used chiefly in midwifery.

1902   The Frenchman Stephane Leduc tries to induce narcosis by electricity.

1905   The German chemists Einhorn and Braun discover novocaine, the leading cocaine substitute, which is far less toxic. Later Lövenhart and A. Schmidt discover another substitute, isocaine.

1910   About this time, James Taylor Gwathmey introduces narcosis by the rectal route, giving a mixture of ether and oil as an enema. Pitha, working independently, tries to induce anesthesia by belladonna enemata.

1917   Eichholz discovers avertin, the foundation of what is termed basal narcosis.

1923   Two American biochemists, A. B. Luckhardt and Carter, isolate ethylene, one of the most recent substances used for producing anesthesia by inhalation.

Index